American Social Science Series

GENERAL EDITOR
HOWARD W. ODUM

*Kenan Professor of Sociology and Director of the School of
Public Welfare in the University of North Carolina*

American Social Science Series

Under the Editorship of

HOWARD W. ODUM

Introduction to Social Psychology. By L. L. BERNARD

American Masters of Social Science. Edited by HOWARD W. ODUM

The Science of Social Relations: An Introduction to Sociology. By HORNELL HART

Man's Quest for Social Guidance: The Study of Social Problems. By HOWARD W. ODUM

The Science of Public Welfare. By ROBERT KELSO

American Marriage and Family Relationships. By WILLIAM F. OGBURN and ERNEST R. GROVES

The American Community in Action: Case Studies of American Communities. By JESSE F. STEINER

The Range of Social Theory. By FLOYD N. HOUSE

A Social Interpretation of Education. By JOSEPH K. HART

Essentials of Civilization: A Study in Social Values. By THOMAS JESSE JONES

Principles of Rural-Urban Sociology. By PITIRIM SOROKIN and CARLE C. ZIMMERMAN

An Introduction to Social Research. By HOWARD W. ODUM and KATHARINE JOCHER

An Introduction to Social Anthropology. By CLARK WISSLER

The Housing Problem. By JAMES FORD

The Negro in American Civilization. By CHARLES S. JOHNSON

Introduction to Mental Hygiene. By ERNEST R. GROVES and PHYLLIS BLANCHARD

Sociological Theory and Social Research. By CHARLES H. COOLEY.

Social Pathology. By N. B. BOND.

The Sociological Method. By ROBERT E. PARK and FLOYD N. HOUSE.

The History of Sociology in America. By L. L. BERNARD.

The Philosophical Foundations of Social Science. By JOHN DEWEY.

The Educational Teachings of Sociology. By FRANKLIN H. GIDDINGS.

Social Morality. By JAMES H. TUFTS.

Social Psychology. By L. L. BERNARD.

Industry and Society. By ARTHUR J. TODD.

Youth and Society. By IVA L. PETERS.

Social Planning. By JAMES FORD.

The Technique of Social Progress. By HORNELL HART.

INTRODUCTION TO
MENTAL HYGIENE

BY

ERNEST R. GROVES
RESEARCH PROFESSOR OF SOCIOLOGY
UNIVERSITY OF NORTH CAROLINA

AND

PHYLLIS BLANCHARD
PSYCHOLOGIST
PHILADELPHIA CHILD GUIDANCE CLINIC

NEW YORK
HENRY HOLT AND COMPANY

PRINTED IN THE
UNITED STATES OF AMERICA

PREFACE

On no application of science to human needs are modern men and women more willing to stake their hopes than on mental hygiene. Mental hygiene represents a distinct purpose and viewpoint, rather than a definite sphere of science. It cuts across many of the divisions that have resulted from the study of human conduct. Of these, psychiatry, psychology and sociology yield most to the accumulating fund of mental hygiene. The authors of this book are deeply conscious of the difficulty of drawing together the various expressions of the mental hygiene movement in the effort to give it synthesis. Any such attempt must be pioneering, but in spite of great differences of opinion regarding certain aspects of mental hygiene, there now appears to be need of providing for the college student and the general reader an introduction to this movement which promises so much for individual and social welfare.

The book was in progress before announcement was made of the International Congress of Mental Hygiene now soon to meet at Washington. It gave the authors, who were already committed to a broad interpretation, encouragement in the execution of their task to see that the program of this most important gathering of scientists recognizes the width of the area of human interest to be included in this subject.

Chapters 1, 2, 3, 4, 6, 8, 11, 13 and 14 are by Phyllis Blanchard; the rest by Ernest R. Groves.

The author of Chapter 13 expresses her thanks to her

v

friends, Lorine Pruette and William van Meter, and to her husband, Walter W. Lucasse, for reading the first tentative outline of this chapter and giving her suggestions for the final revision; and acknowledges her indebtedness to her colleagues, Miss Almena Dawley and Miss Goldie Basch, of the social service staff of the Philadelphia Child Guidance Clinic, for suggestions that have proven invaluable in the construction of Chapter 14, and to Dr. G. H. Pearson, also of the clinic staff, for his critical reading of several earlier chapters. Both authors are especially grateful to Dr. E. van Norman Emery of Yale University for reading the whole manuscript and giving them the benefit of his valuable criticism. He is, however, in no degree to be held responsible for the content of the book.

ERNEST R. GROVES.
PHYLLIS BLANCHARD.

CONTENTS

INTRODUCTION TO
MENTAL HYGIENE

CHAPTER I

THE ORIGIN AND DEVELOPMENT OF MENTAL HYGIENE

The organization of mental hygiene societies. The story of the beginnings of the mental hygiene movement is a dramatic one. In 1908, Clifford Beers, a Yale graduate, who had been a patient in both public and private hospitals for the insane, published a book telling of his experiences in these institutions. With the recovery of his health, he had determined to devote the remainder of his life to rousing interest in the prevention of mental disease. His book, *A Mind That Found Itself*, was only one of his efforts in this direction. Through personal interviews and letters he interested in his plan those prominent people who could give the necessary professional direction and financial support.

The same year that his book appeared, Mr. Beers succeeded in organizing the Connecticut State Committee for Mental Hygiene. In 1909, the National Committee for Mental Hygiene was formally organized. The first three years of its existence passed in raising funds to carry out its program, and in securing the coöperation of physicians, educators and others who could be of service by virtue of their professional training.

Early mental hygiene activities. The National Committee for Mental Hygiene sponsored various types of activities. In order to help raise the standards for care and treatment of the insane, surveys were undertaken which resulted in reports of the actual conditions in state

3

and county institutions with recommendations for improvement. The rousing of the public conscience by the presentation of facts and concrete plans for better care of the insane was followed by legislative changes which enabled the suggestions to be put into effect. In a similar fashion, by utilizing the survey method, reforms were brought about with respect to the care of mental defectives. Penal institutions—reformatories and prisons—were investigated and the public was awakened to the necessity for humane treatment of offenders, and more especially to the advantages of scientific study of delinquents and criminals, many of whom were found to be mentally deficient or insane and therefore in need of custodial care in institutions equipped for this purpose.

By 1927 reports of these surveys in ten states had been published:—Arizona, Georgia, Kentucky, Maryland, Missouri, North Dakota, Rhode Island, South Carolina, Texas and Wisconsin. Surveys had also been made of three cities—Cincinnati and Cleveland, Ohio, and St. Louis, Missouri. Both types of surveys, city and state, were coöperative, local officials working with representatives of the National Committee for Mental Hygiene.

Although the survey work has been limited to thirty-two states, it has awakened many communities to their mental hygiene needs for the care of the insane, the mentally deficient, and criminal classes. The recommendations given with reference to one place are often applicable to another. Thus the results have more than a local significance. Moreover, this work has not been abandoned with the growth of new activities; a survey is going on in New York state at the present time, and others will undoubtedly be made in the near future.

Encouraged by the National Committee, state societies for mental hygiene have been organized in some twenty-eight states. Both the national and state organizations have been active in promoting the establishment of out-patient clinics in connection with hospitals for mental disease, independent mental hygiene clinics, and many other facilities for the treatment and prevention of mental disease and delinquency.

Educational activities. Perhaps one of the most strik-ing accomplishments of the National Committee for Men-tal Hygiene is in the field of education. In 1917 was first published the quarterly journal *Mental Hygiene,* in which have appeared articles upon a range of topics as wide as the whole scope of human adjustments. The magazine is moderately priced, and in general the contributors write in a style that is intelligible to the educated layman as well as to professionals. Leaflets, pamphlets and longer reports upon various mental hygiene subjects are also published by the National Committee and distributed either free of charge or at cost. Thus the most progres-sive literature in mental hygiene is made easily available to the public.

The first director of the National Committee for Mental Hygiene, Dr. Thomas W. Salmon, and his successor, Dr. Frankwood E. Williams, have given generously of their time and energy in the effort to educate the public in matters of mental hygiene. They have given lectures before professional, semi-professional and lay groups in addition to performing the arduous labors of the execu-tive. It is impossible to estimate the debt owed to these two men, who, by virtue of their exceptional abilities and the position they were called upon to fill, have exerted so wide-spread an influence for human welfare.

Spread of the mental hygiene movement to other countries. The second national organization, the Cana-dian National Committee for Mental Hygiene, was established in 1918. Profiting from the ten years' experience in mental hygiene in the States, the Canadian program was from the first a comprehensive one. It included plans for "an active participation in war work, a comprehensive study of immigration, elaborate statistical institutional studies, the establishment of a library, special investigations of delinquency and a series of lectures to be given in various parts of the Dominion." [1]

Province surveys, similar to our state surveys, have been made in Canada for the purpose of improving methods of caring for the insane and mentally defective. New institutions have been provided and mental hygiene clinics opened. Educational work has not been neglected; the *Canadian Journal of Mental Hygiene* having been first issued in 1919. In the public schools, studies of the intelligence of pupils have been conducted and the curriculum reorganized to furnish specialized instruction for the intellectually retarded. Vocational guidance for mentally handicapped individuals has also been instituted by the Canadian National Committee, with the result that many persons who otherwise would have been relegated to institutional life have been helped to make adjustments in the industrial world.

The roll of mental hygiene organizations has increased steadily. The French League for Mental Hygiene was founded in 1920; the Belgium National League in 1921; the British National Council for Mental Hygiene in 1923; the Brazilian National League for Mental Hygiene in 1923. South Africa has a National Committee for Mental Hygiene and also the Cape Province Society for Mental Hygiene. Within the last five years national mental hygiene organizations have been founded in Spain, Italy, Switzerland, Germany, Hungary, New Zealand and Bul-

[1] James V. May, *Mental Diseases*, p. 128. Boston, 1922.

garia. Others are in the process of formation in Holland, Australia, Denmark, Norway, Sweden, Russia, India, Japan, Greece and Czecho-Slovakia. Thus, in the twenty years since its inception in the United States, the mental hygiene movement has become world wide. That the movement would become international was recognized in 1922, when the first steps were taken to form an International Committee for Mental Hygiene. It is planned that the First International Congress of Mental Hygiene will be held in Washington, D. C., in 1930, and that the International Committee will be formally established at that time.

Later mental hygiene activities. If at first mental hygiene appeared to center its attention upon the treatment and prevention of mental disease and delinquency, it was only because these were urgent public health problems. The leaders of the movement clearly visualized its functions as extending much farther, and saw it as concerned with the whole life adjustment of the human individual. Thus education, marriage, parenthood, industry —all the relationships of individuals to each other and to their environment—have their mental hygiene aspects. All need to be studied in order to determine wherein they contribute to human adjustment or undermine mental health, and all need reconstruction in keeping with this point of view.

Initiated directly by the National Committee, or indirectly instigated through its educational activities, mental hygiene has indeed begun to enter into all these fields. Psychiatric and psychological examinations for school children, for employees, and for college students; psychiatric inquiry into the causes of domestic difficulties and marriage maladjustments; education for parenthood, and many other departures have become familiar to our thoughts and their practice is being rapidly extended. Indeed, we may almost fear that the public demand for mental hygiene will exceed the resources as to personnel and technique, which are necessarily limited in so recently organized a branch of applied science.

Financial resources, which in the early years of the mental hygiene movement were sometimes lacking, have been made available through the coöperation of certain philanthropic enterprises, notably the Rockefeller Foundation, the Laura Spellman Memorial Fund and the Commonwealth Fund. Some of the finest achievements of the National Committee for Mental Hygiene have been made possible by grants from these foundations.

Mental hygiene for children. The National Committee for Mental Hygiene was active, from the time of its foundation, in stimulating the establishment of psychiatric and mental hygiene clinics. There was an early realization that if these clinics were to do effective preventative work they must serve children as well as adults, for childhood, as Dr. William White once said, is the golden age for mental hygiene. Although a certain number of children could be served through the out-patient departments of psychopathic hospitals and at mental hygiene centers offering clinical facilities, these means were exceedingly inadequate. The first clinics exclusively for children were still somewhat limited, by virtue of being connected with Juvenile Courts and primarily concerned with delinquent types, or in other instances because the chief purpose was to diagnose the mentally deficient and provide them with proper instruction in the public schools or at state institutions.

There are large numbers of maladjusted children whose difficulties are not sufficiently serious to make them court cases or suitable patients for the ordinary type of psychiatric clinic. They are well developed intellectually, but present personality and behavior patterns which bid fair to handicap them in the economic and social adaptations of adult existence. To meet the needs of these common problems of childhood, the National Committee for Mental Hygiene, aided by the Commonwealth Fund, launched a campaign (in 1922) for the establishment of child guidance clinics. Two "field clinics" were kept in operation over a five year period, demonstrating methods of child guidance in seven cities—St. Louis, Los Angeles, St. Paul, Minneapolis, Cleveland, Dallas (Texas) and Philadelphia. Without exception, these communities provided for the continuation of the child guidance clinics on a permanent basis, securing financial support through boards of education, community chests, local philanthropic foundations or private subscriptions.

Meanwhile, the Commonwealth Fund also financed the Bureau of Child Guidance in New York City for a five year period, replacing it by the more elaborately organized and equipped Institute for Child Guidance at the end of that time. At these centers, in addition to the actual service rendered to problem children, there were affiliations with educational institutions of the city which provided for the training of personnel in child guidance methods and technique. The Institute is particularly generous in offering fellowships to psychiatrists, psychologists and psychiatric social workers who wish to obtain this kind of training.

The necessity for trained workers in these branches of child guidance resulted from the interest in the movement which was very shortly manifested by many cities. Requests for aid in organizing clinics and in selecting personnel became so numerous that at the close of the demonstration program the National Committee continued to maintain a Division on Community Clinics to meet these demands. A recent news-letter of the Commonwealth Fund states that approximately 300 mental hygiene clinics for children have come into existence since 1922. At least 125 of these, besides those listed above as growing directly out of the demonstration program, refer to themselves as "Child Guidance Clinics." The staff unit consists of psychiatrist, psychologist and psychiatric social worker, the size of personnel varying with community needs and adequacy of financial support. Some operate on a full time and others on a part time basis, again dependent upon the two factors just mentioned. In the Commonwealth Fund news-letter, there is an estimate that last year more than 40,000 children were examined and treated in psychiatric clinics in the United States.[2]

England has a child guidance clinic which was opened in London in the spring of 1929. The financial support is to be provided, for a time, by the Commonwealth Fund.

Orientation of the mental hygiene movement. Although the driving force of Clifford Beers' personality was a potent factor in the development of the mental hygiene movement, its rapid growth could not have taken place but for the fact that the times were ripe for it. The hour and the man coincided, as in all successful movements for social progress. Progressive leaders in psychiatry, psychology and education had already begun to think in terms of mental hygiene. William James had spoken of it and William Burnham had published an article on the subject. It was Adolf Meyer who suggested

[2] The News-Letter of the Commonwealth Fund, October, 1928. Division of Publications of the Commonwealth Fund, Fuller Building, 57th St. and Madison Ave., New York.

to Mr. Beers that "mental hygiene" epitomized the idea expressed in his book and the purpose in his mind.[3]

The organized movement was initiated at a time when it was possible for it to draw upon a number of sciences, both pure and applied, in order to obtain its technology. It made use especially of physiology, psychology, psychiatry, medicine, sociology and even mathematics.[4] Without modern psychology and psychiatry, however, it would be far different from what it is to-day, if it could have come into existence at all without them, which is doubtful. Since they have been so important for mental hygiene, it seems appropriate to devote a chapter to its setting in the psychiatric and psychological background. With such an orientation, we shall see that a point had been reached in the development of these two sciences which had not only prepared the way for mental hygiene but made its coming almost inevitable.

SUGGESTIONS FOR CLASSROOM DISCUSSION

1. Read *A Mind That Found Itself*. Describe the experiences that led Mr. Beers to become an advocate of mental hygiene. How did he accomplish his purpose?
2. How many mental hygiene activities can you enumerate?
3. In what ways has the education of the public in mental hygiene principles been accomplished?
4. Describe the spread of mental hygiene to other countries.
5. What is the function of child guidance?

[3] As far back as 1863 a book had been published under the title of *Mental Hygiene*. For a discussion of the origin of the term, see "The Clinical Psychologist at Work," by R. H. Paynter, *The Personnel Journal*, 1927, Vol. VI, pp. 283-294.

[4] The last named may seem surprising until we recall the use made of statistical reports to forge a weapon to drive home to the public the need of better methods for the treatment and prevention of mental disease. This list of sciences is quoted from "The Clinical Psychologist at Work," p. 287.

SUGGESTIONS FOR WRITTEN REPORTS

1. Make an outline for the mental hygiene survey of a community.

2. From the references given in the accompanying bibliography, and other sources which you may discover for yourselves, write a paper describing the clinical work in child guidance.

3. Look over the volumes of the journal *Mental Hygiene*. Make a list of the topics which have been treated therein.

SELECTED BIBLIOGRAPHY

ABBOT, E. S. "Outline for a State Society of Mental Hygiene." *National Committee for Mental Hygiene*, 1921.

ALLEN, F. H. "Evolution of Our Treatment Philosophy in Child Guidance." *Mental Hygiene*, 1930, Vol. XIV, pp. 1-11.

AVERILL, L. A. *The Hygiene of Instruction*, Chap. XV. Boston, 1928. *The Child Guidance Clinic*.

BARKER, L. F. "First Ten Years of the National Committee for Mental Hygiene." *National Committee for Mental Hygiene*, 1918.

—— "Some Phases of the Mental Hygiene Movement and the Scope of the Work of the National Committee for Mental Hygiene." *National Committee for Mental Hygiene*, 1912.

BEERS, CLIFFORD. *A Mind That Found Itself*. Revised edition. New York, 1923.

—— *The Mental Hygiene Movement*. *National Committee for Mental Hygiene*, 1923.

BLANCHARD, PHYLLIS. *The Child and Society*. New York, 1928. See Chap. XV, "The Child and the Clinic"; also pp. 291-295.

BLANCHARD and PAYNTER. "Changing the Child's Behavior." *Journal of Applied Sociology*, 1925, Vol. IX, pp. 338-350; 425-436.

EMERY, E. V. "The Child Guidance Clinic." *Pacific Coast Journal of Nursing*, October, 1926.

MAY, JAMES V. *Mental Diseases,* Chap. VII, "The Mental Hygiene Movement." Boston, 1922.

PAYNTER, RICHARD. "The Clinical Psychologist at Work." *The Personnel Journal,* 1927, Vol. VI, pp. 283-294.

SINGER, H. D. "The Possibilities of a State Society for Mental Hygiene." *National Committee for Mental Hygiene,* 1921.

WILLIAMS, FRANKWOOD E. "Community Responsibility in Mental Hygiene." *The American Review,* January, 1923.

WINSLOW, C. E. A. "Twenty Years of Mental Hygiene." *Mental Hygiene,* July, 1928, Vol. XII, pp. 504-515.

SYMPOSIUM: *The Child Guidance Clinic and the Community.* The Commonwealth Fund, Division of Publications, Fuller Building, 57th Street and Madison Avenue, New York, 1928.

Mental Hygiene Surveys

ANDERSON, V. V. Report of the Mental Hygiene Survey of Cincinnati, 1922.

—— Mental Defect in a Southern State (Georgia), 1919.

—— A Report of the South Carolina Mental Hygiene Survey, 1921.

—— A Report of the Wisconsin Mental Deficiency Survey, 1921.

HAINES, THOMAS. Report of the Arizona Mental Hygiene Survey, 1922.

—— Report of the Mental Hygiene Survey of Kentucky, 1923.

—— Report of the Maryland Mental Hygiene Survey, 1921.

—— Report of the Missouri Mental Deficiency Survey, 1922.

—— Report of the North Dakota Mental Hygiene Survey, 1923.

HAMILTON, S. W. A Report of the Rhode Island Mental Hygiene Survey, 1924.

—— Mental Disease and Mental Deficiency in Cleveland, Ohio (Part 6 of the Cleveland Hospital and Health Survey), 1920.

—— Report of the Texas Mental Hygiene Survey, 1924-25.

—— Report of a Mental Hygiene Survey of Delinquency and Dependency Problems in St. Louis, 1922.

(These surveys, and the other material published by the National Committee for Mental Hygiene and referred to in the above bibliography, may be obtained from The National Committee for Mental Hygiene, 370 Seventh Avenue, New York, N. Y., Some of the material has also been published in the journal *Mental Hygiene*.)

The Commonwealth Fund, Tenth Annual Report (for 1928). February, 1929.
Report of the Institute for Child Guidance, 1928.
Directory of Psychiatric Clinics for Children for 1928.
Progress Report, Commonwealth Fund Program for the Prevention of Delinquency, 1925.

(These reports are published by the Commonwealth Fund, Division of Publications, Fuller Building, 57th Street and Madison Avenue, New York.)

CHAPTER II

THE PSYCHIATRIC AND PSYCHOLOGICAL
BACKGROUND

Ancient attitudes toward mental disease. In any historical survey of the treatment of mental diseases, however briefly sketched, we cannot avoid entering a chamber of horrors in which we become acquainted with some of man's most distressing family skeletons. It is necessary to view these unpleasant reminders of the past in order to acquire an adequate perspective and to realize what an enormous advance is represented by modern psychiatry and mental hygiene. Fortunately, the points of view to be encountered in this chapter have long since been left behind, and we are now progressing in a far happier direction.

In the early ages before medicine became a science, it was a part of magic and of priestcraft. Insanity, along with other human ills, was ascribed to demons taking possession of the body, or to magic wrought upon a person by some enemy. The records of Egyptian and Babylonian medicine describe the incantations, ceremonials and exorcisms to be used for freeing the insane person from supernatural influences or releasing him from magical spells. The folk lore of primitive peoples contains similar allusions.

For a long time, the Christian era held that mental disease was a punishment for some sin, that it was therefore sent by God, who might remove it if sufficiently propitiated by prayer and sacrifice. It is interesting to

15

note, however, that pagan civilizations and Christian peoples utilized what knowledge of herbs and drugs they possessed in the treatment of insanity, rather than depending entirely upon magic rites or divine intervention.

During the hundreds of years known as the Middle Ages, insanity was regarded as a manifestation of the powers of evil. One conception attributed it to the habitation of the human body by wicked spirits. Therefore many individuals suffering from mental disease were confined at the monasteries, where they were scourged and submitted to other physical tortures in order to drive out these demons from their human habitation. Outside the monasteries, insane persons were often burned, hanged or drowned because of the belief that they were practicing witchcraft and sorcery.

It is not strange that the acts of the insane were so interpreted in a pre-scientific age, where any mystery savored of black magic. If we consider the symptoms that characterize certain forms of mental disease, we shall be able to understand how the popular opinion was formed. To-day, when we see a patient in a hospital who appears to be talking to some other person invisible and inaudible to us, we know that he is suffering from visual or auditory hallucinations. To a people without our scientific knowledge, what other explanation could be given than that he was in communication with evil spirits? Or, if we take the case of hysterical anesthesia, without modern psychiatric theory, how else could the insensitiveness to pain be interpreted except as an indication of some more than human force? We cannot but be horrified at the cruelties practiced upon the insane by the early Christians, yet we must remember that the motivation was fear growing out of ignorance and superstition rather than any innate desire to inflict suffering upon fellow creatures.

The first hospitals. Even after insanity came to be regarded as a disease there was little amelioration of the treatment accorded persons so afflicted. It is said that there was a hospital for the insane opened at Jerusalem in 491 A.D., but this was the first of its kind, so far as we know, and a second did not appear until the twelfth century, when the "House of Grace" at Bagdad provided a refuge for patients with mental disease. Garrison, in his *History of Medicine,* states that: "The Arabians were far ahead of their European contemporaries in their kindly treatment of the insane." [1] This was true for more than five centuries. The first European "insane asylum" was St. Mary of Bethlehem, converted from a monastery into a hospital in 1547. But while the Arabian institutions were made comfortable for the patients, with especial attention to attractive food and soothing music, the English asylum just mentioned became the infamous "Bedlam," a theme for artists who wished to depict infernal terrors. Both at "Bedlam" and at the Viennese Narrenthurm, or "Lunatic's Tower" (opened in 1784), "the public were allowed to view the insane, like animals in a menagerie, on payment of a small fee." [2]

During the sixteenth and seventeenth centuries, and most of the eighteenth, although several new insane asylums were opened, little else was accomplished. In all these institutions, in France, England and Germany, the patients were kept in chains, beaten by the keepers, almost starved for want of proper food and permitted to die of cold. To quote Garrison again: "They were either chained or caged when housed, or, if harmless, were

---

[1] F. H. Garrison, *An Introduction to the History of Medicine,* third edition, p. 126. Philadelphia, 1921.

[2] Garrison, *op. cit.,* p. 418.

allowed to run at large, the Tom o' Bedlams of England
or the wizards and warlocks of Scotland." [3]

Early medical theory and practice. As late as the
last part of the eighteenth and first of the nineteenth centuries, insanity was still attributed to "yellow and black
bile"; mania was described as due to "increased secretion
of the nervous fluid," and melancholia was said to result
from a "torpor of brain and nerves" or a "diminished
secretion of the nervous fluid." [4] The texts of this period
discuss such methods of treatment as bleeding, "leeches
to the scalp," and various drugs, including opium.[5] However, it is also to be noted that these books have begun to
speculate, although in a rather vague and philosophical
fashion, about psychogenic factors—fear, grief, love—in
the causation of insanity. Moreover, they begin to question the efficacy of bleeding, and to advise the use of elec-
trical treatments, tepid baths, and "more tenderness and
kindness." The soothing effect of music is also mentioned, and the need of protecting insane patients from
the rigors of cold, "which they do not feel, but from which
they may die."

Garrison summarizes the medical methods in vogue
during the eighteenth century as follows: "Melancholia
was treated by opium pills, excited states by camphor,
. . . and a mysterious power was ascribed to belladonna
. . . a mustard plaster on the head, venesection at the
forehead and both thumbs, clysters, and plasters of Span-
ish fly, were other resources. . . . A melancholic woman
was treated with a volley of oaths and a douche of cold

[3] Garrison, *op. cit.*, p. 418.
[4] Alexander Crichton, *An Inquiry into the Nature and Origin of
Mental Derangement.* London, 1798.
[5] John Syer, *A Dissertation on the Features and Treatment of
Insanity.* London, 1827. E. Esquirol, *Mental Maladies.* (Transla-
tion.) Philadelphia, 1845.

water as she lay in bed. . . . A sensitive, self-conscious
patient was confined in a cold, damp, gloomy, mephitic
cell, fed on perpetual hard bread, and otherwise treated
as a criminal." [6]

There were, in these times, not even any satisfactory
classifications of the different types of mental disease.
Indeed, many ills which we should now classify otherwise—for example, vertigo, or dizziness, and delirium due
to fever—were considered to be forms of insanity. The
few hospitals designed to care for the insane were exceedingly inadequate, and the unfortunate people suffering
from mental disease were often thrown into prison or
herded into almshouse stables. Many of them were still
secured by chains, or at least by manacles.

Milestones of progress. In 1803, Johann Christian
Reil wrote a book advocating psychological treatment for
the insane. Two years later he founded the *Magazin
für psychische Heilkunde*—the first journal devoted to
psychiatric problems. But the most important reform
was brought about by Philippe Pinel, in France. "At the
risk of his own life and liberty, he initiated the reforms of
striking off their chains, placing them in hospitals under
lenient physicians, and doing away with the abuses of
drugging and blood-letting to which they were subjected." [7] Esquirol, who succeeded Pinel (in 1810),
vigorously followed up the reforms in regimen and housing introduced by the latter. He founded ten new asylums and gave the first course of lectures in psychiatry
ever to be offered. England adopted the French methods
some years later, when Gardner Hill introduced the system of no restraint at Lincoln Asylum (1836) and John

[6] Garrison, *op. cit.*, pp. 418-419.
[7] *Ibid.*, p. 433.

Conolly discarded all mechanical restraint at the Hanwell Asylum (1839).[8]

In Germany, it was Griesinger, one of Reil's pupils, who became the advocate of the humane treatment of the insane. He also wrote on *Mental Pathology and Therapeutics* (1845), a treatise which gave clearly described clinical pictures of certain types of mental disease. Other German scientists continued the clinical study of insanity, until Emil Kraepelin finally (1883-1903) evolved a classification which is the basis of that used in contemporary psychiatry.

The status of the insane in the United States. If we turn to America, we shall find that it was no more progressive or humane in its treatment of individuals suffering from mental disease than was the Old World. In the colonial days, witchcraft persecutions persisted up to the close of the seventeenth century. Pennsylvania was the first of the colonies to provide institutional care for the insane, at the Philadelphia Almshouse (1732). This was exceedingly inadequate, however, and twenty years later the Pennsylvania Hospital was founded, with the avowed purpose of caring for insane patients as well as for other types of illnesses. At this institution, according to the records of the time, the insane patients were confined in cells and the curious or sportive citizens were able to visit them freely. For a time a small fee was charged for the privilege of looking at and conversing with these victims of mental disease, just as at the English Bedlam.

The first state hospital designed exclusively for patients with mental disease was at Williamsburg, Virginia (1773). New York opened a hospital to which the insane were admitted some years later (1791), and Maryland soon followed suit (1797). During the first half of the nine-

8 Garrison. *op. cit.*, p. 795.

teenth century, hospital care for the insane was provided in Massachusetts, Connecticut, Kentucky, Vermont, South Carolina, New Hampshire, Rhode Island, Indiana, Maine and Georgia. By 1850, the idea of the state hospital as the proper provision for the care of mental disease was widely accepted, and the next twenty-five years saw the erection of these institutions in many other states.

These early hospitals were far from ideal with respect to the methods of treatment. May states that "strong rooms, padded cells and mechanical restraint of all kinds were used extensively." [9] Moreover, the housing space was inadequate to the numbers of insane patients, many of whom were therefore placed in county "poorhouses" and other similar institutions.

One exception to the general run of hospitals should be noted. In 1817, the Society of Friends founded a hospital for the insane at Frankford, Pennsylvania. It is still in existence, and has the distinction of being, in all probability, the only one in America in which there was never any of the usual confinement in chains or other severe mechanical restraint. Unfortunately, the humane methods in vogue at this institution had no wide influence upon the general tendencies of the day.

Dr. Stephen Smith, recounting his experiences as state commissioner of lunacy in New York from 1882 to 1888, gives a picture of conditions as they existed there at that time. When he began his work, "every form of appliance for the restraint of the disturbed insane was to be seen in common use. They were found in manacles, in 'stocks,' in dungeons, chained to posts, strapped in bed." While some of the insane were properly treated as patients in the state hospitals, many others were in poorhouses and private institutions. "In one almshouse a man was daily

[9] James V. May, *Mental Diseases,* p. 46. Boston, 1922.

brought out of a stall in an out-building where he had
been confined twelve years, arms pinioned and led by his
keeper precisely as a dangerous animal is treated. Mean-
time, another man cleaned the stall and supplied fresh
straw for his bed. In another almshouse seven women
were found in separate stalls in a barrack in a state of
indescribable filthiness. Their attendant, or keeper, as
he was called, was a demented man who could scarcely
answer a question." [10]

In 1883, Dr. Smith drew up a bill providing for the
gradual transfer of the insane from county institutions to
the state asylums. It was opposed by the county officials,
because it would take away some of their revenues. The
opposition was so strong that the bill did not become a
law until six years later, despite the fact that the conditions in the county institutions cried aloud for relief.

This account of the status of the insane in New York
state is an example of what was happening in many other
places in all parts of the country. Everywhere, drastic
reforms were needed, and a few leaders were striving to
bring these about in the face of opposition from politicians
who were influenced by other than humanitarian motives.
Gradually, conditions were ameliorated; training classes
for nurses and attendants were established, and rudimentary courses in psychiatry were introduced into the
curricula of a few medical schools.

The longest struggle was that to accomplish the abolition of the severe mechanical restraints to which reference
has previously been made. The Boston state hospital was
probably the first to abandon them (1842), but their use
was continued in many institutions down to the close of
the nineteenth century. Even to-day we have occasional
reports of these abuses.

[10] Stephen Smith, *Who Is Insane?*, p. 172. New York, 1916.

Developments in the twentieth century. The enormous acceleration of the progress of science which is an outstanding characteristic of the twentieth century was reflected in the development of psychiatry. The whole of the nineteenth century had been devoted to securing humane treatment for the insane and providing them with custodial care. Compared to this, the accomplishments of the next twenty-five years assume a kaleidoscopic speed. From the time when the Pathological Institute of New York became the Psychiatric Institute (1902) and widened its investigations to include all methods of approach, the scientific study of mental diseases spread to different parts of the country. Psychopathic hospitals— the first in this country being that at the University of Michigan in 1906—were established for the treatment of mental disease, only the chronic cases being sent to the state hospitals for prolonged periods of treatment or for life care. Extra-institutional treatment for patients capable of remaining in the community under proper management became a prominent concept, and out-patient clinics multiplied. Meanwhile, the mental hygiene movement became firmly established, as we have seen, and the idea of prevention found expression in the foundation of psychiatric clinics for children.

While the plan for psychopathic hospitals and clinics may have originated in Europe, with the German scientists, the United States may well be proud of its leadership in mental hygiene and preventative work with children. Even here, however, a part of the intellectual inspiration came from Europe, where the study of psychopathology had its inception, and where child psychology had its beginnings, although the latter was soon taken over and developed much further by American psychologists.

The organic approach. Scientific psychiatry has approached the investigation of the causes of mental disease in two distinct ways. The earliest was through the study of the brain and other bodily structures as influencing mental processes. This method was probably most successful in the case of the mental disorder known as general paresis, which was definitely shown to be due to syphilitic infection of the nervous system.[11] The organic viewpoint was also successful in the diagnosis of certain other diseases, such as brain tumors.

In many types of mental illness it has been impossible, to date, to establish specific physical causation. But the sterility which has resulted from this approach has not discouraged many neurologists and psychiatrists from continuing to place their hopes upon it. The professional journals are full of papers reporting their findings, and it may be that these painstaking researches will some day prove fruitful, again, as was the case with general paresis. The search for gross lesions in the brain cells has for the most part been replaced with study of the physio-chemical processes, such as research concerning the changes in blood chemistry in certain types of psychoses or the functions of the endocrine glands. Some of the findings, if not of major etiological significance, have added to our knowledge of the bodily changes that accompany mentally diseased states.

With a few exceptions, the status of these physiological findings may be considered analogous to the old controversy surrounding the James-Lange theory of the emotions: Do we fear because we tremble, or do we tremble because we are afraid? There might well be raised the

[11] Neurosyphilis (or syphilis of the nervous system) does not always attack the brain and interfere with normal functioning of the higher mental processes. Its effect may be confined to the spinal nerve centers.

similar question: Do we become mentally unbalanced because of changes in blood chemistry (or other physical states), or are these changes a result of the mental illness? Each viewpoint has its advocates, but the latter seems to be increasingly emphasized.

The Psychogenic approach. Many scientists concerned with the causation of mental diseases have emphasized the psychogenic factors. Janet's famous studies of hysteria represent pioneer work in this field, but it is the psychoanalytic school which has pushed this approach to its utmost advantages. Sigmund Freud, of Vienna, was the originator of the psychoanalytic method. His first studies were published nearly thirty-five years ago. His later work has become so well known that it seems almost trite to mention his name. It was he who pointed out the important rôle of the "psychic trauma" in the etiology of the psychoneuroses, and who worked out a technique for the discovery of the trauma and the reëducation of the patient without the use of hypnosis.

Freud's brilliant work attracted many pupils to his clinic. Some of them have elaborated his discoveries and furnished new interpretations, so that there is now an extensive literature on the theory and practice of psychoanalysis. For a time, many of the American psychiatrists were repelled by Freud's concentration upon the sexual impulses in relation to psychoneurotic symptoms, and rejected psychoanalysis because it appeared to them as nothing more than sex psychology. With the modifications of the original doctrine to be found in the later works of Freud, and in the contributions of Adler, Jung, Maeder, Rank and other analysts, this attitude toward psychoanalysis has no present basis in fact. The place of sex is still recognized as an important one, but it no longer is offered as the sole explanation of the psychoneuroses.

The most significant contribution of psychoanalysis is its insistence upon the long incubation period required for functional nervous and mental disorders, and the major importance assigned to environmental influences in the production of abnormal personalities. One of the foremost principles is that childhood experience, especially with reference to relationships within the family group, is the chief determinant of the future mental stability or instability of the individual—a tenet which has also come to have a prominent part in the teachings of academic psychology.

Twentieth century psychology. In the field of psychology changes have been no less rapid and striking than in psychiatry. From the laboratory analysis of isolated sensory experiences and separate mental processes, psychology awakened to an interest in the whole organism as reacting to all the complexities of environmental stimuli. It also became concerned with the internal drives to activity—the instinctive and emotional impulses of the lower animals and of man. At first satisfied to describe these from a somewhat philosophical viewpoint, depending primarily upon anthropological data or personal observation and speculation, it soon undertook a controlled laboratory study of the behavior of animals and children. The scope of the investigations was soon widened to include clinical material.

The beginnings of this psychological awakening were European (German and Russian), but the impetus given to child study and the psychology of the emotions by G. Stanley Hall and William Burnham at Clark University, and by the later work of Watson, Baldwin and Gesell with infants and pre-school children, soon placed the United States in the lead. Precise and exact information concerning the child's mental and emotional development was sought. Particularly important, in relation to mental hygiene, were the evidences that emotional responses and attitudes could be built up readily, and in many instances permanently, through the experiences of the child's early years.

Of great importance also, from the mental hygiene viewpoint, were the psychological tests which had been devised for measuring the intelligence of the child and for gathering information to be used as a basis for educational and vocational guidance. The development of a clinical psychology, with methods which could be put to practical use, provided a technique which could be utilized to advantage for mental hygiene aims. Thus psychology, in its pure and applied branches, as well as the existence of a scientific psychiatry, helped to set the stage for the appearance of mental hygiene and to insure its success.

The emergence of mental hygiene. Thus, along independent lines of thought, the workers in psychiatry and psychology had advanced toward a conception of many mental hygiene principles. The more progressive psychiatrists and psychologists were beginning to think not only in terms of therapy, but also in terms of prevention when confronted by problems of human adaptation. There were, to be sure, wide gulfs between the workers in different fields; between psychologists and psychiatrists, and even between the leaders of the different schools of thought in each of these sciences. But these divergencies were reconciled, as Schmalhausen well describes, "in the synthetic movement called Mental Hygiene. . . . We escape from historic futilities by focussing our attention upon man and his realistic milieu, and conceiving it good psychology (excellent, in sooth) to understand man as a product of analyzable social forces, and so understanding him, to devote our psychological devices and insights to an amelioration of his baffled and maladjusted state. This profound task of salvaging human nature . . . is the humble task set for itself by mental hygiene." [12]

No new disciplines were necessary for the practice of mental hygiene; it had simply to avail itself of the tools already at hand but thus far not employed with maximum efficiency because used independently. The strength of mental hygiene lay partly in its triumphant seizure of all these tools and by its skillful use of them to supplement one another. But the rapid growth of the mental hygiene movement was also due to the need for it which human beings had—a need growing ever greater as their biological organisms were called upon to make more complex adjustments to the complicated social organization which they themselves had created.

By virtue of its synthetic nature, mental hygiene was able to avoid the limitations which almost inevitably follow acceptance of a single doctrine and rejection of all others. It placed its emphasis upon the importance of understanding the whole organism in relation to the total environmental stimulation. To reach this understanding required a compound of general medicine, neurology, psychiatry, psychoanalysis, sociology and the art of social case work, behaviorism and mental testing, and from each of these fields (as well as from many others) mental hygiene selected whatever could be useful in the accomplishment of its task. Since it is not committed to any one theory and perhaps accepts none in toto, it is not held to lost causes. If any of its choices do not meet the pragmatic test, they can be discarded and replaced. This capacity for change and advance together with its human-

[12] S. D. Schmalhausen, *Why We Misbehave,* pp. 192-193. New York, 1928.

istic attitude are the characteristics which make mental hygiene a vital social force in contemporary life.

The stimulating influence of mental hygiene. If in its origins mental hygiene owes a debt to psychology and psychiatry (in particular), it has more than repaid it by the stimulating and broadening influence it has exerted on those two sciences. In its mental hygiene aspects, clinical psychology has advanced far beyond the simple task of mental testing and has become concerned with educational and vocational maladjustments, motivation of conduct, personality development, and many other dynamic and vital phases of human life and adjustment. As for psychiatry, which was originally limited to the treatment of mental disease, in response to the mental hygiene demands upon it, it has been re-created.

"Consider . . . some of the problems which in clinics and in private practice crowd upon the modern psychiatrist. . . . There are peculiar mental attitudes and behavior manifestations found in family situations; . . . there is a host of school problems being presented, relating both to conduct and to educational progress; there is the work for juvenile courts and for parents who come with delinquents, asking for psychiatric clues to the causes and treatment of conduct disorder; there are the social agencies . . . more and more asking psychiatry to step in and help develop a plan of life adjustment, or actually to undertake psychotherapeutic treatment in difficult cases. And less well developed conceptions of the service that psychiatry should render come . . . in connection with industrial relationships, studies of divorce and other social irregularities, teaching the principles of mental hygiene, of good parental relationships and what not." [13]

[13] William Healy, "'The Newer Psychiatry," *American Journal of Psychiatry,* January, 1926, Vol. V, p. 391.

SUGGESTIONS FOR CLASSROOM DISCUSSION

1. What were the magical and supernatural explanations for mental disease?
2. How were the insane treated during the Middle Ages?
3. What people were the first to accord humane treatment to patients suffering from mental disease?
4. What were the achievements of the nineteenth century with respect to treatment of mental disease?
5. What were the two principal methods of scientific study of mental disease?
6. What did twentieth century psychology have to offer the mental hygiene movement?
7. In what way has mental hygiene made use of psychiatry and psychology?
8. What has been the effect of mental hygiene upon those two sciences?

SUGGESTIONS FOR WRITTEN REPORTS

1. Magic and folk lore in relation to mental disease.
2. The state hospital movement.
3. Development of the psychopathic hospital and its functions.
4. The types of problems with which modern psychiatry is concerned.
5. The development of clinical psychology.

SELECTED BIBLIOGRAPHY

Samples of Early Texts in Psychiatry

BUCKNILL and TUKE. *A Manual of Psychological Medicine.* Philadelphia, 1858.

CRICHTON, ALEXANDER. *An Inquiry into the Nature and Origin of Mental Derangement.* London, 1798.

ESQUIROL, E. *Mental Maladies.* Philadelphia, 1845.

GRIESINGER, W. *Mental Pathology and Therapeutics* (published in Germany, 1845). London, The New Sydenham Society, 1867.

SYER, JOHN. A *Dissertation on the Features and Treatment of Insanity.* London, 1827.

Samples of Modern Texts

MAY, JAMES V. *Mental Diseases.* Boston, 1922.

MORGAN, JOHN J. B. *The Psychology of Abnormal People.* New York, 1928.

SANDS and BLANCHARD. *Abnormal Behavior.* New York, 1923.

SCHILDER, PAUL. *Introduction to a Psychoanalytic Psychiatry.* Nervous and Mental Disease Publishing Co., 1928.

STRECKER and EBAUGH. *Practical Clinical Psychiatry.* Philadelphia, 1925.

TAYLOR, W. S. (Editor). *Readings in Abnormal Psychology and Mental Hygiene.* New York, 1926.

WHITE, W. A. *Outlines of Psychiatry.* Nervous and Mental Disease Publishing Co., 1919.

Collateral Readings

ABBOTT, E. S. "What Is Mental Hygiene?" *American Journal of Psychiatry,* 1924, Vol. IV, pp. 261-284.

BARRETT, A. M. "The Broadened Interest of Psychiatry." *American Journal of Psychiatry,* 1922, Vol. II, pp. 1-14.

BOSSARD, JAMES H. S. *Problems of Social Well-Being,* Chap. XXV. New York, 1927.

BURNHAM, W. H. *The Normal Mind,* Chap. I. New York, 1924.

FERENCZI, S. "Freud's Importance for the Mental Hygiene Movement." *Mental Hygiene,* 1926, Vol. X, pp. 673-676.

GARRISON, F. H. *An Introduction to the History of Medicine,* pp. 2-70; 124-129; 418-419; 433-434; 700-702. Philadelphia, 1921.

GROVES, E. R. *Social Problems and Education,* Chap. III. New York, 1925.

HALL, G. STANLEY. *Life and Confessions of a Psychologist,* Chap. VIII. New York, 1923.

HART, BERNARD. *Psychopathology,* pp. 1-57. New York, 1927.

HEALY, WILLIAM. "The Newer Psychiatry." *American Journal of Psychiatry,* 1926, Vol. V, pp. 391-402.

LURIE, LOUIS A. "The Relation of Endocrinopathic States to

Conduct Disorders of Children." *American Journal of Psychiatry*, September, 1929, Vol. IX, pp. 285-305.

MAY, JAMES V. *Mental Diseases*. Part I, especially Chaps. II, VI and XIII. New York, 1922.

MEYER, ADOLPH. "Twenty-five Years of Psychiatry in the United States and Our Present Outlook." *American Journal of Psychiatry*, 1928, Vol. VIII, pp. 1-31.

MORGAN, JOHN J. B. *The Psychology of Abnormal People*, Chaps. I and XVII. New York, 1928.

OGDEN, C. K. *The Meaning of Psychology*, Chaps. I and XV. New York, 1926.

PAYNTER, R. H. "Humanizing Psychology in the Study of Behavior Problems in Children." *School and Society*, November 6, 1926, Vol. XXIV.

POLON, ALBERT. "The Growth of Psychotherapy and the Evolution of Psychoanalysis." *Mental Hygiene*, 1924, Vol. VIII, pp. 55-68.

RIVERS, W. H. R. *Medicine, Magic and Religion*. London, 1924.

SCHMALHAUSEN, S. D. *Why We Misbehave*, Chap. VIII. New York, 1928.

TERMAN, L. M. "The Mental Test as a Psychological Method." *Psychological Review*, 1924, Vol. 31, pp. 93-117.

YOUNG, KIMBALL. *The History of Mental Testing*. Pedagogical Seminary, 1923, Vol. XXXI, pp. 1-48.

WELLS, F. L. *Mental Tests and Clinical Practice*. Yonkers, 1927.

CHAPTER III

THE PROBLEM OF MENTAL DISEASE

Prevalence of mental disease. From the careful statistical studies of the prevalence of mental disease in the United States it is possible to make reliable general statements. Strecker and Ebaugh summarize these facts as follows:

"It is known that 50,000 new patients are admitted annually to the state institutions for the insane. When one takes into consideration the many patients who never reach public hospitals (being cared for privately) and, further, the numerous psychopathological border-line conditions such as the psychoneuroses, which are often just as serious and disabling in their consequences as the psychoses, yet do not require institutional care, it becomes clear that mental disease constitutes a serious and far-reaching economic problem."[1]

We could perhaps take a more optimistic attitude toward the problem of mental disease if a survey of the statistics showed that it was tending to decrease. But the evidence of the figures shows, on the contrary, that mental disease is still increasing. In 1910, the state hospitals were giving custodial care to 187,791 patients; in 1920 there were 232,680 patients in these institutions,[2] and the 1927 census shows that the numbers are still

[1] Strecker and Ebaugh, *Clinical Psychiatry,* p. 1. Philadelphia, 1925.
[2] Pollock and Furbush, "Patients with Mental Disease," *Mental Hygiene,* January, 1921, Vol. V, p. 145.

growing steadily.[3] In 1910, the number of state hospital patients per 100,000 of the general population was 204.2; in 1918 it was 217.5; in 1920 it was 220.1; in 1923 it was 218.5, and in 1927 it was 226.9. Thus there is a consistent tendency toward the increase of mental disease as measured by admissions to state hospitals. It has been suggested that people have acquired a better understanding of mental illness and therefore turn more frequently to the hospitals for aid. But we must remember that there has recently been remarkable· improvement in methods of treatment and prevention which, other things being equal, should balance the effect of lay education.

Modern civilization and mental strain. It may well be that the increasing prevalence of mental disease comes from the very nature of modern civilization. We live in an age dominated by machinery, and this has keyed up the speed at which we work and play and carry on many other activities to a rate which is far in excess of our capacity for biological adaptation. This accelerated tempo of living is productive of enormous mental tension and fatigue. Again, modern life stimulates conflict. Large scale production, with its advertising calculated to induce desire for material objects, extends the number of human wants indefinitely and far beyond the means to acquire satisfaction except for those who are financially well-to-do. The unsatisfied desires of the individual tend to increase tension and to breed emotional conflicts.

In a democratic society, where the social philosophy stresses equality of opportunity, the mass of less able individuals must always be discontented with their lot. The failure to achieve reacts upon the personality to cause feelings of insecurity and inferiority, and nothing

[3] H. M. Pollock, "State Institution Population Still Increasing," *Mental Hygiene*, January, 1928, Vol. XII, p. 103.

is more productive of mental maladjustment than prolonged feelings of this kind. Thus the bitterness of failure, which is such a common experience, plays a part in
the causation of mental breakdowns.

Still another factor in modern life is the increasing
dominance of the city. The movement of the population
in the last twenty years has been steadily toward urbanization. Not more than half the population of the country
has remained in rural districts. And the rural population
is dominated by the city, in these days of rapid travel and
communication, to an extent which was formerly impossible. This urban domination has imposed more complex
adjustments upon the individual and it may be that personalities become disintegrated under this pressure which
might have preserved normality under simpler conditions
and faced with less drastic demands.

Organic and functional mental disorders. Modern
psychiatry divides mental diseases into two classes—the
organic and the functional. To the former belong those
which have a definite physical basis involving pathological
changes in brain tissue. About thirty per cent of mental
diseases, according to recent figures, are of the organic
type. The names and frequency of occurrence are given
in the following table: [4]

General Paresis.....................10.6 per cent
Senile Psychoses...................12.1 "   "
Psychoses with Cerebral Arteriosclerosis. 2.1 "   "
Epileptic Psychoses................ 2.7 "   "
Psychoses with Huntington's Chorea,
    Brain Tumor and Other Brain and
    Nervous Diseases................ 1.2 "   "
Traumatic Psychoses............... 0.3 "   "
Encephalitis..............No statistics available.

[4] Taken from Strecker and Ebaugh, *Clinical Psychiatry,* p. 55.
New York, 1925.

In the functional mental disorders, there is no pathology of the brain structure; at least it has thus far been impossible to demonstrate structural changes even with the aid of all the instruments modern science has at its command. The functioning of the brain is obviously abnormal, however. The most common functional mental disorders are: [5]

Dementia Præcox.................27.0 per cent
Manic Depressive Psychoses.........16.0 " "
Involution Melancholia............. 3.3 " "
Paranoid conditions................ 2.8 " "
Psychoneuroses and Neuroses......... 2.1 " "

Not falling in either of these two main groups is a small number of mental disorders of which the most frequent are the alcoholic psychoses (estimated at about five per cent), psychoses due to use of drugs (slightly over one per cent) and the psychoses which occur in association with certain physical diseases (between three and four per cent).[6]

Heredity and mental disease. There is a very pessimistic view, taken by some investigators who have been unable to find a satisfactory explanation of the functional mental disorders in any other manner, of the relation of heredity to the incidence of mental disease. Rosanoff, for example, advances the proposition that its onset is predetermined in the inheritance of the individual in harmony with the Mendelian laws.[7] But there are many psychiatrists who feel satisfied that the life experiences

[5] *Op. cit.,* p. 12.
[6] The percentages given here and in the two tables preceding do not make 100 because certain very rare forms of mental disease have not been mentioned.
[7] A. J. Rosanoff, *Manual of Psychiatry,* pp. 2-6. New York, 1920.

of the individual molding his reaction patterns into certain habitual modes of response have far more to do with his normality of mind and his ability to resist mental strain than the presence or absence of psychopathic individuals in his ancestry. As William A. White has summed it up:

"In dealing with the subject of heredity, however, it must not be forgotten that our ideas are of necessity largely founded upon hypotheses, as biological science has not yet unfolded a sufficient number of facts to make it possible for us to tell just how much, in any individual case, must be attributed to the inherent qualities of the germ plasm and just how much to the influences of environment." [8]

Strecker and Ebaugh comment that undue stress has often been placed on heredity, to the exclusion of such other factors as the environmental influences of childhood, endocrine imbalances and other conditions. They conclude:

"While the student of psychiatry must needs respect the rôle which heredity plays, yet he should not permit himself to be overwhelmed by its unknown significance, nor should he become at all pessimistic in his psychiatric point of view. Probably, some individuals inherit less resistant cardio-vascular systems than others; but this is no reason why the cardiologist should become fantastic in his conception of heart and blood vessel diseases." [9]

As a matter of fact, the fatalistic attitude which makes heredity all-powerful retards our understanding of mental

[8] W. A. White, *Outlines of Psychiatry,* p. 35. Nervous and Mental Disease Pub. Co., 1923. Dr. White also points out that insanity, which is the name applied to various groups of symptoms, differing from one another in the different types of psychoses, can hardly be considered a unit character in the Mendelian sense (p. 27).

[9] *Clinical Psychiatry,* p. 8.

disorders and interferes with the development of preventative methods. For the psychiatrist, it is all too easy an excuse for ceasing further research into the facts of causation; for the lay person who happens to have had a close relative that suffered from any mental disease, it often becomes a veritable nightmare. In the latter instance, the fear is far more apt to become a predisposing cause of mental instability than the biological inheritance. Moreover, there is at the present time considerable data concerning personality development which suggests that many traits formerly accepted as hereditary are in reality acquired; these data throw grave suspicion on earlier studies of heredity.[10]

Controllable etiological factors. Mental hygiene, in its concern with the prevention of mental disease, is eminently practical and deals with facts. Many of the organic and functional mental disorders are undoubtedly preventable. General paresis, in the organic group, is certainly susceptible to prevention. We know that it is caused by syphilis and medical science offers a treatment which is capable of arresting the course of this disease and also prophylactic measures which protect the person who has been exposed to infection. The social attitude toward the venereal diseases interferes with the use of these methods to considerable extent, the idea of shame and disgrace causing the person who has been exposed to syphilis or who has contracted the infection to hesitate in seeking medical aid. If public health education were employed in the interests of preventing general paresis the present situation could be overcome and the percentage

[10] For a brief summary of the data concerning emotional responses, attitudes, etc., in their genetic development, see Blanchard, *The Child and Society,* Chaps. I and II. New York, 1928. See also W. A. White, *Mechanisms of Character Formation.* New York, 1918.

of mental patients suffering from this disorder could be greatly reduced.[11]

Although we have somewhat less specific knowledge in the case of the senile psychoses (which, with general paresis, form the two largest groups among the organic mental diseases) and in psychoses with cerebral arteriosclerosis, here, too, prevention can be at least partially assured by early medical treatment and careful guarding of the health in those types which show susceptibility to these conditions. If the habit of annual health examinations could become widespread, treatment could be instituted, in many instances, sufficiently early to ward off the later development of psychotic symptoms with respect to these two types of mental disorder.[12]

Despite the evils of bootlegging and the fashionable status of drinking (even at the risk of blindness or death from poisonous beverages) which have resulted from federal prohibition, psychiatrists agree that there has been a noticeable decrease in the number of psychoses directly traceable to alcoholism. In nineteen state hospitals, in 1910 the admissions showed eleven per cent suffering from psychoses due to alcoholism; in 1922 the percentage of admissions of this kind was only 3.9 per cent.[13] Thus we see what can be accomplished by preventative methods, even when these depend upon legal restraints and are enforced from without.

The above illustrations represent only a few examples of the way in which the etiological factors of mental disease may be brought under control in the interests of pre-

[11] I. J. Sands, "The Controllable Etiological Factors in Insanity, and How to Utilize Them," *Neurological Bulletin,* April, 1919, Vol. II, pp. 159-164 (see pp. 159-160). Strecker and Ebaugh, *Clinical Psychiatry,* p. 56.

[12] I. J. Sands, *op. cit.,* pp. 160-161.

[13] Pollock and Furbush, "Prohibition and Alcoholic Mental Disease," *Mental Hygiene,* April, 1924, Vol. VIII, pp. 548-570.

ventative medicine. There are many psychiatrists who believe that the functional mental disorders are as much, probably more, capable of yielding to preventative methods. The situation is more complicated, however, and will therefore be discussed in separate sections in a later part of this chapter.

Psychiatry and psychology in the war: an experiment in prevention. Under the conditions of modern warfare, two types of men proved unfit for service. These were the mentally deficient individuals, whose intellectual capacity was so limited that they could not become adapted to the demands made upon them, and the individuals who showed early symptoms of mental disease or displayed characteristics indicating a tendency to mental disorder which could be expected to break out into an open psychosis or psychoneurosis under undue environmental strain. It became the duty of the psychological and neuropsychiatric services of the army to weed out these types from the enlisted men and recruits. Although undertaken in the interests of building an efficient army, the results were significant from the mental hygiene viewpoint. Many individuals were protected from entering into an enterprise which would have caused them to become the victims of mental disease. The army was guarded against inefficiency, to be sure, but at the same time an important piece of preventative work was accomplished.

Through the army psychological examinations, 7,800 men were found to be of very inferior intellectual status and were recommended for discharge. Another 8,000 were referred for special psychiatric examination and discharge, on the basis of the psychological findings.[14] The

[14] Figures quoted from Vol. XV of the Memoirs of the National Academy of Sciences, "Psychological Examining in the United States Army," p. 99 and p. 116.

work of the psychological division in devising methods for maintaining morale is less easily evaluated from statistical data. But who can say whether the maintenance of morale, although instigated in order to produce an effective fighting spirit among the troops, may not also have helped to sustain their mental integrity and enabled them to withstand the painful situations with which they were confronted better than they could otherwise have done?

The psychiatric achievements were even more striking. By the advice of the neuropsychiatric examiners, more than 72,000 men were rejected from the drafted army. "Largely as a result of this remarkable work," says Clifford Beers, "the rate of mental and nervous cases evacuated to the United States from France was less than that from any expeditionary force in history. The incidence of mental disease in the A.E.F. was one-third lower than the rate among the troops on the Mexican border in 1916. The total number of men sent home for the neuroses ('shell-shock') was a little over 2,000. The rate for suicides in the A.E.F. was phenomenally low, being only one-tenth that in the regular army in 1915. The elimination of mentally defective and psychopathic soldiers in the camps at home was also a factor of prime importance in the remarkably low prevalence of serious crime in the A.E.F. Of the 2,000,000 men who left this country for France only 1,700 were returned as general prisoners." [15]

Out of the study of the war neuroses came a new understanding of this form of mental disease. In case after case, the patient's real difficulty was shown to be one of

[15] Clifford Beers, *The Mental Hygiene Movement,* National Committee for Mental Hygiene, 370 Seventh Ave., New York, 1923, p. 343. (Also in *A Mind That Found Itself.* New York, 1923.)

unwholesome personality development, with origins extending back into the early years, rather than the immediate physical trauma or mental shock. This discovery gave a new impetus to the personality studies already undertaken by many of the leaders in the field of psychiatry. Thus, besides its immediate practical value, the neuropsychiatric work in the war was a contribution to the scientific study of mental disease.

Personality studies in relation to mental disorders. For a considerable period, psychiatry was concerned with the classification of mental diseases and with problems of differential diagnosis,—a necessary stage in the development of the science but not a very fruitful one in yielding therapeutic and preventative measures. Then came Adolf Meyer's emphasis on "the living patient" and the necessity of "adjusting individual and environment, and the individual to a whole lifetime." [16]   Contemporaneously, other psychiatrists and psychologists were occupied with studies of personality types from the viewpoint of the development of personality traits and the part played by these in determining the adaptability of the individual to environmental situations. Outstanding contributions in this direction were made by Hoch and Amsden, F. L. Wells and the Allports.[17] These studies brought a new leavening into psychiatry and helped to formulate a con-

[16] "Twenty-five Years of Psychiatry in the United States and Our Present Outlook," *American Journal of Psychiatry,* July, 1928, Vol. VIII, pp. 1-31.

[17] Hoch and Amsden, "A Guide to the Descriptive Study of the Personality," *State Hospital Bulletin,* November, 1913.   G. S. Amsden, "Systematic Study of the Personality in Estimating Adaptability," *Archives of Neurology and Psychiatry,* March, 1919, Vol. I, pp. 301-312.   F. H. and G. W. Allport, "Personality Traits; Their Classification and Measurement," *Journal of Abnormal Psychology,* April, 1921, Vol. XVI, pp. 6-40.   F. L. Wells, "The Systematic Observation of the Personality in Its Relation to the Hygiene of the Mind," *Psychological Review,* July, 1914, Vol. XXI, pp. 295-333.

ception of the functional mental disorders as something other than distinct disease entities.

Our present understanding indicates that the abnormal personality differs from the normal in degree rather than in kind. The personality traits and behavior patterns which characterize such functional mental disorders as dementia præcox, manic depressive psychoses, paranoid conditions and psychoneurotic states are found also in everyday life among individuals who are adapting themselves fairly well to economic and social demands. The picture is exaggerated in the maladjusted person, to be sure, but it is nevertheless recognizable as the same.

Distinct personality types may be seen even among children. There is the seclusive or shut-in type, for example. Children and adults belonging in this group do not mingle readily with others but are quiet and reserved, preferring reading, daydreaming or other isolated pleasures to group activities. Some of these seclusive persons become fairly well adjusted, fitting into a vocation that does not require the ability to be "a good mixer" and maintaining a family life which is not subjected to wide social demands. A few may be found among the scholarly figures to whom we look for intellectual leadership. But others become more and more seclusive and retreat from reality into the inner world of dreams. In extreme cases, we find that they break down completely in the functional mental disorder called dementia præcox.

Another abnormal personality appears in its extreme degree in the manic depressive patient of the psychiatric clinic or hospital. The manic depressive psychosis is characterized by marked fluctuations of mood, varying from the heights of elation to the depths of depression—hence its name. In the elated or manic mood, the person is talkative, facetious, restless and at times excited and boisterous. In the depressed phase, he is quiet, talks little or none, moves slowly or sits sunken in sadness, is oppressed by a feeling of guilt, and may be constantly tearful.

Many normal individuals show similar mood variations to those which characterize the manic depressive patient, the principal difference being one of degree. They do not reach the same intense pitch of elation or the marked state of depression shown in the psychosis. Indeed, when the manic depressive temperament is not carried to the extremities of psychotic reactions, it may be an asset rather than a liability. Especially is this true of individuals in whom the buoyant (elated) phase is predominant. They have an abundant supply of energy and, given a high intelligence, often show a distinctly creative bent. One author of clever and witty short stories possesses this type of personality. The rapid stream of verbal imagery which is a distinct manic trait is well adapted to the profession of writing so long as the associations are fairly logical. In the psychotic state, the associations become illogical and may depend upon superficial relationships such as clang or rhyme qualities of words.

The personality traits which accompany paranoid conditions and neurotic and psychoneurotic symptoms are also to be met in everyday experience. Typical of the paranoid is the suspicious attitude toward other people and the belief that they intend to inflict some injury. The neurotics and psychoneurotics are particularly marked by their inability to face reality. They may be fearful, indecisive, oversensitive and hypochondriacal. They become discouraged easily and abstain from making efforts to adjust to work situations or they seek refuge in physical ill-health which seems to them serious although medical examination usually shows them to be fairly well and at the most suffering only from minor difficulties which should not prove at all incapacitating. Hysterical reactions and the war neuroses (shell shock) are illustrations of an extreme development of the psychoneurotic personality. Less severe but of a similar nature are complaints of illness put forth by children who lack the courage to face some unpleasant school situation or by adults who find their work uncongenial.[18]

A genetic conception of personality. There is considerable evidence that personality traits are developed gradually as acquired characteristics which eventually become habitual and an integral part of individuality. The different situations to which the child is exposed set up patterns of response and if the same patterns are continually repeated they are apt to become permanent. There is probably a tendency toward the repetition of those responses which are accompanied by emotional satisfaction and cessation of reactions which do not gratify the emotional needs. Thus the process of personality formation depends somewhat upon trial-and-error, trial-and-success procedure, if the analogy may be permitted in this field. The child may respond differently to very similar situations until he happens upon a response which brings with it satisfaction; thereafter he tends to repeat it, to make it an habitual pattern, and in time it becomes a fairly fixed element of personality and behavior.[19]

Let us consider, for example, how the shut-in type of personality may be formed in early years. Here is a six-

[18] For a more elaborate study of these abnormal personality trends see Sands and Blanchard, *Abnormal Behavior*, Chap. V. New York, 1923.

[19] In this connection see "The Formation of Life Patterns," by Leslie B. Hohman, *Mental Hygiene*, January, 1927, Vol. XI, pp. 23-37, and "The Family Situation and Personality Development," by Phyllis Blanchard, *Mental Hygiene*, January, 1927, Vol. XI, pp. 15-22.

teen year old boy, of dull intelligence, who has always
been unfavorably compared with an elder brother. His
parents find their eldest son admirable in every way but
have always been critical of the youngest. He has taken
refuge in daydreams in which he pictures himself as a
much more successful person, and the habit of daydreaming has increased as he has grown older until now it
occupies much of his time. He has been made sensitive
by his parents' criticisms and therefore interprets even
a mild reproof from his teachers as having a much more
serious intent than is actually implied. He also has a
tendency to see criticism where none is intended. Recently, he wonders whether anyone who looks at him is
thinking of him in critical terms. He is even beginning
to think that strangers are laughing at him.

From such a state of affairs it is a comparatively short
step to a real dementia præcox with paranoid trends.
Unless the boy's situation can be changed, his rapidly
growing sensitiveness and feeling of failure may lead him
to develop hallucinations. Perhaps he will begin to hear
strangers talking about him and ridiculing him. Such
auditory hallucinations and delusions are not uncommon.
Then he will be forced to shut himself up more tightly in
his dream-world, where he can create more satisfactory
conditions. We can conceive of his retreating further and
further into daydreams until he loses all contact with
reality. The hallucinations then will die away, his feeling
of failure will no longer trouble him, but he will also have
lost all knowledge of his own identity and that of his parents and teachers; in short, he will be a patient in a hospital for mental diseases.

That is what may happen, but the future for this particular boy is probably brighter than this, because at this
critical stage in his affairs he has been provided with aid.

A psychiatrist is helping him to talk over his difficulties, and this process in itself provides a wholesome touch with reality and furnishes him with the first person, perhaps, in all his experience, who seems non-critical. The parents will be helped to understand the boy's trouble and will (it is to be hoped) see the need for encouraging the boy about the things he can do instead of demanding of him achievements above his capacities. At the school, if the teachers are able to realize his sensitiveness and his inability to attain to the highest scholastic standards, his situation may be made a much more pleasant one.

As the matter stands, we have in this boy's case a rather well-defined type of personality with which we must deal. The treatment measures do not rest upon so simple a foundation as altering habits (which is only to be described as simple by comparison). Rather we must seek below the habit level and provide experiences which will bring forth responses of a different kind. Specifically, in this instance, we must make reality sufficiently tolerable so that he will not be forced to take refuge in a dreamland, and we must help him to make friends through insuring that some of his personal contacts will offer encouragement instead of criticism. Thus we shall insure emotional satisfactions as a result of his new experiences and his reactions thereto, for without such satisfaction we cannot hope to build them into his individuality. The task would be easier if his reactions had had less time to crystallize, if the aid could have been proffered when he was eight or ten or twelve years of age. Then we would have been engaged more in prevention and less with therapy. But whether we are applying therapy or prevention in the field of personality and behavior, we are involved in very complex and subtle matters.

Mental disease symptoms in relation to normal mental processes. The various symptoms associated with the different types of mental disease involve disorders of nearly all the mental processes. We have the hysterical anesthesias, for example, in which the cutaneous sensations are no longer registered in the consciousness of the individual; the hallucinations, which interpret sensory experiences incorrectly, giving false perceptions; the delusions, which are somewhat like errors in judgment but with the error persisting because of emotional factors. Morgan, in his exceptionally fine treatment of mental abnormalities,[20] has shown very clearly how the normal process becomes disordered in a gradual fashion, usually passing over by slow degrees into open abnormality and becoming a symptom of mental disease. He also brings out vividly the underlying causes of these symptoms as found in emotional maladjustments and unfortunate personality development.

As has been previously intimated, for purposes of treatment and prevention we must be chiefly concerned with etiology; therefore we shall devote no further time to the discussion of symptoms in the present text. The interested reader is referred to Morgan's work, where he will find a thorough treatment of the subject which is all the more valuable because of the presentation, the relationship between symptoms and causal factors being carefully worked out.

Present conception of functional mental disorder and prevention. The fundamental principle in our present conception of the etiology of mental disease stresses the long incubation period which precedes the frank psychosis or neurosis. "It is commonly believed," writes

[20] J. J. B. Morgan, *The Psychology of Abnormal People,* Chaps. II-VIII, inclusive. New York, 1928.

Frankwood Williams, director of the National Committee for Mental Hygiene, "that individuals become insane suddenly. No one ever became insane suddenly. Mental disease develops over a long period of time. From small beginnings it grows insidiously, until, to the uninitiated, it blossoms forth in full bloom to the distress and consternation of those taken by surprise. And yet, before their eyes and the eyes of school teachers and ministers and friends and family physician, the thing has been developing all these years—only they have called it by other names." [21]

It is this conception of mental disorders which has been an incentive to the development of psychiatric clinics for children and of student personnel work in the colleges and universities. When the mental maladjustment has advanced to the stage of unmistakable mental disorder a long period of therapy is necessary, involving unhappiness of the individual, his relatives and friends, and also an economic and social loss in terms of the months, even the years, of treatment and readjustment. When unwholesome personality trends are detected in early life, and reconstruction of the personality undertaken at that time, the outcome is less problematical and far more hopeful.

Physical health a basis for mental health. The modern emphasis on personality adjustments as fundamental for mental health does not imply a neglect of physical hygiene. The effect of bodily ills upon the functions of the mind has been amply treated in medical literature, however, and seems to require no more than a passing emphasis in a text of this nature. It is generally recognized that, other things being equal, the sound mind is most apt

[21] "Community Responsibility in Mental Hygiene," *American Review,* January, 1923. Reprinted in *Mental Hygiene,* July, 1923, Vol. VII, pp. 496-508.

to be found in a healthy body. Along with attention to wholesome development of personality and character should go obedience to the principles of physical hygiene.

There are certain somatic diseases which undoubtedly carry with them the possibility of weakening or destroying mental integrations. Certain diseases of the heart, lungs, brain, endocrine glands and other organs of the body may bring about marked changes in personality and impair the mental health of the sufferer. It is axiomatic, for good mental hygiene, that all such bodily defects be treated and, if possible, corrected.

But, on the other hand, the possession of a sound physical organism is not in itself enough to insure mental health. It is a very favorable factor, certainly, but in spite of its possession the social stresses to which the individual is subjected may be great enough in themselves to bring about a mental breakdown. Illness may follow mental strain rather than being a contributory cause, for intense emotional disturbances are likely to levy a toll upon physical as well as mental well-being. Nevertheless, we may be justified in assuming that physical health is an asset which aids in the resistance to mental disease, and that illness renders the personality more vulnerable to other unwholesome influences.

ILLUSTRATIVE CASE

Mary Smith's early childhood was spent in a home where parental disharmony was acute. After her birth, her mother refused to have further marital relations with her husband, and the latter turned to other women for the satisfactions denied him by his wife. Mary was a witness to frequent quarrels between her parents until her father left home permanently when she was eight years old. Mary's mother became still more embittered and assumed a domineering attitude toward the child. She was not permitted to bring any of her girl friends to the home for play, and as she grew older her mother constantly warned her that she must have nothing to do with boys, although she never gave her any information about sex matters. The girl's life was so carefully guarded that she obtained very little information elsewhere, since her mother's strict discipline had prevented her from forming the usual intimate and confidential friendships with other girls.

At the age of fifteen, Mary met a man of thirty-five, whom she married three days later. Her marriage was nothing more than an attempt to escape from the harsh domination of her mother, but she was utterly unprepared for the sex side of marriage. When her husband attempted to have sexual relations with her after their marriage, she was terrified and refused to go to bed with him. Instead, she spent two nights sitting on the floor, and then ran away from her husband and returned to her mother's home.

For several weeks, she lived with her mother. Her husband came to see her frequently, and begged her to return to him. After these visits, Mary appeared to be in a rather excited state, and one day she began to complain that her husband was causing peculiar feelings to creep through her body and that she feared he would do her physical harm. After this her actions became increasingly peculiar. If she went out on the street, she would return home saying that the men she met had tried to do things to her. Soon she could not be induced to leave her own room or to eat her meals. She insisted that the food was being poisoned. She also stuffed cotton in her ears to shut out voices which she claimed were telling her to do wicked things.

Mary's mother took her to a psychopathic hospital. At first Mary was very suspicious and resentful, and would not talk to the doctors. But after a time she stated that men were following her and trying to have immoral relations with her. Because she refused them, they were trying to poison her food. She did not dare to sleep at night for fear these men would break in and abuse her. She was finally committed to a state hospital for the insane, having been diagnosed as suffering from dementia præcox.

There was no history of insanity in Mary's family, and had her life experiences been different, she would probably never have developed psychotic trends. Her mother's unhappiness had prevented the child from making social contacts and forced her into a seclusive kind of existence. Her complete ignorance of sex matters made her ill prepared to understand the normal sexual impulses which come with adolescence, and she interpreted these feelings as something imposed upon her from without and came to have delusions of persecution.

SUGGESTIONS FOR CLASSROOM DISCUSSION

1. What is the difference between the organic and the functional mental disorders?

2. Are mental diseases inherited?

3. Would it be possible to prevent any of the organic mental diseases?

4. What part did psychiatry play in the World War?

5. What is the relationship between personality types and mental disorders?

6. Is mental disease ever of sudden inception?

7. When is the best time to introduce preventative methods?   Why?

SUGGESTIONS FOR WRITTEN REPORTS

1. The introvertive and extrovertive types of personality have not been discussed in this chapter. Read the literature which treats of these types and write a paper describing the introvert and extrovert, including a discussion of the genetic development of these two types.

2. Read the literature on daydreaming and write a paper on the subject, considering both the normal and abnormal aspects of this mental activity.

3. The rôle of inferiority in personality development.

4. The formation of personality patterns in childhood.

SELECTED BIBLIOGRAPHY

Collateral Readings

GROVES, E. R. *Social Problems and Education,* Chap. III. New York, 1925.

MAY, JAMES V. *Mental Diseases.* Especially Chaps. VIII and XI. Boston, 1922.

MORGAN, JOHN J. B. *The Psychology of Abnormal People,* Chaps. II-VIII (inclusive), and XIII-XVI (inclusive). New York, 1928.

POLLOCK and FURBUSH. "Prohibition and Alcoholic Mental Disease." *Mental Hygiene,* 1924, Vol. VIII, pp. 548-570.

POLLOCK, H. M. "State Institution Population Still Increasing." *Mental Hygiene,* 1928, Vol. XII, pp. 103-112.

RIGGS, A. F. "The Psychoneuroses: Their Nature and Treatment." *American Journal of Psychiatry,* 1923, Vol. III, pp. 91-110.

ROSANOFF, A. J. *Manual of Psychiatry,* Chap. I. New York, 1920.

SANDS, I. J. "The Controllable Etiological Factors in Insanity, and How to Utilize Them." *Neurological Bulletin,* 1919, Vol. II, pp. 159-164.

SANDS and BLANCHARD. *Abnormal Behavior,* Chap. V. New York, 1923.

STRECKER and EBAUGH. *Practical Clinical Psychiatry,* Chaps. I and II. Philadelphia, 1925.

TAYLOR, W. S. (Editor). *Readings in Abnormal Psychology and Mental Hygiene,* Chaps. I, III, XXIII, and XXIV. New York, 1926.

THOMAS, W. I. and THOMAS, D. S. *The Child in America,* Chap. X. New York, 1928.

WECHSLER, I. S. *The Neuroses,* Chaps. I, II, and III. Philadelphia, 1929.

WHITE, W. A. *Outlines of Psychiatry,* Part I. Nervous and Mental Disease Publishing Co., 1923.

Literature on the Formation of Personality Patterns

BAGBY, ENGLISH. *The Psychology of Personality,* Chaps. I, II and III. New York, 1928.

BLANCHARD, PHYLLIS. *The Child and Society,* Chaps. I, II, IV, V, X and XIII. New York, 1928.

BURNHAM, W. H. *The Normal Mind,* Chaps. I-VII, inclusive. New York, 1924.

FLÜGEL, J. C. *The Psycho-Analytic Study of the Family.* International Psychoanalytical Press, 1921.

GROVES, E. R. *Personality and Social Adjustment.* New York, 1923.

HOHMAN, LESLIE B. "The Formation of Life Patterns." *Mental Hygiene,* 1927, Vol. XI, pp. 23-37.

MYERSON, A. *The Foundations of Personality,* Chaps. I, II and XI. Boston, 1921.

WATSON, J. B. *Psychology from the Standpoint of a Behaviorist,* Chap. VI. Philadelphia, 1924.

WHITE, W. A. *Mechanisms of Character Formation.* New York, 1918.

Literature on Extrovert and Introvert Personality Types

ALLPORT, F. H. *Social Psychology,* Chap. V. Boston, 1924.

FREYD, MAX. "Introverts and Extroverts." *Psychological Review,* 1924, Vol. XXXI, pp. 74-87.

HINKLE, BEATRICE. *The Re-creating of the Individual,* Chap. V. New York, 1923.

JUNG, C. G. *Psychological Types,* Chap. X. New York, 1923.

MARSTON, R. L. *The Emotions of Young Children.* (An Experimental Study in Introversion and Extroversion.) Univ. of Iowa Studies in Child Welfare, 1925.

MORGAN, J. J. B. *The Psychology of Abnormal People,* Chap. X. New York, 1928.

WICKES, FRANCES G. *The Inner World of Childhood,* Chap. VI. New York, 1929.

Literature on Daydreaming

BAGBY, ENGLISH. *The Psychology of Personality,* Chap. X. New York, 1928.

GREEN, GEORGE. *The Daydream.* University of London Press, 1923.

LONG, CONSTANCE. *Collected Papers on the Psychology of Phantasy.* London, 1920.

Morgan, J. J. B. *The Psychology of the Unadjusted School Child,* Chaps. VII and VIII. New York, 1924.

Robinson, E. S. "The Compensatory Function of Make-Believe Play." *Psychological Review,* 1920, Vol. XXVII, pp. 429-439.

Wickes, Frances G. *The Inner World of Childhood,* Chap. VII. New York, 1929.

Literature on Inferiority

Adler, Alfred. *A Study of Organic Inferiority and Its Psychic Compensation.* Nervous and Mental Disease Publishing Co., 1917.

—— *The Neurotic Constitution.* New York, 1916.

Bagby, English. *The Psychology of Personality,* Chaps. VIII, IX and XII. New York, 1928.

Burnham, W. H. *The Normal Mind,* Chap. XV. New York, 1924.

Groves, E. R. *Personality and Social Adjustment,* Chap. XV. New York, 1923.

Morgan, J. J. B. *The Psychology of the Unadjusted School Child,* Chap. XI. New York, 1924.

Myerson, A. *The Foundations of Personality,* Chap. XI. Boston, 1921.

CHAPTER IV

DELINQUENCY AS A MENTAL HEALTH PROBLEM

Popular attitude toward delinquency. Despite scientific studies of human conduct, which establish clearly the sequence of cause and effect relationships in the behavior of the individual, the average citizen still clings to a belief in the old doctrine of free will and heartily affirms that every man is captain of his fate and master of his soul. Antisocial behavior presents no problem to popular opinion because it appears as the deliberate choice of wrongdoing, without regard to circumstances which may have operated to enforce this choice. From this viewpoint, the question of how to deal with the delinquent and criminal is readily answered: he should be punished. If further inquiry is made concerning the prevention of delinquency, there is an equally simple popular solution: make the punishment for crime so severe that those who might wish to do wrong will be afraid to follow their impulses in this direction.

These are just the principles which, in all societies, have governed the treatment of offenders against the folkways or the legal code. But fear of neither torture, death nor incarceration in prison has been effective in preventing criminal behavior. The majority of prison inmates are recidivists, whose previous experience with prison sentences has not stopped them from continuing a criminal career upon their release. Nor is this fact wholly due to

the difficulty which confronts the discharged prisoner
when he tries to secure work in order to make an honest
living, although this may be a factor in some instances.
Rather is it the result of the manner in which his behavior patterns have been formed, as we shall see in suc-
ceeding pages. But the average layman, ignorant of statistics regarding repeated offenders, sees crime as something which can be met by punishment alone. He may
even go so far as to oppose the movement for reform in
prison management, on the grounds that the chief function of a prison should be that of making the sentence as
unpleasant as possible for the criminal.

Scientific studies of the delinquent. Psychiatric
studies of delinquents show that by a conservative estimate one-half are either mentally deficient or suffering
from mental disease. At least, this is true of the legal
offenders who are found in the jails and prisons of the
United States. To substantiate this statement, let us
glance at the figures from some of the surveys made in
penal institutions.

In 1918, Dr. Glueck published his findings from a
psychiatric study of 608 prisoners at Sing Sing. This was
an unselected group, the individuals being those consecu-
tively admitted to the institution during a nine months'
period. He found that 28.1 per cent of these prisoners
were mentally defective, 18.9 per cent were psychopathic,
and 12.0 per cent were suffering from frank psychoses.
Altogether, then, 59.0 per cent were mentally abnormal,
and their mental abnormalities had directly conditioned
their behavior.[1]

In the Maryland Mental Hygiene Survey, we find the

[1] Bernard Glueck, "Concerning Prisoners," *Mental Hygiene,* April,
1918, Vol. II, pp. 1-42.

following figures given concerning the mental condition
of seventy-five inmates of six county jails:

Diagnosis	Total	White	Colored
Normal	23	12	11
Dull normal	10	3	7
Borderline mental defect	7	3	4
Mental defect	2	1	1
Character defect	10	8	2
Psychopathic personality	16	14	2
Mental disease or deterioration..	4	3	1
Epilepsy	1	0	1
Endocrine disorder	2	1	1
Total	75	45	30

And concerning the inmates of the Maryland Penitentiary
and House of Correction, the following diagnoses were
reported for 1,386 prisoners: [2]

Diagnosis	Total	White	Colored
Normal	202	106	96
Dull normal	392	116	276
Borderline mental defect	151	26	125
Mental defect	163	30	133
Character defect	128	54	74
Psychopathic personality	234	128	106
Psychoneuroses and neuroses ..	73	49	24
Epilepsy	3	2	1
Mental disease or deterioration	40	24	16
Total 1,386		535	851

[2] See the Report of the Maryland Mental Hygiene Survey (*National Committee for Mental Hygiene,* 370 Seventh Ave., N. Y.),
pp. 36 and 44. In this report the figures are also given by sex, although we have quoted only the totals here.

Thus, in the Maryland survey, we find that of the prisoners in the six jails 12.0 per cent were mentally deficient in greater or less degree, while 28.0 per cent had mental disorders of one kind or another; and in the case of the 1,386 inmates of the Penitentiary and House of Correction, 22.7 per cent were mentally deficient, and 25.3 per cent were suffering from mental disorders.

When a mental hygiene survey was made in Cincinnati, Ohio, 200 unselected prisoners of the Hamilton County Jail were given psychiatric study, with the following results:

Diagnosis	Total	White	Negro
Normal	51	35	16
Subnormal (or dull normal) ...	27	14	13
Borderline mental defect	14	7	7
Feebleminded (mental defect) ..	57	6	51
Psychopathic	36	30	6
Psychoneurosis	7	6	1
Mental disease	4	3	1
Epilepsy	2	1	1
Undiagnosed	2	1	1
Total	200	103	97

Here we find 35.5 per cent mentally deficient, and 23.5 per cent with some form of mental or nervous disorder.[3]

In the St. Louis mental hygiene survey, 142 inmates of the city jail were diagnosed as follows:

[3] Report of the Mental Hygiene Survey of Cincinnati, 1922 (*National Committee for Mental Hygiene,* 370 Seventh Ave., N. Y.), p. 36.

Diagnosis	Total	White	Negro
No abnormality noted	29	15	14
Subnormal	21	4	17
Feebleminded	12	2	10
Psychopathic personality	65	47	18
Psychoneurosis	4	4	0
Epilepsy	1	0	1
Mental disease	4	4	0
Unclassified	6	4	2
Total	142	80	62

Here we find only 8.5 per cent mentally deficient, but
52.1 per cent suffering from other mental abnormalities.
In the same survey, of 178 prisoners (an unselected
group) examined at the city workhouse of St. Louis, 69.0
per cent "were found to be classifiable in terms of deviation from average normal mental health; were handicapped by nervous and mental conditions which . . .
are important factors in their delinquent conduct." [4]

From these studies of unselected groups of prisoners
in different parts of the country, which may be justifiably
considered a fair sampling of the population within our
jails and prisons, we see that it is indeed a conservative
statement when we claim that one-half of the criminal
class is so by virtue of mental abnormalities. What then
becomes of the popular idea that delinquency represents
deliberate, free willed choice? Certainly it does not apply
to mentally deficient or psychopathic individuals. And as
to the other half, which consists of normally intelligent

[4] Report of a Mental Hygiene Survey of Delinquency and Dependency in St. Louis, 1922 (*National Committee for Mental
Hygiene,* 370 Seventh Ave., N. Y.), p. 20. The figures in the table
concerning the 142 prisoners in the city jail are taken from page 14
of the same report. The original tables also give figures for male
and female, but these are omitted in the table reproduced above.

persons who cannot be classified under any of the diagnostic headings which we use to denote mental pathology, there is evidence from the scientific studies of juvenile delinquency that even here the concept of deliberate choice of a criminal career must be abandoned. This evidence will be presented in later pages of the present chapter. Meanwhile, we must consider more concretely the ways in which delinquent conduct is an outcome of pathological mental states.

Mental disease and antisocial behavior. In order to comprehend how mental disease may lead to delinquency, we have only to understand that the patient is living in an unreal world and that he reacts to his hallucinations and delusions as if they were actual occurrences. The action of a passenger on an elevated train in New York, when he suddenly struck the guard, is not inexplicable when it is learned that he has for some time been having auditory hallucinations that people are saying things about him and calling him bad names. While riding on the elevated these hallucinations troubled him, he attributed the voice which he heard to the guard, and struck him in retaliation for the supposed insults.

Again, a twenty-six year old man was arrested for throwing his younger sister, a girl of twenty, out of the window of their home. This young man was suffering from delusions that he was the chosen prophet of God, and believed that God talked with him and gave him directions. On the day when he attacked his sister he had heard God telling him that the world was doomed to destruction unless some human sacrifice was made to avert it. He explained his behavior by saying that God had told him to make a sacrifice as he had told the prophet Abraham; that his sister had looked at him just then in a hypnotizing manner which meant that God had given him the signal to make the sacrifice through her.

Sometimes we can trace the chain of events which led to the development of delusional and hallucinatory trends. For example, there was a nineteen year old boy, arrested for attacking his stepmother and slashing her with a knife and sent to the psychopathic hospital for observation. During his adolescence he had learned to masturbate from some of his companions, but when his stepmother discovered this habit she had frightened him by telling him it was wicked and that it would cause him to become insane. She also declared that it was immoral. The boy tried to control the habit, and succeeded in doing so during the day, but would wake up mornings to find that he had masturbated in his sleep. His fear and feeling of guilt became unbearable. He began to think that perhaps he had not done this himself, but that someone else came into his room and did it to him. He had never liked his stepmother and believed that she hated him. He thought that she might wish to injure him and was taking this method. Gradually these ideas became systematized into an active delusion and he was convinced that the stepmother was actively to blame for his troubles. "I am not sorry that I hurt her," he said to the psychiatrist. "I am only sorry that I did not kill her. She deserved it, for she was trying to make me crazy."

Antisocial behavior is very common in patients with general paresis, a mental disorder due to syphilitic infection of the brain. The following case is typical:

A man, forty-five years of age, was brought to the psychopathic hospital from a municipal court. For the past six months he had refused to support his wife, had spent his money lavishly upon prostitutes, when at home was irritable and struck his children frequently. The neurological examination showed all the signs of syphilitic destruction of the brain, and laboratory tests gave a positive Wassermann for both blood and spinal fluid. He was elated in mood; said that he was the strongest man in New York, that he owned all the gold mines in the world and that all the girls were in love with him. He thought his wife was too old fashioned and he preferred chorus girls. He admitted that he had been forging checks, but said that he did not need to worry about the false signatures because all the banks in the city belonged to him, anyway. The neurological examinations and laboratory tests established the fact that he had contracted general paresis.

The records of psychopathic hospitals are full of such cases as these, where patients sent from court are found to be suffering from some form of mental disease which was the direct cause of their antisocial conduct. Had the early symptoms of mental disorder been noted and psychiatric treatment or hospital care provided, these criminal acts would have been avoided in many instances.[5]

Mental deficiency and delinquency. Most of the scientific studies of adult criminals indicate that the proportion of mental deficiency in this particular group is somewhat higher than in the population at large.[6] At one time, this inclined many of the early investigators to regard mental deficiency as linked very closely with po-

[5] For further case reports, see Sands and Blanchard, *Abnormal Behavior*, Chaps. VI, VII and VIII. New York, 1923.

[6] Murchison, however, has published an extensive statistical study comparing the intelligence of criminals with the intelligence of men drafted into the army during the late World War, and finds that: "In terms of Army Alpha scores the criminal group seems superior to the white draft group. Not only is this true if we make a general comparison, but it is true if we make the comparison in separate units according to the states from which the draft quotas and criminal groups were drawn." Carl Murchison, *Criminal Intelligence,* p. 57 (Clark University Press, 1926).

tentiality for criminal behavior. More careful studies of
the problem have led us to believe that if mental defectives receive proper educational and vocational guidance,
and if they are not subjected to improper environmental
influences, there is no reason to expect that they will lead
delinquent careers. There is certainly no doubt that
many feebleminded individuals adapt themselves to community life, are self-supporting and never become involved in legal transgressions. The lowest grade mental
defectives, the idiots and imbeciles, seldom have any share
in the social group; because of their inability to care for
themselves they are usually placed in custodial institutions. They have neither the ability nor the opportunity,
for the most part, to engage in antisocial acts.

About all that we can say is that because of poor judgment, lack of foresight and suggestibility, the mentally
deficient individual may, under appropriate circumstances, be led into delinquency. A typical example is
the fifteen year old boy, with a mental age of about six
years, who was taught to steal by a group of boys living
in his neighborhood. He had been arrested four times
and spent some months in a reformatory. After each
arrest, he had returned home, associated with the same
group of boys, and repeated the same offense. Because
of his dullness, he was always the one to be caught by
the police, while his friends, more alert mentally, were
able to escape very frequently, leaving him to bear the
brunt of the common crime.

The suggestibility of the feebleminded girl, plus her
inability to realize ultimate consequences, accounts in
part for her offenses against the sex code, although her
environmental circumstances also have a share in determining her conduct. Take the case of a twenty-three
year old girl, with a mental age of ten and a half years,

already mother of three illegitimate children. Her first child was born when she was only fifteen years of age. The father married her but soon deserted. After that she lived with several different men, but had to return to her mother when she became pregnant as none of them would assume her care at those times. After the birth of the third child, her mother lost patience with her and preferred the charge of incorrigibility against her. The girl herself could not see that she had done anything wrong or that she had given her mother cause for dissatisfaction.[7]

The making of the delinquent. Although from the figures presented in the preceding pages it appears that mental disease or mental deficiency are contributing factors in approximately one-half the cases of adult delinquency, the existence of these abnormalities is by no means a full explanation of the origins of criminal conduct. For a more complete understanding of this problem, we must turn to studies of behavior difficulties in children and of juvenile delinquency, for there we may see the adult offender in the making. Whenever we are able to obtain the life history of the child or adolescent who exhibits antisocial traits we find a clearer picture of the forces that have operated to produce misconduct.

As a typical case history, let us briefly review that of a twelve year old boy who was repeatedly brought to juvenile court for running away from home and stealing. His parents had not been successful in making their marriage adjustments, and the home was the scene of frequent family quarrels. The mother often told the child that

[7] For other case reports and discussions of the relationship between mental deficiency and adult delinquency, see *Abnormal Behavior*, Chap. III; Wallace, "Are the Feebleminded Criminals?" (*Mental Hygiene*, January, 1929, Vol. XIII, pp. 93-98) ; Murchison, *Criminal Intelligence*, Chaps. 4, 5, 6, 21, 22 and 23.

the father hated them both and wished them out of his way. The boy was afraid of his father and his fundamental feeling of security at home was destroyed. Whenever the quarreling between the parents became unusually severe, the child slipped out of the house and ran away. After a time, as he grew older, he began to stay away from home all night, and then two or three days at a time. With these extended absences arose the necessity of procuring food. At first he took fruits from stands or purloined things to eat from stores. Then he grew bolder and broke into a cash register in order to obtain money to buy food. Court experiences had no deterrent effect upon his increasingly delinquent tendencies. In fact, as he explained to a psychologist, he preferred being at the Detention Home to staying with his parents.

Another typical case is that of a fifteen year old girl who had been in court three times because of repeated truancies from school. Her family was in poor circumstances and she was very anxious to go to work in order that her wages might be contributed to the family income. She had always made poor school progress, however, and had only reached the fifth grade, while according to the laws of the state in which she lived, she could not leave school until she had completed the sixth grade or reached the age of sixteen. She was large for her age and could easily pass for sixteen or seventeen. While looking for work she claimed to be over sixteen years old. But there was a record of her real age at school and her absence was reported to the attendance department. The attendance officer assigned to make the investigation of her absences had no choice but to make them a court issue. When she appeared in court for the third time she was committed to an institution for juvenile delinquents.

With this particular girl, the fundamental cause of her misconduct was the failure of the school and of the compulsory education laws to meet the needs of the individual child. Her intelligence was below average, yet she had not been transferred to a special class where she could have advanced more regularly through being given easier work. She took the only way which occurred to her to escape from an unsuitable situation, with the result that she came into conflict with the legal code.

Not all studies of delinquent careers are as simple or as readily understood as these two. In many instances it is not one situation but rather a combination of circumstances which occasions antisocial behavior. But many undesirable behavior patterns are best understood as reactions to environmental pressure.

Mental conflict is also a prominent factor in the development of misconduct. This is particularly true with reference to emotional disturbances about sex matters, and to compensations for feelings of inferiority. Healy has cited many cases of juvenile delinquency in which stealing is a substitution for sexual impulses. To illustrate the connection between sex conflicts and stealing, we may mention a six year old boy whose playmates had tried to teach him to masturbate and at the same time had persuaded him to accompany them on expeditions for petty thieving. The boy's parents had discovered one episode of sex play, and had punished him severely, besides scolding him for it. Thus it was impressed upon his mind that such sex play was exceedingly wicked. Thereafter he steadfastly refused to join in it, covering his eyes to shut out of his sight the acts of his playmates. The matter assumed an obsessive character in his mind, however, and being so closely associated with stealing also brought that more often into his thoughts. He succeeded in repressing overt sex acts, but yielded more and more readily to the impulse to steal. His propensities in this direction came to be a source of anxiety to his parents, although not treated with the same degree of horror as the sex episode had occasioned. Psychiatric study and treatment disclosed the relationship between his sex experiences and his habit of stealing, and when the conflict over the former was cleared up the latter ceased also.

Delinquent conduct as a compensation for feelings of inferiority is clearly shown in the behavior of a ten year old boy who because of glandular imbalance was too obese to hold his own in competitive games on the playground at school. The other boys made fun of him, and he felt that he had to "put himself across" with them in some fashion. He began to invent tales of himself as a daring burglar, but the boys laughed at these. Then he actually began to take money, at first from his parents, and displayed it flourishingly in treating his companions. Next he advanced to stealing from his teachers and others outside the family circle. His misdemeanors soon brought him to Juvenile Court, but this was only an added advantage to his boasting. He succeeded in winning the respectful admiration of his comrades by his antisocial behavior when he had been unable to do so in any other way. Medical treatment and a strenuous course of athletic training which reduced his weight and enabled him to participate successfully in group games solved his problem.

Social causes of juvenile delinquency. Statistical studies of juvenile delinquency offer some interesting indications of the frequency with which different environmental factors operate to produce antisocial behavior. On one point, nearly all the investigations are agreed: the relationships within the family are those which most often appear in a causal relationship to misconduct.   One of the most exhaustive studies is Cyril Burt's report on two hundred youthful offenders, which is especially impressive because he compares the items taken into consideration with similar data for non-delinquent children.   Some of the pertinent points of his work may be briefly stated as follows:

Poverty characterizes the homes of 52.8 per cent of the delinquents but of 38.2 per cent of the non-delinquents (used as a control group).

Defective family relationships (one or both parents dead, one parent deserted, parents divorced, illegitimacy, and other conditions which have caused a gap in the parental care) are found in 57.9 per cent of the juvenile delinquents but in only 25.7 per cent of the controls.

Defective discipline (in the sense of over-strictness, laxity, or absence of any attempt at control) occurs in 60.9 per cent of the cases of delinquency, but in only 11.5 per cent of the non-delinquent group.

Homes in which there is sexual immorality, alcoholism, quarreling, neglect or ill-treatment of the children include 25.9 per cent of the homes from which the delinquent children come, while only 6.2 per cent of the homes of the non-delinquents can be so described.[8]

These figures speak for themselves as to the effect of family life upon development of antisocial behavior.   It should be noted that poverty is a far less significant factor than defective family relationships, defective discipline or the existence of immorality or alcoholism in the home.

With respect to environmental situations outside the home, Burt presents the following figures:

[8] Cyril Burt, *The Young Delinquent,* pp. 51 and 62; tables III and IV.   New York, 1925.

Condition	Delinquents	Non-delinquents
Bad companions of same age ..	17.7%	0.5%
Companions of same age not bad	7.6	2.7
Corrupted by adult companions or strangers	2.0	0
Excessive local amusement facilities	10.6	11.2
Deficient local amusement facilities	3.0	4.2
Uncongenial school situations..	4.1	0.2
Uncongenial employment	4.1	0.7
Unemployed	5.1	0.7

As compared to the percentages concerning undesirable home conditions, these figures are exceedingly small. Moreover, when the delinquent and non-delinquent groups are contrasted, the only factors which seem to be more frequently found in association with delinquency are those involved in the influence of companions, in uncongenial school and work situations, and lack of employment.[9]

With reference to the types of mental conflicts discussed in the preceding section, Burt finds sex conflicts in 8.1 per cent of his delinquent children and inferiority feelings with compensatory antisocial behavior in 10.6 per cent. Both types of conflicts were absent from the control group.[10]

Healy and Bronner have recently published a statistical analysis of the cases of four thousand juvenile offenders. Two thousand were studied in Chicago from 1909 to 1915, and two thousand in Boston from 1917 to 1923. Their findings may be briefly summarized, as follows:—

[9] The Young Delinquent, p. 125, table VI.
[10] Ibid., p. 540, table XX.

| | *Approximate* |
Conditions in the Home	*percentages*
Poverty	20
One parent dead	27
Both parents dead	4
Parents separated or divorced (desertion included)	15
Illegitimacy	2
Mother working outside the home	17
Lack of parental control (no attempt at discipline)	40
Parental neglect (Boston cases only included)....	22
Excessive quarreling in the home	12
Alcoholism, sexual immorality or criminalism in home	21

Further to emphasize these unfortunate home conditions, Healy and Bronner also state that in two thousand·cases (in both Boston and Chicago) only 7.6 per cent were living under reasonably good conditions.[11]

Other factors which were found to be important in the causation of antisocial behavior in the cases studied by Healy and Bronner include:

Bad companions, which in three thousand cases reached as high as 62 per cent; mental conflicts in 6.5 per cent of the total four thousand; early sex experiences 12.5 per cent; school dissatisfaction 9 per cent; poor recreation 20 per cent; street life in excess 15 per cent; vocational dissatisfaction 3 per cent.[12]

For the most part, the findings from Burt's investigation agree with those from Healy and Bronner's analysis. Burt found defective family relationships associated with delinquency in about 60 per cent of his cases; Healy and Bronner place it at 48 per cent (items two, three, four and

[11] Healy and Bronner, *Delinquents and Criminals: Their Making and Unmaking,* Chap. XII.   New York, 1926.
[12] *Ibid.,* Chap. XVIII.

five in the table on home conditions being combined for this figure). Burt reports defective discipline for nearly 61 per cent of his cases, Healy and Bronner for 40 per cent. Immorality, alcoholism, neglect of children and quarreling are found in approximately 26 per cent of the homes of delinquent children, according to Burt; in 55 per cent of the homes according to Healy and Bronner. Both studies agree fairly closely as to the incidence of mental conflicts, uncongenial school situations and vocational maladjustments. The only point on which there is any marked disagreement is the influence of companions; Burt puts this factor at 20 per cent only, while Healy and Bronner find it important in 62 per cent of their cases. The findings concerning recreational facilities are not so readily comparable, but it seems as if this is also emphasized much more in the Healy and Bronner report than in Burt's data. Other investigations of juvenile delinquency confirm the results given by Burt and by Healy and Bronner.[13]

Mental deficiency and juvenile delinquency. As in the case of adult criminals, we find that a certain number of juvenile delinquents are mentally deficient. Healy and Bronner, in the study to which reference has been made in the preceding section, state that 13.5 per cent of their 4,000 cases were mentally deficient.[14] Slawson's figures for 1,543 delinquent boys in the correctional institutions of New York State are almost identical, for he reports 13.4 per cent of feeblemindedness.[15] Burt, on the

[13] See John Slawson, *The Delinquent Boy*, Chap. VI. Boston, 1926. Also, Breckenbridge and Abbott, *The Delinquent Child and the Home*. Survey Associates, New York, 1916.
[14] *Delinquents and Criminals*, p. 151.
[15] *The Delinquent Boy*, p. 192.

other hand, considered that only 8 per cent of his 200 cases were feebleminded.[16]

While there is some evidence that a greater percentage of mental deficiency is to be found among delinquent than non-delinquent juveniles, Slawson points out that there would be very little discrepancy if the delinquent group were compared with non-delinquents of similar economic and social level. He states: "When comparisons of the performance on intelligence tests of delinquents are made with that of non-delinquents coming from a social status somewhat similar to that of the delinquents, the difference in performance is not large." [17] Moreover, he offers statistics to validate this conclusion. Certainly, when we contrast the data on mental deficiency with those for environmental factors, we must perceive that there is no such striking association between deficiency and delinquency as there is between family relationships and antisocial behavior.[18]

Mental disease and juvenile delinquency. Mental diseases have no very high incidence among the juvenile population, whether delinquent or non-delinquent. So far as the delinquent group is concerned, Burt reports 10 per cent of functional nervous disorders for his 200 young offenders, and also 3.5 per cent post-encephalitic or post-meningitic disorders, as well as 1.0 per cent epilepsy. The total score for mental disease processes which might possibly occasion antisocial conduct is thus slightly under 15 per cent, according to Burt. Healy and Bronner give

[16] *The Young Delinquent,* pp. 285-286.
[17] *The Delinquent Boy,* p. 193.
[18] For further discussion of the relationships between mental deficiency and juvenile delinquency, see *The Child and Society,* Chap. XIV; *The Young Delinquent,* Chap. VII; *The Delinquent Boy,* Chap. II, but especially pp. 191-194 and 442-444.

it an even smaller place: 5.6 per cent mental disease and
5.6 per cent epilepsy for the Chicago cases, and only 1.0
per cent mental disease and 1.6 per cent epilepsy for the
Boston group.[19]

The whole matter of mental disease and mental deficiency in relation to juvenile delinquency may be
summed up, on the basis of these and other studies, by
saying that approximately three-fourths of young delinquents are non-defective and are not suffering from any
form of mental disease which could cause antisocial behavior. Thus, in about 75 per cent of delinquent children, we must seek the explanation of their antisocial
conduct in the environmental conditions which we have
previously considered and in the child's emotional reactions to those conditions.

The early beginnings of delinquency. If we wish to
study the very early inception of delinquent behavior, we
must not wait for the child to become a court case. In
the Child Guidance Clinic we have the opportunity to
see the first manifestations of delinquent trends and are
enabled to enlarge our knowledge of etiology. It is appropriate at this point, therefore, to introduce a somewhat detailed analysis of certain of these clinic cases.
For this purpose it was decided to select all the cases
referred for clinical study during the period of one year
for the major problem of stealing.

In going over the records [20] from April, 1927, to April,
1928, it was found that of the whole 220 children given
intensive study and treatment during that length of time,

[19] *The Young Delinquent,* pp. 256-268 and 556-570. *Delinquents
and Criminals,* pp. 151-153 and 273.

[20] These cases are taken from the files of the Philadelphia Child
Guidance Clinic.

only 80 presented the problem of stealing.[21]   But since this number represents all the children brought to the clinic for that reason during twelve consecutive months, it may be regarded as a fair sample of the clinic stealing cases.   The offenses varied from minor ones to a more serious type for which fourteen of the children had at one time or another been taken to court, although none had been placed in correctional institutions.   Besides stealing, lying was a serious problem in 72.5 per cent, and truancy in 43.75 per cent of the 80 cases.   The frequent occurrence of lying and truancy in association with stealing is not surprising.   The child who steals often resorts to lying in order to escape punishment.   Truancy, on the other hand, is likely to precede stealing; the truant child is apt to fall in with companions who teach him to steal.

Of the 80 stealing cases, 61 were boys and 19 were girls.   The non-stealing group of clinic cases for the same twelve months' period was composed of 91 boys and 49 girls.   The non-stealing group is divided by sex in a ratio of approximately two to one, while the stealing group presents approximately a three to one ratio.   This would suggest the possibility of stealing being slightly more prevalent among boys than girls.   In view of the small number under consideration, however, this can only be mentioned tentatively; further research is necessary before any definite conclusion can be reached.

The life ages of the 80 children who steal range from six to twenty years.   All but five are under sixteen years

[21] By "intensive study and treatment" we mean the combination of medical, psychiatric, psychological and social study.   Consultation cases, in which only the services of psychiatrist, psychologist or social worker were utilized, are not included in this number.

of age.[22] Twenty-one of the children were between the ages of six and ten; nineteen were between ten and twelve years; twenty between twelve and fourteen; fifteen between fourteen and sixteen; five between sixteen and twenty. From this age distribution, it appears that stealing is as characteristic of the young school child as of the preadolescent and adolescent. It is to be noted, however, that there are no preschool age children in this stealing group.[23]

When the 80 children are classified on the basis of intelligence we find that one is mentally deficient; five are borderline; nineteen are dull normal; thirty-eight are average; eleven are superior, and five are very superior. One child (from an institution for the blind) was not given an intelligence test. Thus, only 7.5 per cent are subnormal, while 23.75 per cent are dull normal, 47.5 per cent are average, and 20 per cent are superior or very superior.[24] These figures do not lend themselves to any formulation of the relationships between intelligence and stealing, since the clinic plans to serve normally intelligent children, and retarded types are usually referred to organizations existing especially for them. Such evidence as these figures offer is therefore negative. It merely indicates that the possession of average or superior intel-

[22] This is largely determined by the age limits set for receiving patients at the clinic, which aims to serve children between the ages of three and sixteen. Older patients are taken only in exceptional instances.

[23] Dr. G. H. Pearson of the Philadelphia Child Guidance Clinic has just completed a study of the preschool cases. He found that stealing is not one of the problems arising in the child under five years of age. His study is to be published shortly.

[24] Classifications follow Terman's. The subnormals have intelligence quotients between 60 and 80; dull normal, I.Q. 80-89; average, I.Q. 90-109; superior, I.Q. 110-119; very superior, I.Q. 120 or above. The highest I.Q. in the superior group was 150.

lectual endowment is no barrier to the development of such conduct disorders as stealing.

Since mental deficiency can be ruled out as a factor in nearly all of these 80 cases, the importance of the social and emotional factors is all the more apparent. The social facts relative to these children are presented in the following table:

Social situation	Number of cases
Broken home	25
Foster home	14
Institutional care	7
Poverty	46
Moderate or comfortable circumstances	34
Over-strict discipline	21
Inconsistent discipline	33
Very lax discipline	6
Sexual immorality of mother	3
Alcoholic parent	5
Illegitimacy	1
Recreational deprivations	16
Member of gang	19
Uncongenial school situations and truancy	35
Delinquent parent	8
Delinquent brother or sister	11
Other relatives delinquent	3

The outstanding data in the above table are: 57.5 per cent of the children are not living with both parents; 57.5 per cent come from very poor homes; discipline is very poor in 75 per cent of the cases; 20 per cent are deprived of recreational outlets (including playthings); gang associations (bad companions) figure in nearly 24 per cent; alcoholism and sexual immorality occur so seldom as to be practically negligible; delinquency of parent, brother or sister, or other relatives occurs in 27.5 per cent.

Out of the deprivations suffered by these children arise drives to obtain emotional satisfaction. Some of the children, in foster homes or institutions, or in broken homes where there is a step-parent, feel keenly the loss of security in parental affection. They seek the acceptance which they cannot find in normal relationships with parents from the gang or from brothers or sisters. Others, who feel that they are unwanted at home because they cannot live up to too strict or inconsistent standards of discipline, must also seek substitute satisfactions. Still others feel themselves to be failures because they have not succeeded in their school work or have been unable to make proper adjustments on the playground, and are seeking compensations for their feelings of inferiority. Some turn to sex play, in lieu of more wholesome recreation which is denied them, and this becomes associated with stealing. Others long for playthings or for seats at the movies.

Sometimes a single child is responding to complex motives, but usually some one factor is more powerful than the others. The major drives apparent in the stealing of these 80 children may be classified as follows:

Major drive	Number of cases
Compensations for feelings of inferiority	28
Desire to be accepted by gang	18
Substitute for or associated with sex activities	16
Desire for recreational or play outlets	10
Desire to be accepted by delinquent sister or brother	5
Escape from unhappy home (using money to run away)	3

Undoubtedly, in these children, the home situation is the fundamental one. Had they lived in wholesome

homes, where they were sure of the affection of both
parents, they could have withstood the pressure of school
maladjustments, poverty and bad companions, to a much
greater extent. But because the family situation was unsatisfactory and because they had lost the fundamental
security of parental acceptance, they were left especially
vulnerable to these other environmental influences. We
know, from clinical studies, that given reasonably good
parent-child relationships the incidence of antisocial behavior may be kept very low for children living under
much worse economic conditions and gifted less highly in
intelligence.[25]

The results of treatment instituted by the clinic bear
out the above interpretation. The primary effort in treatment has been directed toward improvement of the relationships between parents and children. The parents
have been able to work out their own problems, with the
aid of the clinic social workers, and as they have become
better adjusted they have been able to meet the needs of
the children.[26] As the latter are accepted by the parents
on a more comfortable basis, their behavior has improved.
Supplementary to this chief treatment goal has been the

[25] See Blanchard and Paynter, "Socio-Psychological Study of
Children from Marginal Families," *The Family*, March, 1927, pp.
3-10. This study shows that 80 children from 23 families dependent
upon financial relief from a social organization were 68.8 per cent
free from behavior difficulties, and that serious misconduct appeared
in only 13.7 per cent. This freedom from behavior disorders is
explained as follows: "Economic deprivations are their portion, to
be sure; their homes are poor and over-crowded; sanitary conditions
are far from good; and the house-keeping standards are often very
lax. But they have something in their relations with their parents
which neither institutional nor foster-home care can offer. . . .
Almost all of them were fond of their parents and happy with them,
despite the wistfulness which they displayed in talking of the play
life which was more or less denied them."

[26] The methods of social work are discussed in Chap. XIV.

provision of more wholesome outlets for the children whenever camp experiences, recreation center contacts or other community resources could be utilized for this purpose.

Since the children were studied by the clinic for the twelve months prior to April, 1928, many have been under treatment for more than a year. In forty-five cases the treatment is still being continued. This means that while there has been considerable progress toward adjustment, more work is necessary before it seems wise to leave the children entirely to parental direction without any supervision from the clinic. Thirty-five cases have been closed. Twenty-five of these closed cases were considered partially or completely adjusted at the time of closing. In two of the closed cases, the families moved away shortly after the initial study; while eight others were closed because the parents refused to coöperate with the clinic plans. It is probable that the results would show a larger number of successful terminations of treatment but for the fact that twenty-one of the children are in foster homes or institutions, so that it has been impossible to give them parental affection and not easy to find substitutes for this which would satisfy their needs.

Heredity and delinquency. If popular opinion be robbed of the theory of deliberate choice as an explanation of delinquent behavior, it often falls back upon the scapegoat of heredity. The individual is an offender against the law, says the average citizen, because his parents, or if not his parents, other close relatives, were criminals. How do actual figures support this belief?

Burt, in the study of young delinquents from which we have already quoted, states that: "Within the whole group of delinquents studied there were only 11 per cent whose relatives had been sentenced for crime; and only 19 per cent whose relatives, whether sentenced or not, were known to have committed some gross offense. As many as four-fifths of the children could plead no history among their kindred of any definable crime." [27]

Healy and Bronner, analyzing the heredity of 675 juvenile repeated offenders, find that 45 per cent had delinquent relatives. They add, however, that treatment measures were just as frequently successful in those cases with bad heredity as in those in which the heredity was clear. This suggests that the delinquent traits were not congenital but acquired.[28]

As we have seen, in the 80 Child Guidance Clinic cases of children who steal, there were eight cases in which one parent was delinquent and three more in which other relatives were delinquent. Yet intensive case studies showed little indication that inheritance was necessary to be considered in explaining the children's behavior; much more significant were the drives for emotional satisfactions. In eleven cases there were delinquent brothers or sisters, but inheritance with respect to this relationship could hardly be postulated.

There is surely no factual basis for the popular assumption that behavior traits may form part of biological inheritance. The most that could be said, from the scientific viewpoint, is that some physical defect or neurological condition, which would afford a fertile soil for the growth of delinquency, might be inherited.

Undoubtedly, the rôle of heredity in the production of criminal conduct, has been too much stressed in popular thinking. Indeed, we do not need to call upon biological inheritance to explain the presence of antisocial conduct in children of criminal parents; the force of suggestion

27 *The Young Delinquent*, p. 50.
28 *Delinquents and Criminals*, Chap. VIII.

and imitation is a more adequate explanation. Again, the child may fear that he will develop similar traits to those of criminal family stock, and this fear may become so obsessive that it operates in the manner of auto-suggestion. Thus the individual may be driven by his fears in the very direction which he desires to avoid.

Is juvenile delinquency increasing? Because of the sensational press notices of striking examples of juvenile delinquency, the average reader of the newspapers is likely to gain the impression that the number of youthful delinquents is rapidly increasing. This kind of reasoning from the particular to the general is always liable to be fallacious. Certainly it seems to be in error in this instance. The Children's Bureau of the United States Bureau of Labor, after careful statistical studies, reports the following facts concerning juvenile crime in fourteen of our leading cities:

"In nearly all of these fourteen cities, the delinquency rates per 1,000 children . . . were decidedly *lower* in 1924 or 1925 than in 1915. There was a not very surprising increase during the war period, 1917 to and including 1919, but in most cities the downward trend thereafter was marked. . . . Typical of the general trend is the condition in Chicago, where the rate formerly averaged around five or six delinquents per annum per thousand children and since 1920 has been three or four; or New York, where it dropped from 11.1 to 6.8. Boston, Buffalo, New Orleans, Providence, Richmond, St. Louis and Washington all showed a decrease from the first to the last year studied, while Minneapolis, Philadelphia and Seattle showed slight increases. In none of these three cities, however, were 1925 figures available." [29]

[29] "How Wild Is Wild Youth?", *The New Republic*, May 5, 1926, pp. 318-319.

Although the above figures do not indicate what has been happening in the last four years, it is very probable that the youthful "crime wave" is good newspaper copy and little else.

Delinquency as a mental health problem. On the surface, some of the facts presented in the preceding pages may seem to be somewhat inconsistent. In surveys of adult prisoners, for instance, a higher percentage of insanity and mental deficiency seems to be associated with crime than is the case in studies of juvenile delinquents. Certain scientific investigations of delinquency lay chief stress upon environmental influences. There is, however, an interpretation of delinquent behavior, sponsored by psychiatrists and psychologists who have been working in close contact with children showing the early beginnings of misconduct, which serves to unite these various facts.

As we have previously suggested, such environmental factors as poverty, lack of proper recreational facilities and bad companions cannot be taken as inevitably productive of antisocial behavior. More fundamental are the psychological aspects of the child's environment, particularly with respect to the parent-child relationship. If the child has a feeling of security and ease in the family, if he is certain of the affection of his parents, he is able to withstand considerable environmental pressures of other kinds. Lacking this fundamental emotional comfort, he is open to these pressures. Indeed, the absence of such security is in itself sufficient to cause undesirable behavior in many cases. Thus we find that a certain proportion of young delinquents and pre-delinquents come from homes which seem to provide an excellent environment until the psychological situation within the family circle is understood.

The family, considered as a psychological organization, is infinitely subtle in its interactions of the component parts. Criticism which may seem to be entirely justifiable to parents often appears to the child as an evidence of unfair discrimination and is interpreted to mean that he has forfeited parental love. Jealousy of brothers or sisters may be an origin of similar feelings on the part of a certain child. There are many ways in which the belief that he is unwanted may come about.

While personality and behavior patterns are shaped in accordance with all the manifold influences to which the individual is subjected, there seems to be an especial vulnerability with reference to circumstances which undermine the feeling of security in parental affection. Unhappy relationships within the family do not always lead to antisocial behavior, however. Abnormal personality traits may be a result. In certain instances, as we have seen in preceding chapters, mental disease may be the outcome of unwholesome childhood experiences. Sometimes the onset of the psychosis is expressed in delinquent acts. Very likely, therefore, if we knew the early life of insane criminals, we should find that their difficulties can be traced back to psychological factors arising in parent-child relationships.

The legal situation. The legal code is not predicated upon any desire to understand criminal behavior. It exists for the purpose of protecting the social group. Unfortunately even this aim may be easily perverted. The trial by jury does not so much represent an attempt to discover whether the prisoner at the bar would be dangerous to others, if allowed to remain at large, as a combat between opposing lawyers. As Dr. William A. White describes it: "The method of trial of a criminal case before a jury is in the nature of a combat in which two opposing forces are lined up against each other and the battle goes to the strongest.   The judge acts as a sort of referee whose business it is to prevent fouls and the taking of unfair advantages." [30]

Moreover, legislation is slow to respond to the findings of science.   It represents popular opinion and lags far behind scientific progress.   We have only to consider the recent passing of legal acts to prohibit the teaching of evolution (in certain states), or the scientifically obsolete laws forbidding dispensation of birth control information, to understand the power that mass prejudice exerts in this field.

On the other hand, popular conduct with respect to laws which do not fit in with prejudices is such as to undermine the efficiency of the legal code.   The national prohibition law is daily disregarded with impunity.   Public officials, entrusted with enforcement of the law, accept graft and wink at the traffic in liquor, until some occasion precipitates an investigation revealing these conditions. [31]

As a whole, the legal profession has no understanding of the psychiatric interpretation of crime and consequently is entirely out of sympathy with it.   Even when professional opinion is required in order to settle a legal question, the statement of the medical expert is often set aside in favor of some legal technicality. [32]   The judge is so used to the exercise of authority that he is apt to consider himself infallible.   Many examples might be given. For instance, there is the judge who assured two psychiatrists that he knew more about mental disease than they did, refusing to commit to a state institution a woman

[30] William A. White, *Insanity and the Criminal Law*, p. 56.   New York, 1923.

[31] Witness the investigation of police protection of bootlegging interests conducted by the district attorney in Philadelphia in 1928.

[32] See *Insanity and the Criminal Law*, Chap. X.

suffering from dementia præcox with paranoid trends. Two days after her release the patient shot and wounded a former employer, against whom she had delusions of persecution. Another illustration is that of the judge who refused to commit a feebleminded girl who had given birth to several illegitimate children, because the psychological examination had been made by a woman and he did not believe that one woman could be fair to another. He was entirely unaware of the methods and technique of administering mental tests, which rules out the possibility of personal opinion; nor did he understand that the clinical expert is unlikely to introduce questions of moral judgment into a diagnosis.

A mental hygiene view of court procedure. There is more than a relic of barbarity about modern court procedure. Sensation-seeking crowds of spectators are permitted to throng the courtroom in a way that is peculiarly reminiscent of ancient gladiatorial spectacles. Nowhere is this to be more severely censured than in cases involving children. To some extent this has been avoided by the establishment of the juvenile court, which has usually become too socialized to pander to an audience and insists on private hearings. But when the criminal is an adult and a child witness is involved, the latter often has to take the stand in the face of a multitude of spectators. This experience frequently assumes a traumatic value, especially in relation to sex offenses.

Consider the young girl who appears as witness in a case of attempted rape. The attitude of her family may have been such that she has already developed a strong feeling of guilt. Yet she may be required to testify publicly concerning experiences which have become a source of shame to her despite the fact that she was in no way at fault. She thus comes to believe that her disgrace is known to everyone. This feeling may cause her to with-draw from social contacts and to develop a seclusive personality, brooding over her sense of guilt. Or she may adopt an attitude of bravado to conceal her emotional conflict, talking continually of her experience in order to assert her sophistication and obtain attention.[33]

Just as destructive is the court experience for a boy who has been a victim of homosexual acts. His family is determined to punish his assailant. The boy must go on the stand and describe in detail the acts to which he was subjected, then submit to a grilling cross-examination by the defense lawyer, who takes him again and again over the same ground in the hope of trapping him into some confusion of details. The reactions of the spectators are of a nature to impress the boy deeply with a sense of shame and disgust. Moreover, in securing a conviction of the offender, nothing really constructive is accomplished. He may receive a short prison sentence, but while he is serving his term his homosexuality will be intensified. A clinical treatment of such cases, without their being brought to court, would be of far more value to the individuals concerned and to society in general.

Fortunately, present day legal procedure is not open to adverse criticism alone. There are healthy signs of its socialization, and of its interest in the rehabilitation of the criminal. The use of probation is widespread, although it varies in efficiency from one community to another. Probation officers are assigned the duty of investigating the conditions which bring about delinquency

[33] Hamilton and Macgowan contrast the diametric results in two cases of rape. One grew up to be a healthy woman, because she had earlier received realistic sex education. The other, brought up to believe that sex is obscene and revolting, became an hysteric after the sex aggression and has remained such. See "Physical Disabilities in Wives," in *Sex in Civilization,* p. 575.

in individual cases and they also assist in the social adjustment of the person released upon probation. The parole system provides a way of releasing prisoners who are ready to attempt adjustment to group life prior to the expiration of their sentence. Educational and recreational opportunities are provided in many penal institutions for both juveniles and adults, and vocational training has been initiated, all with the aim of preparing the delinquent for economic and social adaptation after his return to society.[34] The separate court for juvenile offenders and the use of very different methods in handling their cases, has already been mentioned.

One of the most hopeful signs of the times is the recognition, from within the professional legal group itself, of the need for the law student of a revised curriculum of study which will place more emphasis on the human side of the problem. Much may be expected from the establishment of the new Institute of Human Relations at Yale University, which, in the words of President Angell, will "give to our law teachers, as well as to their students, opportunity to face and study directly the more important influences which create crime, lead to disorganized social conditions and precipitate premature or ill-advised legislation." President Hutchins, formerly Dean of the Yale School of Law, visualizes the well-trained lawyer of the future as follows: "He should certainly have a knowledge of economics and sociology. He should not overthrow the empirical wisdom of the ages, but he should be insinuated into the atmosphere of modern science. It is not difficult to imagine, for instance, what aid psychiatry can be in the just disposition of persons who fall afoul of the law." With leaders in the legal profession taking

34 See E. R. Groves, *Social Problems and Education,* Chap. II. New York, 1925.

such a socialized stand there is every reason to hope that many of the contemporary barbarous customs will sometime be replaced by methods more in accord with the findings of modern science.

Mental hygiene aims. Meanwhile mental hygiene, having for its aim the purpose of prevention of crime and social rehabilitation of the offender, suggests certain practical plans:

1. Professional training for probation officers, so that they will be better equipped for their tasks, and reduction of their case load so that they will not be handicapped by insufficient personnel.

2. Proper use of the parole system, which is now all too frequently perverted, through political or other influence, to secure the release of prisoners who are not at a point where they are capable of making necessary social adjustments.

3. Extension of the best type of juvenile court procedure to all communities and to all types of cases involving children.

4. The provision of clinical study and treatment for all juvenile offenders.

5. Increased facilities for the psychiatric and psychological examination of adult offenders.

6. Adequate clinical facilities for the treatment of children showing early behavior difficulties, in the interests of prevention.

7. Humanitarian treatment of prisoners in correctional institutions, and the extension of education, recreation and vocational training in these institutions.

8. Revision of the law school curriculum to include courses in psychiatry, abnormal psychology and the other social sciences.

9. The abolition of trial by jury in criminal cases and

the establishment of a permanent board of experts under the leadership of trained and enlightened psychiatrists and psychologists to replace the jury chosen by lot. In view of the popular faith in the custom of trial by jury, this will probably not be accomplished for some time to come.

These mental hygiene aims, although they emphasize a humanistic attitude toward the delinquent individual, have keenly in mind the need of protecting the social group from its antisocial members. Under the present legal system, the convicted prisoner is sentenced to a longer or shorter period of segregation according to the nature of his crime. Whether or not he will still be a menace to society upon his release is all too rarely taken into consideration. Extension of mental hygiene service in the courts would tend to emphasize the interests of society. It would favor the indeterminate sentence, with return to the community depending upon the later mental condition of the individual and his capacity for making the proper adjustments to a freer life. It would promote the permanent segregation of the insane and defective delinquents in institutions properly equipped for their care and treatment, instead of temporary confinement in penal institutions. Compulsory sterilization of defective and psychopathic types, to prevent the birth of children to persons who could not provide them with a reasonably good heredity or with a wholesome family environment, would also be advocated. These measures would be of infinitely greater social value than the present standardized routine with its general disregard of individual differences in offenders.

ILLUSTRATIVE CASE

Joseph was a boy who had never felt secure in his parents' affection. His mother had not wanted children because they would interfere with her work and her social activities. She left Joseph to the care of nursemaids, who were not always well trained and used threats and punishments as a means of discipline. His father was fond of the boy, but worked late at night at his office frequently, and therefore did not see very much of him.

By the time Joseph was ten years old, he was turning to friends outside the home for the acceptance which he did not have from his parents. He found a gang of boys at school who were willing to admit him to their intimate circle provided he conformed to their patterns of behavior. Unfortunately, these boys were accustomed to playing truant and to stealing, and in order to maintain his position with them, Joseph was forced to join in these activities.

When these misdemeanors were reported to the parents, Joseph was scolded and punished. This made him feel even more rejected at home and forced him to cling still more strongly to his companions of the gang. Because of his truancy, he began to get poorer reports from school, and was criticized by his teachers both for this and for his misbehavior. Soon the boys in the gang must have seemed to Joseph the only friends he had left, and he began to slip away from home at night to be with them. The whole group of boys were caught in misdemeanors of various types, and after a period of probation, during which their truancy and stealing continued, several of them, including Joseph, were sent to a state school for boys.

SUGGESTIONS FOR CLASSROOM DISCUSSION

1. What is the popular interpretation of delinquent behavior?

2. To how great an extent do we find mental deficiency among the delinquent classes?

3. What is the incidence of mental disease among adult offenders?

4. How can mental disease cause a person to commit a crime?

5. How can mental conflicts occasion antisocial behavior?

6. What social conditions contribute to the production of juvenile delinquency?

7. What part does heredity play in the production of crime?

8. What would be a scientific interpretation of delinquency?

9. Discuss criminal court procedure from the mental hygiene point of view.

10. What would be the chief points in a mental hygiene program for the prevention of delinquency?

SUGGESTIONS FOR WRITTEN REPORTS

1. Mental Disease in Relation to Crime.

2. The Social Factors Contributing to Delinquency.

3. Mental Deficiency and Delinquency.

4. The Development of the Delinquent Personality.

5. Criminal Court Procedure in the Light of Modern Criminology.

6. The Childhood Beginnings of Delinquency.

SELECTED BIBLIOGRAPHY

ALLEN, F. H. "Psychic Factors in Juvenile Delinquency." *Mental Hygiene*, 1927, Vol. XI, pp. 764-774.

BARNES, HENRY E. *The Repression of Crime*, Chaps. I, V, VIII, IX and XI. New York, 1926.

BLANCHARD, P. *The Child and Society*, Chaps. XIII and XIV. New York, 1928.

BRIGGS, ARTHUR E. "Social Distance Between Lawyers and Doctors." *Sociology and Social Research*, 1928, Vol. XIII, pp. 156-163.

BURT, CYRIL. *The Young Delinquent*. New York, 1925.

CAMPBELL, C. M. "Crime and Punishment from the Point of View of the Psychopathologist." *Journal of Criminal Law and Criminology*, 1928, Vol. XIX, pp. 244-251.

DAHLSTROM, S. "Is the Young Criminal a Continuation of the Neglected Child?" *Journal of Delinquency*, 1928, Vol. XII, pp. 97-121.

DAVIES, S. P. "Social Control of the Mentally Deficient," New York, 1929.

ESTABROOKS, G. H. "Moral Responsibility in the Light of Certain Psychological Facts." *Mental Hygiene*, 1828, Vol. XII, pp. 768-771.

GLUECK, SHELDON. "Psychiatry and the Criminal Law." *Mental Hygiene*, 1928, Vol. XII, pp. 569-595.

—— "Principles of a Rational Penal Code." *Mental Hygiene*, 1929, Vol. XIII, pp. 1-32.

—— "Psychiatric Examination of Persons Accused of Crime." *Mental Hygiene*, 1927, pp. 287-305.

—— "State Legislation Providing for the Mental Examination of Persons Accused of Crime." *Mental Hygiene*, 1924, Vol. VIII, pp. 1-19.

—— "A Tentative Program of Coöperation Between Psychiatrists and Lawyers." *Mental Hygiene*, 1925, Vol. IX, pp. 686-698.

GLUECK, S. and GLUECK, E. "Five Hundred Criminal Careers," New York, 1930.

GROVES, E. R. *Social Problems and Education*, Chaps. I and II. New York, 1925.

HEALY, WILLIAM. *Mental Conflicts and Misconduct*. Boston, 1923.

HEALY and BRONNER. *Delinquents and Criminals: Their Making and Unmaking*. New York, 1926.

MURCHISON, CARL. *Criminal Intelligence*, Chaps. 4, 5, 6, 21, 22, 23. Clark University, 1926.

OVERHOLSER, WINFRED. "Psychiatry and the Treatment of Offenders." *Mental Hygiene*, 1927, Vol. XI, pp. 306-323.

—— "Psychiatric Service in Penal and Reformatory Institutions and Criminal Courts in the United States." *Mental Hygiene*, 1928, Vol. XII, pp. 801-838.

PLANT, J. S. "The Relationship of the Psychiatric Clinic to the Juvenile Court," *Mental Hygiene*, October, 1929, Vol. XIII, pp. 708-718.

PARSONS, H. C. "The Learned Judge and the Mental Defective Meet—What Then?" *Mental Hygiene*, 1928, Vol. XII, pp. 25-37.

SANDS and BLANCHARD. *Abnormal Behavior*, Chaps. II, III, VI, VII and VIII. New York, 1923.

SLAWSON, JOHN. *The Delinquent Boy*. Boston, 1926.

SLESSINGER, DONALD. "Human Relations at Yale." *Survey Graphic*, May, 1929, Vol. LXII, pp. 182 ff.

THOMAS, W. I. and D. S. *The Child in America*, Chaps. I and II. New York, 1928.

WHITE, WILLIAM. *Insanity and the Criminal Law*. New York, 1923.

CHAPTER V

MENTAL HYGIENE AND CHILDHOOD

Interest in parenthood problems. With the development of the mental hygiene movement it was inevitable that attention should be directed to the problems of childhood. As from every quarter new light was thrown by scientific investigation upon the meaning of personality it became increasingly evident that not only was childhood the golden age for mental hygiene, but that the influence of parents was in most instances predominant in shaping the life of the child. In recent years mental hygiene has been chiefly concerned with the child and his parents. This interest is new only in the sense that it represents an effort to use science in dealing with problems of the child and of his father and his mother. It is not at all new in its recognition of the need of helping offspring and parents in their home contacts since this idea stretches far back. Even in pre-literate people we discover a definite understanding of the importance of childhood and the significance of parenthood influence. The initiation so commonly found among primitive people demonstrates the clearness with which it was understood that the child had to accept the social responsibility of the matured individual. Studies of savage children, of which Margaret Mead's *Coming of Age in Samoa* is a striking example, reveal the definiteness with which parental policy was limited with the aim of making the child socially responsible. Not only did savage parents as a rule treat their children kindly but, by comparison with their other conduct, they showed in dealing with their offspring surprising insight. With the coming of the historic era every culture shows appreciation of the significance of childhood and emphasizes the duties of the parent.

The philosophic interest. The philosophers from the first have recognized the large place that family association has in the development of character. Both Plato and Aristotle gave testimony to their great interest in the problems of parenthood, and from their time until the present philosophy has constantly discussed the problems of family life as related to the physical, ethical, and social values of the child and of society. Even mental health in the more narrow sense has at times received attention. Rousseau, Locke, and Kant were three philosophers who gave considerable thought to problems of parenthood and childhood and who because of their interest exerted much influence on the subsequent behavior of those in charge of children.

The pre-scientific interest. Previous to the emergence of mental hygiene, the medical doctor and the minister divided between them the responsibility for parenthood guidance, which of late has been taken over by the science of mental hygiene. Because of a wide-spread confidence in the doctor as a student of human nature, who could also be trusted not to gossip, parents and sometimes children came to him with their problems. From wide experience and close observation, the doctor usually proved a wise counselor when dealing with concrete difficulties of family relationships. Since these problems were often ethical in their expression the minister and the priest were also looked to for help by parents, and although their viewpoint was less objective as a rule than that of the doctor, their influence was considerable. One of the most common topics in pulpit exposition was that of the duties of parents, and, while this sermonizing stressed religious training, it also abounded in counsel regarding the care and discipline of children.

The scientific period. The first distinctive application of science to the problems of childhood and family life appears in the movement to conserve the physical welfare of infants. Progress in this direction has been so extensive and fruitful that it is hard to realize that it has come about in practically the last twenty-five years. A quarter of a century ago there were not more than half a dozen children's specialists in the United States. At that time no medical school had a department of pediatrics, and no laboratory was equipped to investigate the medical problems of children with the exception of diphtheria. We were also destitute of milk stations, baby health stations, state and municipal departments of child hygiene, and public health nurses.[1] In so short a time as twenty-five years, medical science has found its greatest triumph in its preventive work along lines of child care and everywhere the most effective service of public health departments concerns itself with the physical protection of children.

The rapid progress of medical science, including surgery, during the last two decades became a challenging stimulus to those who were concerned with problems of mental health. As described in Chapter II, the first emphasis was upon the structural causes of mental malady, but the attention of the specialist was irresistibly turned to the larger problem of functional disorders. With the advent of psychoanalysis, as a result of the work of Freud, investigation turned to the inner life of the neu-

---

[1] Bernard Glueck, "Constructive Possibilities of a Mental Hygiene of Childhood," *Mental Hygiene,* July, 1924, p. 650.

rotic in an effort to discover the origins of mental disease. Not only was the field of investigation greatly increased, but much that before was dismissed as of no significance, such as the mutterings of the insane or the dreams of those suffering from milder forms of mental disorder, was studied seriously in the expectation that it would yield insight into the causes of the various forms of mental trouble. One of the first results of this new attack upon the problems of mental disorder was the bridging of the chasm that previously had existed between the insane and those who were thought of as sound-minded individuals. The sharp line separating the normal from the abnormal faded away and the conviction grew that the real task of the psychiatrist was the understanding of human behavior and of the mechanisms that, developing in the personality pronounced mentally disordered, were also found in milder form within the group of healthy minded persons. As the searching of the personality for clews to the causation of mental disorders continued, the importance of childhood became more impressive. This in turn brought the parent within the field of investigation, since the child's problem was most often the consequence of an environmental situation in which the father or mother occupied the most prominent place. Since mental maladjustment rather than a disease-entity appeared as the problem of the specialist he had to turn from his laboratory to the larger task of bringing about the patient's graduation from family ties and of studying the construction of his personality in the experiences of life itself.

Fortunately medical science in its attempt to conquer physical disease was committed to prevention. It was inevitable that the specialist in mental disease should feel the same impulse to prevent rather than to cure, and this meant applying the principles of mental hygiene to problems of childhood and the home. Investigation had already traveled far enough to disclose the great importance of the emotional life of the individual and the large part that childhood experience played in developing and establishing the direction of the emotive life. The significance of jealousy, for example, between the ages of one to five as a cause of the adult's later difficulties in social adjustment when the emotion was cemented into character became apparent. The fact that the early life of the child, if badly handled by the parent, becomes a fixed source of trouble for the adult in his later coping with life reveals how largely the consummation of mental health depends upon the wholesome interplay of family members and upon a wise parental policy.

Pleasure motivation. It is easy to see in the early life of the child the basic drive of the human organism toward pleasure and away from pain. No less swiftly than he snatches back his hand from a hot radiator does the infant scramble away from the raucous voice of a stranger or spew out of his mouth the unliked new food put there by his mother. Anything that does not attract him he flees, just as he does physical pain. In the same way he runs to meet the few pleasures he knows, whether milk-drinking or parental fondling or the exercise of his muscles. Let the child of eighteen months suddenly notice a stranger paying unwanted attention to him as he teeters into the living room, and he stops as suddenly as if he had run into a solid wall, yells his protest, and runs away to find his nurse or a favorite nook to comfort him. If he is a thumb-sucker he may stand his ground and thrust into his mouth his ever-present pacifier, then dreamily give himself up to this pleasure of his earliest days and pay little heed to the disturbing stranger.

Whatever has been long associated with comfort spells

pleasure for the tiny child, and pain is represented by anything that suggests earlier discomfort. As he grows older the range of situations that bring him pain or pleasure grows wider, and the classifying of any particular situation less simple. At two years the child who, six months before, was driven by strangers to take flight—either into the playroom, or the apron of his nurse, or his own thumb-sucking habit—alternates between his old program and a new one that puts strangers among the pleasures of his life. First he runs up to the caller and shouts or tugs at her dress, then, when he receives the attention he is demanding, hangs his head, or hides behind mother, only to repeat his performance with variations as soon as he is forgotten.

On up through the years of childhood, into and throughout his maturity, he still switches back and forth in this way as he reacts to social experiences as productive of pain or pleasure. At six years he craves the companionship of any and all people, hangs around the washerwoman, sticks close by the plumber, and suffers agonies of deprivation if not allowed at least to see every grocer's boy, messenger and dignified visitor at his home. Yet, so painful may he still find it to be looked at by a stranger that he cannot put his tongue to the questions he aches to put to the worker, but begs his nurse to ask for him, and only peeks around the corner at front door visitors, lest they ask him questions he cannot trust himself to answer. The pleasures and pains his first six years have tied up with the coming of outsiders to his home are still pulling him toward opposite ways of acting, while the new pleasures and pains he meets as he wobbles between wanting and not wanting contact with people keep changing the strength of his impulse toward flight or approach.

Six years or so later the balance may for a while be

so heavy on the side of flight that he can never be found when any outsider comes, but hides himself away in the attic, reading for hours on end about the doings of those fascinating people outside his daily round, with whom he yet craves contact even while he most dreads it. The pain of being looked at and spoken to by any but his immediate family and schoolmates does not quench his thirst for the pleasure of knowing how strange people think and talk and act, so for the time he satisfies his hunger for social contact pleasures at secondhand, through books that do not assail his self-consciousness and cause him pain by focusing their attention on him. Farther on in his development, the balance is likely to hang more evenly between his attempts to gain pleasure by being with people and his efforts to avoid pain by escaping from them, but always he oscillates between these two drives, now approaching what promises him pleasure, and now running away from what threatens pain. Although this unveiling of an inner mechanism which drives the individual toward this act and away from that one is not so near the surface in the adult period it still persists, for it is a human characteristic, built upon the purpose of the organism itself, whose fundamental reaction to its environment is expressed in the effort to avoid discomfort and pain and to attain and continue pleasure. In these two activities originate the momentum that drives the human individual throughout his life experience. With the development of the personality, these pain-pleasure processes are not confined to the physical satisfaction of the organism. Just as the six months old baby, well fed and refreshed by nap and bath, is disturbed by the excited tones of his mother's voice and the tenseness of her hands and arms as she holds him while heatedly scolding another child or quarreling with her husband, so the more mature individual reacts against the painfulness of situations that are embarrassing or productive of anxiety, even though entirely free from physical discomfort. Whatever seems to threaten security, whether physical or emotional, bespeaks pain to child or adult, and everything that makes the person feel secure or important, whether by adding to his material possessions—a bottle of milk or a legacy—or by building up his prestige—a smile from mother or favorable newspaper publicity—is interpreted as pleasure.

In his veering toward this pleasure and away from that pain experience nobody is untouched by the appraisal of pain-pleasure situations in the evolution of the particular culture of his time and place. One person finds a tightly closed dwelling pleasant because of its warmth, while another, whose racial and geographic background are different, is pained by its stale odors but takes pleasure in a colder house which allows free circulation of fresh air. Even one's reactions toward the food necessary to support the physical body are affected by social attitudes that have been built up by the group's experiences in past generations, and as a consequence appears an elaboration of food preparation and technique of table manners through which satisfaction is achieved, and without which discomfort and chagrin are felt.

As the child grows he does not merely multiply his needs by beginning to want and fear an increasing number of situations. He also builds up habits and attitudes as a result of the pleasures and pains that he experiences under the tutelage of his parents. Although the urge toward pleasure and away from pain is fundamental to the organism, its direction is not fixed, aside from a few distinctive reactions, but instead is formed out of experience, the product of the conditioning the child receives. One youth reacts pleasurably to the busy hum of a factory because this means that goods are being produced which will in turn bring pleasure to numbers of other people; another is painfully affected by the whir of the same factory, because he sees the painful situation of the employees who are doing uninteresting work for low wages, with little leisure and less hope of bettering themselves. As a result of later episodes which recondition him, either of these young men may at any time take the position of the other in regarding as painful that which he had previously considered pleasurable.

Thus, although pain and pleasure furnish momentum for the child's activities, they do not decide the direction along which he must proceed to achieve his satisfaction. This results from experience. What happens is, to a large extent, determined by the influence of the parents.

An illustration of this is the child's reaction to injury. What may be called the hurt experiences are among the first to appear and to receive the conditioning impress of parental teaching and example. The product of hurt for the child should be caution and self-protection. It is his business to steer away from the occurrences that hurt him and bring him pain. When he bumps his head on the corner cupboard or falls down on a slippery floor, or gets a pebble in his shoe, he should notice how it happened that he got hurt and practice a careful avoidance of similar missteps in future. His reaction to his discomfort or suffering, expressed in tears or anger, attracts the attention of the parent and frequently brings forth from the latter an excessive and uncritical concern and sympathy. As a consequence the child is tempted to make use of the feeling of hurt as a means of getting emotional satisfaction from father or mother, instead of learning to take better precautions for his own safety. When this happens the child easily exaggerates his suffering, and tries to give the impression that he is hurt much more than he is, until he even deceives himself into thinking his hurt is serious.

Often one sees a child of two years take a tumble with no outcry, then begin to howl when he notices his compassionate parent looking anxiously at him, and howl louder and louder as caresses and endearments are heaped on him, until he finally tires of being fussed over and runs off to play again. Such a procedure confuses the issues and makes the child think more highly of himself for making an error in judgment or being clumsy with his hands or feet, since his stupidity has brought him an unusual dose of demonstrative affection. Far from regretting his awkwardness and trying hard to do better next time, he supposes himself a hero when he is buffeted by hard circumstances. It is not difficult for the child to proceed farther in his error until he deliberately uses even a mild discomfort to get emotional satisfaction from the fondling given him by his parents. He magnifies his injuries to such an extent that his discomfort is more fictitious than real. Because of the wrong policy of the parents, the child loses the lesson that his pain should bring him; he learns to prefer fancy to fact, and also discovers an easy means by which he can force the attention of the parent and receive an outpouring of affection. In this way pain-pleasure reactions that should be a basis for sound self-direction stimulate cravings for emotional support. This pushes the child toward a parasitic experience which robs him of self-confidence and vitiates the discipline that his experience offers.

As the child grows older, to achieve happiness he must learn when it is necessary to postpone or give up the satisfaction he craves. Here again he runs the risk of bad conditioning from parents who have never learned self-control when they find their desires frustrated, and by their behavior or their deliberate teaching encourage the child to make a great ado whenever he encounters disappointment and blow off his energy in crying or in rage rather than either facing the defeat from which he cannot escape or giving himself to the effort of finding some way by which he can later attain his wish. This is most likely to happen in families that are torn by discord between husband and wife. The child sees his parents forever quarreling, giving way to rage or displaying hurt feelings, instead of dropping or adjusting the trifles that start their disputes. Much as this wears on him, the child is liable, under provocation, to go through similar contortions of body and emotions. He teases or fights to get whatever is temporarily denied him, cries when he is crossed, or has a tantrum when things do not go his way. The child who because of family influences cannot learn self-mastery when his desires are blocked starts a life policy which is bound to lead him into much unhappiness, inefficiency, and nervous dissipation.

The interaction of the physical and psychic. The physical and psychic mingle in the individual's pain-pleasure reactions as he comes in contact with his environment and it is difficult to separate the two. An interesting illustration of this interaction of the physical and psychic appears in what is recognized by persons familiar with the problems of mothers as one of the most common difficulties encountered in family life. No need of the organism could be more fundamental than the necessity of food, without which life cannot continue. In spite of the obvious physical character of hunger, the experience is one that easily passes over into the psychic so that because of conditioning influences, the outcome of contact with members of the family, the normal appetite of the child is decreased or led into idiosyncrasies. Nature has provided a large element of pain-pleasure reaction in this hunger-food response. Serious and unsatisfied hunger is painful beyond imagination. The pleasure of appeasing hunger is also great as is clearly seen in the behavior of the hungry animal that receives food. With the development of human culture, the pleasure of taste has been extended and refined until the special feature of modern cooking is its skill in catering to the delicate and varied tastes that have been cultivated. Although food satisfies the most compelling of all organic cravings, the influence of social experience can interfere with physical appetite to such an extent as to perplex the mother and leave the child under-nourished.

The food experiences of the child of four or five years are frequently his most dramatic happenings, often culminating in the dislike of certain foods which his parents push upon him because, looking at the matter from the point of view of diet, they believe that his physical welfare demands his eating daily a definite amount of such foods as spinach or carrots. This child easily, especially when some older member of the family sets the example, develops a strong antipathy to foods that are both palatable and wholesome and may even continue his dislike throughout life.

Another variation of the food difficulty of the child appears in the dramatic contests that develop as soon as the child begins eating in the presence of his family. Hostility to certain foods, unwillingness to eat, the eating of merely enough to take away the sharpness of hunger, followed by an effort to escape from the table and play, and an emotional outburst of anger or crying when this is prevented, are common forms of the eating reactions of the child. There are, of course, often physical reasons for the child's conduct, especially when he has changed from having a normal to a poor appetite. Illness frequently causes a loss of appetite; bad posture or unwise sleeping conditions also are among the most common physical causes of food disturbance. Sometimes an eating problem originally came out of a physical situation, but was continued and increased by psychic reaction. This is brought out by Aldrich [2] who describes how the common cold, which temporarily takes away the hunger of the child, may be the origin of serious difficulties on account of the fact that the mother persists in the effort to feed the child who has lost his zest for food. This is a particularly good illustration of how easily the psychic element may be built upon the physical.

The mistakes of parents that lead to bad conditioning in the hunger-food responses of the child fall into three types. One is an attack upon the proper reaction of the organism by trying to force food upon the child when he does not need it. This, as we have seen, may be when the child has a slight cold. The mother is particularly liable to cause trouble when she makes an issue of the child's eating something of dietary value. He at once gets the idea that his eating or not eating is of more concern to his mother than to him. This provides opportunity for the child to create disturbance by protest and even rebellion, thus giving him the means of unwholesome self-assertion. His eagerness to accept his opportunity is sometimes due to unsatisfactory relationships between himself and either parent during the daily routine away from the dinner table. If the child feels that one of his parents does not care for him, he is likely to give vent to

[2] C. A. Aldrich, "The Prevention of Poor Appetite in Children," *Mental Hygiene,* October, 1926, p. 703.

his hidden feeling of bitterness by refusing to do what is expected of him, even expressing his dissatisfaction with life by refusing, as far as possible, to eat. Another origin of bad eating responses comes out of the failure of the mother to use good technique in preparing or presenting food. This is especially true when she does not wisely introduce new food to the child. It is quite common for strange tastes to be at first disliked by the child, who gradually, if he is skillfully handled, cultivates a liking for the new kinds of food. This is an experience familiar to the adult who, in order to dine pleasantly with others or when in foreign countries, deliberately cultivates a taste for a new and strange food.

The family setting. In any interpretation of the influence of the home upon the growing personality of the child it is necessary to consider the family setting in its totality. Every member of the family makes a contribution to the situation in which the child forms his personality. It is, however, from the older members that the child must largely obtain his impressions. Disturbance between family members is bound to recoil upon the child even though it may not distinctly concern him. Usually, the little one has a prominent place in any incompatibility that arises, since he is always in danger of becoming a victim of reactions that, as compensations, bring relief to an unhappy adult. The woman who distrusts her husband or the man who resents his wife's poor team work in making both ends meet is very likely to pour out on the child unrestrained affection, to make up for the choking of the normal outpouring of love toward the mate. This abnormal display of fondness for the child hurts him by giving him a grossly exaggerated idea of his own importance, at the same time that it prevents the turning of his attention toward winning more difficult but more wholesome rewards in the group outside the family.

The child is almost sure to be dragged into any quarrel that originates between husband and wife, and sooner or later becomes the bone of contention when friction has developed in the home. However wise and determined the mother may be in her effort to start the child right, she cannot protect him from the family setting as it is actually maintained. In immigrant families where European traditions are strong and contrary to American culture the presence of a grandmother or a grandfather in the family frequently leads to friction if the parent attempts to discipline the child in accord with American practices. Grandparents so often interfere that they have come to be thought of as a problem whenever they live with their children and grandchildren and have an opportunity to influence parental policy. Difficulties arise not because of the age difference, but because of contrast in attitude and background. When such differences exist between husband and wife the same sort of problem appears. For example, the father may be traditional in dealing with his child and utterly ignorant, indifferent, and even hostile to the science of child care. On the other hand, the wife, more fortunate in her contacts, may have become interested in modern methods of child culture. In the repeated clash between husband and wife and great divergence in their reactions to him, the child deeply suffers.

Older brothers and sisters also provide conditioning influences that are seldom fully appreciated by the parents. Jealousy, discontent, ill-feeling, indeed unhappiness in any form in an older child, usually transfers itself into attitudes toward the younger child that are distinctly harmful. This transference of bad adjustment in the experience of the older becomes a stumbling block in the pathway of the younger family member. It is, therefore, fallacious in any diagnosis of a child problem influenced by family conditions to deal only with the child himself or his relationship to his parents. The diagnosis must consider the total family situation, including the attitudes of the brothers and sisters, and not be content with focusing on any individual difficulty, which, however distressing it may be in itself, has to be regarded as a symptom rather than the main problem.

Integration. The weaning process by which the child turns from looking to his parents as the almost exclusive environment of his life, and becomes accustomed to self-decision and self-maintenance is necessarily gradual. It is unfair to force it upon the child suddenly by a complete change in the policy of the parent, by which, without adequate preparation or sympathetic interpretation, the child is made to depend entirely upon his own guidance. This is both unfair and usually disastrous to the personality of the growing child. The transition from dependence to self-reliance would be more difficult than it normally is, were it not that the child's process of growth and his increase of strength and achievement lead to the drive for new forms of self-expression. This provides the opportunity which the wise parent accepts. Much hangs upon what happens in the first experiences that attend the child's effort to free himself from earlier dependence. Each success in meeting life gives him additional confidence, and it is the business of the adult to provide conditions by which he can achieve, but this must be genuine success, not a fiction substituted by the parent because of the child's failure; it is not for the parent to give the child success, but to provide a situation in which he can obtain it for himself. Chronic defeat will rob him of the feeling of self-reliance. During this weaning process the child may start, because of his experience of defeat, a tendency toward self-depreciation, so that he cannot use his resources, or easy success may give him the spirit of arrogance and a conceit which will cause him always to misinterpret what he does and over-estimate himself. If the emergence of self is seriously thwarted by parental or other authority, the vigorous child may become rebellious and eventually perhaps lawless. This process of release from extreme dependence upon parents may rightly be described as the most critical event in the development of personality.

The Consolidation of Trends. In his movement toward integration, the child needs to have all his various lines of growth consolidated to form the basis of a unified, happy personality. Advancement must go on in his physical, intellectual, emotional, and social life. The emotional element deserves especial attention, because of its many possibilities. Easily perverted from wholesome development, it demands skillful guidance. The occurrences that stamp their impression upon the child have a determining influence upon his career by the conditioning of responses they bring about. These conditioned responses are not limited to their specific origin, but are carried over from one experience to another until they become so well established and automatic that they compel decisions, exercising what might figuratively be called the sovereignty of the personality. They usurp authority over the intellect, and govern the social activities.

Dangers of adult contact. The social and psychic risks of childhood do not come from the operation of a pernicious instinct that arises in the parent with the birth of his child. The history of children committed to the most efficient institutions reveals that they encounter even greater hazards in the orphanage than in the home. The origin of the child's difficulties is his dependency. He has to shape his personality under conditions provided by superior authority. He is at the mercy of the environment provided, as much as the plant is in the power of the soil conditions at the spot where it happens to start its growth. In such a situation, where older persons furnish a quantity of influences and the little one partakes of what is offered, all the dangers of intimate contact are bound to be exaggerated. If the parent frequently errs by unrestrained expression of his love, a mistake which is usually due to his ignorance of the power he exercises and a misinterpretation of what the child needs, the impersonal institution discloses how easily officialism takes possession in an authority-dependency relationship.

Nor should we forget that it is not only a problem of association of adult and child, but that the entire environment of the child is largely directed by the older person. In this setting the most influential conditions spring out of the personal contact of the child and adult, but that is not the exclusive cause of trouble, for the world of things also has influence. The injury that the adult brings the child by faulty control of the physical environment or of his personality contacts, comes either from his unwise attitudes toward himself or toward the child. The parent or older person in this relationship reveals his own maladjustments, especially those of an emotional character. Out of his wrong attitudes toward life and his lack of self-knowledge pours forth unrestrained feeling which interferes with the natural growth of the child and creates obstacles to his integration. On the other hand, mistaken attitudes toward the child occur as a result of failure to see the needs of the little one or of inability to cope with them if they are faintly discerned. In the first case the trouble is primarily personal failure to deal adequately with the problems of life. In the second case the trouble chiefly springs from lack of understanding, which may be nothing more than failure to get the necessary preparation for parenthood.

The child's dependency.   Pain-pleasure experiences loom large in the early years of childhood.   The reactions of the immature individual to his environment are vigorous and crude.   They have none of the subtlety that appears in the complex life of older people.   As a consequence of the vividness of pain-pleasure experiences, the child's reactions are definite and forceful.   From his dependency comes both pain and pleasure.   Pleasure results from the fondling he receives and from his first taste of self-assertion and independent achievement.   In the losses of comfort and security that come to him as he grows up, pain experiences appear.   As he turns from the protection of his parents to go his own way, he encounters ordeals which test him and, if he fails to master them, bring him extremely unpleasant results.   He may contrast his home situation, beside his parents, with all the other conditions that he finds when he is outside the protection of his mother or father.   Thus he easily turns to his association with his parents as a means of saving himself from harder circumstances.   He seeks to continue in his dependency the security which he should obtain by growing up.   He may even endeavor to make this relationship with his parents his constant environment in which he may avoid all testing circumstances that would force upon him new adjustments.   This policy of the child may delight the parent.   Indeed, it is often entered upon because it satisfies the deep wishes of the mother or the father.   A more heroic child, striving to assert himself, finds at the best that he is decidedly limited in self-expression, if he has been over-dependent upon others during his period of helplessness. It is not difficult for the parent or older person to check the faint beginnings that offer the child training in self-control. The child also sees that the environment presented by the parents in this child-adult interdependency may be largely controlled by him if only he can make his father and mother respond to his wishes. By this interference with his parents the child obtains protection against hard circumstances and at the same time a sense of power which gives him the pleasure that comes from an increasing ego.

Mischievous as all this may be because of its final effect upon the character of the child, the status of dependency cannot be forever maintained since growth, except in the lower grades of feeble-mindedness, must take place. What occurs is the postponement of growth, which leads to a personality which clings to past experiences, has little vigor in attempting to adjust to new circumstances, and is marked by lack of confidence. The personality is fundamentally parasitic and this trait, carried over into later life, reveals its weakness when the adult is obliged to meet the ordeals of everyday existence.

The world of dreams. The working of the pain-pleasure principle appears clearly in the child's earliest use of his imagination. At first it is difficult for him to distinguish fact from fancy. The memory of things that have happened, present experiences, and his wishes intermingle, so that with the best of intentions he is confused in dealing with what adults call his real experience. As his contacts increase and his power of interpretation grows he should gradually gain the ability to realize whether he is dealing with things that have happened or things that he wishes to happen. But if his environment is severe, he recoils from it instead of developing greater clarity in his perception of it; he is tempted to substitute desires for facts and to use his power of imagination as a means of creating a refuge to which he can retreat for his satisfactions. Whether he finds his environment repellent or not depends more upon his disposition, as determined by his early conditioning, than upon the character of his material environment. By the time he is able to appraise the circumstances of his life, he has already developed attitudes and habits which tend either to make him eager to deal with life as he finds it or to turn from it and find a substitute in some form of daydream. If the parent has interfered too much already, by pampering the child and not permitting him to begin the development of courage in facing difficulty, he is of course predisposed to magnify the unpleasant features of his real experience and take comfort in the creations of his imagination. This is the more likely to happen if the child who has been over-indulged faces, because of a change of policy of his parent, or because of the death of father or mother, or the coming of hard circumstances to the family, unexpected hardships from which, because of the softness of his character, he is impelled to run away.

The child is also tempted to over-use his imagination as a substitute for the poverty of his experience when the environment is deficient in opportunities which the normal child should have. For example, an American child, living with her parents on a banana plantation, thirty miles by rough road from the nearest white neighbor, with no opportunity for play with other children except when her parents once a month go to town, has developed an imaginary world in which she has association with several self-created playmates. In such an extreme case as this it is easy to see that the child is finding, by compensation, a way out of the deficiency of her environment and that her creatures of fancy, if, as she grows up, her parents lead her to balance her fanciful life with increasing skill in manipulating real situations, offer less danger than her former loneliness.

Facility of imagination, however trying it may be at times to parents in the early life of children, is not a personality defect *per se*, but an equipment for life of great promise. Risk comes when phantasy is used to establish a habit of disguising facts which are unpleasant in the effort to prevent the necessity of disagreeable adjustments to life, or when fictions are developed as substitutes for the reality that the person should either seek in actual experience or abandon as a desire because of no reasonable chance of its attainment.

The guilt feeling. Nothing perhaps better measures the distance we have traveled toward a better understanding of childhood, under the influence of modern science, than does the changed attitude toward the feeling of guilt in children. With the spread of Calvinistic tradition in America went the belief that the climax in the child's religious training was a tremendous sense of personal guilt. Not only was the coming of this feeling of guilt considered normal; its failure to appear was regarded as serious criticism of the parental training, whose solemn duty it was to bring the child, at least by early adolescence, to an overwhelming sense of unworthiness and sin. There is in the history of childhood nothing so morbid as the shadow Puritanism threw over the child. With his eternal destiny at stake, the young person was deliberately driven by fear to find in his experience grounds for guilt. This led to self-deceit and inner strain, alien to the nature of the wholesome child, and forced morbid thinking and feeling which scarred even the happiest disposition. To-day mental hygiene considers this guilt feeling in childhood as one of the most risky happenings of early life, from which the child must be guarded as much as possible by those who minister to his needs.

A striking fact is the triviality of most of the occasions that lead to guilt in children. For example, one of the most common thoughts in young children is that they have done something terribly wrong when they have merely expressed their inevitable and proper curiosity in sex. This usually has nothing to do with any sex impulse, but is merely a desire to know the meaning of what has been made a mystery in the child's experience. The reaction of parent or other adult may be such that forever after the child carries a sense of guilt which attaches itself to anything that has to do with sex even though the original trouble is soon forgotten.

The source of the guilt feeling has nothing to do with the seriousness of the experience, for it is how the child feels rather than how he came to have this emotion that is the significant thing. Naturally the child does not talk about his consciousness of guilt to those from whom he expects blame and even punishment, so that only the discerning parent has opportunity to give relief to the child when guilt arises. By portraying guilt feeling in children as one of the great obstacles to normal growth, mental hygiene has contributed greatly not only to the happiness of childhood, but even more to the security and sanity of adult life.

Fundamental reactions to environment. Pain and pleasure, the fundamental reactions to environment, issue in movements of advance and retreat, out of which develop, with the growth of the child, the various habits and attitudes that form his personality traits, both good and bad. Always the organism attempts to continue and even to increase a pleasurable experience, while consistently trying to escape from unpleasant conditions. In the early days of infancy these contrasting movements are simple. As soon as half an hour after birth, the baby seeks food, turning its head at a touch on its face, getting hold of the finger or nipple presented, and starting sucking. Even before the end of his first day an infant may show avoiding reactions, as in Watson's experiments when the baby lay on its back with legs stretched out and the inner surface of one knee was lightly pinched, the infant struck the experimenter's fingers with his opposite foot in something over half a minute. Babies a few days older reacted in this way in a few seconds, occasionally in less than one second. Sometime in or after the third month the infant responds by the avoiding movement of blinking to a sudden threatening motion of the hand or any other object.

The reactions of approach and withdrawal are rapidly elaborated by experience and are built up into habits characteristic of the individual, who becomes a product of the conditioning that he has received. These reactions are evoked by contact with the environment, both of things and people, but the latter make the stronger impression upon the child, and his movements toward and away from people are more vigorous and generate more emotion than when he is reacting to things. In his contact with people the child is in association with an environment which is also characterized by movements of approach and withdrawal, for the adult makes the same fundamental reactions as the child. Whatever the child does is responded to by the adults in charge of him in terms of advance and retreat. Thus people present to the child an environment that is emotionally charged, and therefore is continually being changed by its reaction to what he does, at the same time that it acts as a stimulus upon him, producing in him a strong emotional reaction. In such an interplay, in which the adult's reactions may be as primitive and unrestrained as those of the child, the character of the latter must construct itself. The child cannot avoid reacting favorably or adversely to the situations in which he finds himself, and whatever he does at once becomes a factor in the shaping of his environment, at the same time that it enters directly into the making of his personality.

Sex. As soon as the child reaches that point in his development at which he becomes observant of the reactions of persons about him, he discovers that a certain sphere of his interests gets a different reception from his parents than any other. This means that his curiosity or some accidental happening of his body exploration has entered into what is known to the adult as "sex." These things that the child does and becomes so curious about are no different to him than other experiences that have arisen with his growth, though for the adult they have a distinctly different meaning from any other events and ideas, because they are saturated with an emotional coloring that comes out of his past and the conditioning that he has himself received. The adult, by a harsh reprimand or shocked tone or self-conscious expression of mingled guilt and pleasure, dramatizes the incident in a way that fixes the child's attention on what he has done or said, which immediately takes on a coloring of differentness from the other happenings of his life.

Sex then becomes not merely a new part of the child's experience, as going to school or getting acquainted with the child who has just moved into the neighborhood opens up additional fields of thought and activity, but, because of the emotional intensity of the parent in dealing with it, becomes a thing apart, more fascinating than anything else, not to be openly discussed or experimented with nor to be lightly dropped and easily lost sight of in the press of other interests. Immediately the child reacts emotionally to the situation to which the adult has unwittingly contributed, and, whether the child advances or retreats, the experience is bound to have an emotional significance for him, in proportion to the excitement he has created and the emotion that the parent reveals. The child may think much of what has happened and add to it every bit of information or experimentation he can get hold of or imagine, or he may flee the subject in panic, only to find it pursuing him whichever way he turns. Oftener, perhaps, he will swing back and forth between these positions, now seeking and now fleeing whatever has even a remote bearing on the emotionally charged subject.

At first these experiences have to do with the child's desire for information; at a later time they are concerned also with the inhibition of impulses that have been brought to expression by the maturing of his body. The older child feels the force of social convention whether he conforms to usual behavior or deviates, and his conduct takes on an emotional coloring which is necessarily built into the personality. Mental hygiene cannot be merely a matter of getting the child's conduct to square itself with social expectation. More significant than the question of conformity is, What emotional attitudes with reference to sex has the situation constructed in the life-trend of the individual? Feverish attempts to impress him with the undesirability of a recurrence of the episode in which he was involved are liable to overshoot their mark and either convince him of the undesirability of all sex conduct even among mature persons, or else they give such prominence to what has happened that it gains a power of fascination which makes it certain to be followed by further vagaries of sex behavior. Morbid tendencies that lead either to chronic sex repulsion or intense but hidden or unacknowledged interest are created in this way and increased in strength by like happenings at a later time, until they become lasting obstacles to good adjustment. Although originating within the sex sphere these morbid trends are not, as this book again and again emphasizes, confined to the special type of experience in which they started, but readily transfer themselves to any other department of life, where they become deeply embedded, vexatious trouble-makers. The person who is trying to suppress a consuming interest in sex is likely to deal severely with the more normal behavior of others, reading a vicious meaning into wholesome occurrences and exaggerating trifling happenings into licentiousness. This morbid concentration on the evils of sex accounts for much slander, meddlesome gossip, and the warm reception of such tales, whether spread by word of mouth or in journalistic tabloids. He who is repelled by sex as a result of early conditioning is apt to become a soured individual, demanding much and giving little in ordinary daily contacts, suspecting the motives of other people and parading his own impeccability.

Fear. The emotional reaction of fear in animal life is common, strongly expressed, and usually useful. Under the circumstances in which modern men and women live, the rôle of fear is decidedly different. In the elaborate setting that the human encounters in his everyday living, there are innumerable circumstances that can bring forth the emotion of fear. In meeting conditions that provoke fear, modern man cannot safely fall back on the simple reactions of the animal that is frightened. Flight or concealment are not always possible or prudential when they can be carried out. In man's life also the forms taken by fear are most variable. It passes by gradations from mild anxiety to abject terror.

At the present time there is much difference of opinion in psychology as to the interpretation of the emotions and their practical application to mental hygiene. In mental hygiene discussions relating to fear, different attitudes are maintained. Partly due to the present state of controversy in regard to man's emotional life, this divergence with reference to the meaning and value of fear is even more the result of unlike definitions of the term fear. Some use the word, fear, to refer merely to the emotional state that accompanies danger, while others have in mind the entire recoil of the individual from the circumstances that menace him. If fear is used in the latter sense, of course it is useful to man as to the animal when it signifies awareness of danger.

In spite of apparent differences of opinion, the leaders in mental hygiene are essentially in agreement that the more understanding prevails over feeling in the midst of a danger crisis, the safer the individual. If the person is captive to his emotional reaction, the difficulty of his acting with prudence is increased. There is also general agreement that it is risky to use fear as a means of frightening the child into desirable behavior. Even in such a perplexing problem as the parent faces in trying to protect his child from automobile risks on the public highway, this appears. Supposing that he can so thoroughly terrorize the child as to prevent his coming into danger, the parent may appeal to fear to impress on the child, for example, the need of his not attempting to cross the street until he has looked in both directions for cars. But this does not assure safety. In spite of the greatest care the child may take, he may at any time find himself in grave danger. Perhaps an automobile seen at a great distance approaches with unexpected speed and reaches the child before he has time to get to the other side. Immediately all the teaching the child has received adds special menace to the confusion that naturally arises as he senses his danger. He may be paralyzed with fear or make discordant and incomplete reactions, costing him his life when it would have been quite possible for him by making the appropriate movements to save himself from being hurt.

The child, however well guarded by his parent, is bound to encounter danger in some form either through suggestion or by the accidents of everyday living, and his reactions powerfully affect his personality. Soon there comes a time when the person, as the result of the conditioning he has received, either lays himself open to fear experiences or encounters danger with self-possession. When the inner life is in a state of tension because of emotional conflict or when guilt feeling has taken possession of the individual, fear responses are encouraged. The policy of parents when fear arises also leads to habit formation in the child. Over-solicitude when fear appears undermines the child's confidence in himself and makes him an easy victim of chronic fear, while indifference leaves him to fight alone a battle that may be decisive in its effects upon character if the child suffers defeat.

Mental hygiene is not content merely to emphasize a protective policy, since the most intelligent parent cannot save the child from danger experiences, indeed will not endeavor to guard his child to this extent. Fear in some form is bound to intrude in every childhood and demands wise treatment. When possible, it should be allied with pleasurable experience. For example, the child may be led to face a situation he fears by appealing to his sense of self-control. Always parents should attempt to detect fear episodes in their children's lives, though the parents must be careful not to suggest fears, by allowing their anxiety to become evident. The parents' recognizing the fears of the child will not only save him often from unnecessary worries, when his fears are only fictitious, but it will eliminate the more serious situation when the fear, driven out of consciousness, remains as an unknown obstacle to good adjustment. The parent who deals with genuine fear will also endeavor to keep it within its proper sphere. If the child has been frightened by a dog, he must be taught to free himself from fear of all animals, including other dogs, and finally if possible even of the one that has troubled him. Fear transferred from a definite occurrence until it grows into a habit-attitude becomes a grievous burden to those whose confidence has been so undermined by the fear reaction that they seldom meet the difficulties of life at any point without misgivings.

Anger. In his reaction to his environment the child frequently expresses anger. This apparently is one of the strongest expressions that issue from environmental contact because it is called forth by extremely disagreeable and menacing circumstances. Rage appears even in the infant as an instinct. Consequently one of the most practical problems confronting the parent is the appearance in the child of what is known as the "temper tantrum." This is nothing more than the free expression of the feeling of rage with the abandonment characteristic of the child. It is a more aggressive reaction to environmental circumstances than is the emotion of fear. Spontaneously expressed by the little child, it often leads him to a realization that he has discovered a means of power by which he can coerce the people about him. Recently in a public restaurant a six year old child obtained his own will and had the food that he insisted upon because his father, a professional man, did not wish to advertise a family situation by withstanding the anger the child expressed when given the food the mother had ordered for him.

If the child wins any success in coercing his elders by his emotional outburst of anger, he comes to regard an expression of temper as one of the most effective means by which he can control his environment. There is also a dramatic element in the temper tantrum which magnifies the ego by the attention it attracts and the fuss it brings about. It is common for the child to attempt to use his outburst of anger as a mechanism for the control of his environment by enlisting the help of his elders, often forcing the assistance of his mother or father to accomplish that which he should learn to do for himself.

In addition to the risk of developing this parasitic attitude toward responsibility and difficult circumstances, the habit of anger tempts the child to reckless acts which he soon regrets. Often these are followed by guilt feeling and penance. In his outburst he may throw and break a most precious toy, and his recklessness may become symbolic of the behavior he is destined to exhibit throughout his life.

The conditioning that encourages display of temper comes from specific situations. These may be grouped in two categories. In the one the child is given an example by the exhibitions of anger by his elders. Through imitation he develops the same faulty reaction that he sees commonly portrayed by one or more members of his family. This need not be the word-slinging, noisy anger that flares up and is gone; more insidious is the resentment one parent cherishes toward the other which overflows onto the child, teaching him that he is the victim of chronic anger he is unable to allay. In one such case the wife, aware that she was being childish in resenting her husband's concentration on his work, to the curtailment of his honeymoon attitude toward her, made a half-hearted effort to reach the mature position of accepting his professional ambition as an ally instead of fearing it as a rival.   Failing in this attempt to grow up quickly she nursed a growing resentment against her husband for putting her in the uncomfortable position of not remaining sole mistress of his attention.   Unable to change either her husband's attitude or her own, Mrs. X. transferred part of her resentment to her five year old son, Jim, who happened to be very irritable and required a great deal of care just at this time because of a prolonged, but mild, illness.   For half a year Mrs. X. consciously disliked her elder son, doing things for him out of a sense of duty alone and pouring the bulk of her affection on her year-old baby.   At last Jim announced his disgust with a world that prized babies and repudiated him.   When his mother first saw him throwing himself on the floor and knocking his things about, she wondered what could possess him to act so like a baby, then suddenly realized that Jim was only trying to win back her love by copying his baby sister's actions.

In the other sort of anger-producing situation the difficulty comes from within and may be broadly characterized as resulting from some kind of irritation. A common form of this is fatigue. The undernourished child is liable to frequent expressions of temper. Whatever the cause of the tantrums of the child, they bring lasting injury to his personality, and make it harder for him to effect adequate adjustments when as an adult he copes with life.

Parenthood hygiene.   It is evident that the mental hygiene of childhood is essentially a problem of efficient parenthood. Parents who understand the emotional needs of their children are in a position to guarantee their young a well-rounded development. The first requisite of the child is that his parents shall have freed themselves from emotional dependence on their own mother and father. The adult who is still infantile in life attitude cannot hope to raise self-reliant children. Efficient parenthood is the work of self-controlled adults, alert to the implications of mental hygiene.

Childhood in itself presents no menace. The dangers of immaturity are, for the most part, the risks that come to the helpless child because he must take from the older people about him the conditions they furnish and incorporate their influences in his growing life. Our modern way of living has made both childhood and parenthood more difficult and it is this that has led to the movement for the training of mothers and fathers.

ILLUSTRATIVE CASE

E. C. was the only girl in a family of four children. From birth she was the favorite of her father, who, throughout her childhood, showered her with excessive affection. He was a man of some means so that he had the leisure to give his child unusual attention. Since the mother was left free to deal with the other children she did not interfere. It is probable, however, that any protest on her part would have made no impression upon her husband. As E. C. developed her father restricted her in play and to a very great degree isolated her from both girls and boys of the neighborhood, especially boys, with whom she was never allowed to have more than a speaking acquaintance. At first she went to the village school, her father carrying her back and forth and exhibiting constantly a morbid concern regarding her health and her school career. The teachers found his interest in his child a good deal of a nuisance, since he constantly bothered them regarding her rank and her physical health. As a matter of fact she had no serious illness and, although encouraged often to stay out of school, she was both well nourished and physically vigorous. Everything connected with her home influences operated to instill in her an idea of self-importance and to build habits of selfishness. When she entered adolescence her father made no change in policy and at that age she still lived a very restricted life as far as contacts with the boys and girls of her own age were concerned. She was not encouraged to enter college. She did travel in Europe and the Orient with her father, making several long trips. Now that the other children had grown up and left the family, the wife increasingly resented the attitude the husband took toward the daughter. Finally, as a consequence of this a bitter quarrel broke out between mother and daughter, under circumstances which forced them both to appeal to the father to decide what was to be done. The mother was so clearly right that the husband had no choice but to render a verdict in her favor. Two or three days later the girl suddenly and without warning left home, and a week later was reported back to her parents from a distant city, where her behavior had become so noticeable as to attract the attention of the police, leading to her commitment to a psychopathic institution. Her disorder was differently diagnosed by the different specialists employed by her father, but after several years of treatment in private institutions, although she had improved, she was not judged competent to go back to her home, nor indeed did she wish so to do. She came to have a great hostility to her father, maintaining the idea that he had injured her, which, in a different way than she understood, was profoundly true, and she eagerly criticized him whenever she obtained a listener. Although her father paid her expenses it was necessary that this be done through the mother, since under no circumstances would the daughter see her father. After six years of institutional care the young woman had only slightly improved.

SUGGESTIONS FOR CLASSROOM DISCUSSION

1. Why has there been so rapid a development of interest in child care?
2. What has Freud contributed to the science of child care?
3. How should parents react to their child's accidental injuries?
4. What suggestions create bad food habits in children?
5. What are the chief dangers of child dependency?
6. What are the stages of the child's interest in sex?
7. How do temper tantrums start?

SUGGESTIONS FOR WRITTEN REPORTS

1. Child training among savages.
2. Rousseau's theory of the meaning of childhood.
3. The conditioning process as interpreted by Burnham in his *Normal Mind*.
4. A critical analysis of Flügel's *The Psycho-Analytic Study of the Family*.
5. An explanation of guilt feeling in children.
6. Common causes of fear in children.

SELECTED BIBLIOGRAPHY

ADLER, ALFRED. *Understanding Human Nature*, Book I. New York, 1928.

ALDRICH, C. A. "The Prevention of Poor Appetite in Children." *Mental Hygiene*, October, 1926, pp. 701-11.

—— *Cultivating the Child's Appetite.* New York, 1927.

BLANCHARD, PHYLLIS. *The Child and Society,* Chaps. I and II.

—— "The Family Situation and Personality Development." *Mental Hygiene*, January, 1927, pp. 15-22.

BROWN, HELEN WILLISTON. "The Deforming Influences of the Home." *The Journal of Abnormal Psychology*, April-May, 1917, pp. 49-57.

BURNHAM, WILLIAM H. *The Normal Mind.* New York, 1924.

CHADWICK, MARY. "Six Months' Experiment at a Nursery School." *The Psychoanalytic Review*, January, 1928, pp. 27-36.

DAVIDSON, JOYCE. "Mental Health in the Nursery School." *Canadian Nurse*, Winnipeg, 25:425-26, August, 1929.

EMERY, E. VAN NORMAN. "The Child Factor in the Teacher-Pupil Relationship." *Mental Hygiene*, April, 1926, pp. 285-93.

FLÜGEL, J. C. *The Psycho-Analytic Study of the Family.* New York, 1921.

FOSTER, SYBIL. "Personality Deviations and Their Relation to the Home." *Mental Hygiene*, October, 1925, pp. 735-42.

GLUECK, BERNARD. "Constructive Possibilities of a Mental Hygiene of Childhood." *Mental Hygiene*, July, 1924, pp. 649-67.

—— "The Significance of Parental Attitudes for the Destiny of the Individual." *Mental Hygiene*, October, 1928, pp. 722-41.

GROVES, E. R., and G. H. *Wholesome Parenthood*, Chaps. I-VII, IX-XV. Boston, 1929.

KASANIN, JACOB and KAUFMAN, MOSES RALPH. "A Study of the Functional Psychoses in Childhood." *American Journal of Psychiatry*, Vol. IX, September, 1929, pp. 307-84.

LINE, W. "A Note on Child Phantasy and Identification." *Mental Hygiene*, Vol. XIII, October, 1929, pp. 754-56.

LOWRY, LAWSON G. "Psychiatric Methods and Technique for Meeting Mental Hygiene Problems in Children of Pre-School Age." *Mental Hygiene*, July, 1929, Vol. XIII, pp. 473-82.

NELSON, LOUISE A. "Why John Ruskin Never Learned How to Live." *Mental Hygiene*, October, 1928, pp. 673-705.

NEUMANN, FREDERIKA. "The Effects on the Child of an Unstable Home Situation." *Mental Hygiene*, October, 1928, pp. 742-50.

OWENSBY, NEWDIGATE M. "Value of Child Training in Prevention of Mental Disorders." *Southern Medical Journal*, July, 1929, Vol. XXII, pp. 629-34.

PRESTON, GEORGE H. "Mental-Hygiene Factors in Parenthood and Parental Relationships." *Mental Hygiene*, October, 1928, pp. 751-60.

Proceedings of the Southern California Conference on Parenthood. *Modern Parenthood*, Part VI. Los Angeles.

RICHARDS, ESTHER LORING. "Practical Aspects of Parental Love." *Mental Hygiene,* April, 1926, pp. 225-41.
—— "The Significance and Management of Hypochondriacal Trends in Children." *Mental Hygiene,* January, 1923, pp. 43-59.
SILVERMAN, BARRUCH. "Some Aspects of the Mental Hygiene of Childhood." *Canadian Public Health Journal,* Toronto, 20:398-406, August, 1929.
TAYLOR, MARIANNA. "The Child and the Home." *Mental Hygiene,* October, 1922, pp. 746-72.
TILSON, MARIE AGNES. *Problems of Pre-school Children; a Basis for Parental Education,* 90 pp. New York. Teachers College, Columbia University, 1929.
WHITE, WILLIAM A. *Mechanisms of Character Formation,* Chap. VII. New York, 1916.
WILE, IRA S. "Mental Hygiene in Childhood." *Journal of the American Medical Association,* 93:1874-78, December 14, 1929.
YOUNG, KIMBALL. "Parent-Child Relationship: Projection of Ambition." *The Family,* May, 1927, pp. 67-73.

CHAPTER VI

MENTAL HYGIENE AND ADOLESCENCE

Adolescence as a period of adjustment. Many children who have not been recognized as maladjusted during the preadolescent period appear to become problems during the period of adolescence. In reality the basis for their difficulties has almost invariably been laid in the earlier days of childhood. Their maladjustments can be traced back to unwise types of experience provided by their parents. That the signs of poor adaptation become more marked at this period of life is due to the fact that the adolescent is faced with larger demands for social adjustment than is the child.

The junior and senior high schools, with the introduction of departmental work and a broader social life through school and class clubs, require the young adolescent to fit into a more complex type of organization. Parents, too, expect the assumption of new responsibilities and a more mature attitude with the coming of this age. Weaknesses that have hitherto been excused, or passed over with the comment that they will be "outgrown," now become an occasion for concern in the family. The problem of vocational choice enters into the picture; parents suggest an occupation which they desire the boy or girl to follow, and toward the end of junior high school a decision must be made concerning the subsequent course of study. The adolescent is asked to decide whether he will take an academic course, in preparation for college, or a business course or a mechanical course. Or, if the family finances are somewhat inadequate, he must make up his mind whether to leave school and go to work, or remain in school for a longer time in the face of his parents' economic struggle.

Both at home and at school, adolescence becomes a critical age. The decisions which are made by the individual, or forced upon him, at this time of life may have a far-reaching effect upon his later career. Much depends, therefore, upon whether the adolescent has been prepared, through wise treatment in childhood, to meet the complex demands which are thrust upon him.

Parental ambitions. During childhood, unless the child is obviously mentally deficient, parents are able to build high hopes of his future. In a democratic society such as ours, there is no limit to the scope of these parental dreams. Very often, parents who have failed to achieve their own youthful ambitions look forward to seeing these accomplished vicariously through their children. For them, they desire better things; they must be pushed on to higher economic and social levels.

It is fortunate, for both parents and children, when the latter are capable of fulfilling the wishes of the former. But all too frequently, in the high school period, the boy or girl finds further scholastic success impossible. The plans for further education must be abandoned, but the disappointment of parents cannot always be concealed at this prospect. Three courses are open to parents when their children begin to fail in junior or senior high school. They can accept the situation quietly and encourage them to look about for suitable work; they can resign themselves to their children leaving school but unwillingly and with an attitude of reproach; or they can refuse to face reality and insist that the children stay on in school, urging that success will be possible by harder work.

If the adolescent has parents who are sufficiently under-standing to pursue the first course, the chances are that happiness will be found in some occupation suitable to his intellectual equipment. If the parents permit the boy or girl to go to work, but maintain their feeling of disap-pointment and make it obvious, the vocational adjustment will bring no great satisfaction, since it will carry with it the sense of failure to make good at a higher level. An even greater feeling of failure besets the junior or senior high school student who is forced to remain in school and repeat grade after grade due to parents' insistence upon what they consider the proper education.

It is not only parents who wish to see their children more successful than themselves who perpetrate these errors. The father who wishes to see his son follow him in business or professional life is prone to make the same mistakes. Again and again we see a boy with no aptitude for his father's vocation forced to prepare for it. If he is unable to struggle through the preparation, almost in-variably the father will consider him a failure, or believe that he has deliberately set aside the paternal ambitions through stubbornness or rebellion.

As has been stated recently by Leta Hollingworth, cases in which an able father tries to force an incompetent son to follow the paternal vocation are often brought to the attention of the educator, the psychiatrist and the psy-chologist. Dr. Hollingworth comments, further, "In this situation parents seem almost never to be able to follow the advice given them. Having cherished for about fifteen years the belief that their son would be what they wish, they cannot reconcile themselves to the disappoint-ment of giving up their cherished dream." [1]

[1] Leta S. Hollingworth, *Psychology of the Adolescent*, p. 86. New York, 1928.

The pressure to live up to family expectations causes considerable emotional conflict with many adolescents. A typical instance is that of a fourteen year old boy whose mother brought him for clinical study because he was failing in junior high school. His father, a college professor, had died four years previously, and his mother had constantly talked of the day when the son would take the father's place in the teaching profession. When examined, the boy was found to have average mentality, but not sufficient to take him through senior high school. The mother, in this particular instance, was willing to forego her ambitions and to permit a change in vocational plans. The boy, however, had become so imbued with the idea that he must emulate his father that he was in an exceedingly depressed frame of mind. A long period of work with him was necessary to induce a different reaction on his part. Eventually, he was able to find consolation in work which enabled him to supplement the mother's inadequate income. Without assistance at this critical period of adolescent readjustment, however, he might have become still more oppressed by the sense of failure created by his inability to live up to the family expectations. Undoubtedly there are many adolescents who do not receive such help and who continue to believe themselves failures in the light of family traditions long into adult life.

Vocational orientation. Even when family pressure is not severe, the adolescent still is troubled, to some extent, by the necessity for vocational choice. Without any real knowledge of what is involved in each occupation, the boy or girl is asked to plan a life career. If there is some outstanding talent to point the way, this decision may not be so difficult, but the vast group of young people are uncertain what occupation would suit them or would prove a pleasant one.

In certain high schools, vocational orientation classes have been introduced in order to provide the pupils with accurate information about different kinds of work, the preparation necessary for success in the different fields, and the opportunities for financial return. In addition to this, there is a tendency, also, to introduce vocational counseling into the schools. This means that the pupils are given intelligence tests to determine their qualifications, and are helped to plan their educational program and to choose a kind of work in keeping with native ability.

In a complex industrial civilization such as ours, this educational guidance and vocational orientation is sadly needed. If it cannot adjust the abilities of the adolescent to make possible the realization of parental ambitions, it can at least prevent him from making plans which he can never carry out, or from selecting a vocation in which he has no chance for success. There is no sadder fate than that of the individual who through parental ambitions or other influences has chosen a profession in which he is unable to meet the competition of others who are more fully equipped than himself. Success in a humble occupation gives far more self-respect than continual failure in a higher calling. The mediocre individual may be just as contented and find just as much satisfaction in life as the more highly gifted person, provided he seeks a life work in keeping with his capacities. It is when he finds himself a misfit that he suffers most from his mediocrity.

Adolescent emancipation. Another problem of adolescence is the need to break away from the parents and to assume some measure of personal responsibility. For the child who has been helped to make decisions in little things and to develop self-reliance at increasingly higher levels, this transition is relatively easy. But for one who has been over-protected, who has been encouraged to remain dependent upon the parents, this is a more difficult process. On the one hand the example of companions of the same age stimulates the boy or girl to want independence; on the other a long period of turning to the parents for decisions makes this personal independence a thing to be feared.

Nearly always, the child who has been encouraged to depend too much upon parental care has been the victim of maladjustments within the lives of the parents themselves. It may be that a father, needing to dominate his children in order to bolster up his own self-esteem, has built the pattern of dependency in the child. Or a mother, dissatisfied with her marriage relationships, may have clung too closely to a son or daughter in order to refresh her own starved emotional life. Whatever the cause, the child who has been too closely tied to the parents is ill prepared to meet the social demands upon the adolescent for assuming some responsibility for his acts and making certain of his own decisions.

The adolescent who has been extremely dependent upon his parents in childhood will react in one of several ways. He may shrink back from the problems that confront him, and refuse to grow up, avoiding outside contacts and clinging to the home more firmly than ever. If this attitude persists, it may result in the formation of a seclusive personality and the tendency to remain permanently withdrawn from the outside world and to refuse to face situations or to make adjustments. If the reaction is less extreme, it may simply mean a lengthening of the period of adolescence, psychologically speaking, and a delay in taking up new responsibilities of economic or social nature. Vocational adjustment may be especially difficult, in this case, and marriage and parenthood relationships seriously affected.

If the desire for independence is stronger than the fear of it, the adolescent who has been too long subjected to parental domination may enter into a state of open rebellion against the family standards. In such circumstances, the parents are apt to complain that all their advice is resisted or disregarded, or that their rules concerning smoking or staying out late in the evening are treated with open defiance. The adolescent effort to win emancipation may even lead to running away from home, to truancy from school, or more serious types of delinquent conduct.

A good illustration is the seventeen year old boy whose mother complained to the psychiatrist that since he entered high school she found him quite uncontrollable. If she told him to come home by nine-thirty or ten o'clock he was sure to stay out until eleven or twelve. Twice he had stolen automobiles and taken his friends for rides. On two other occasions he had taken money from her purse and run away to a neighboring city, leaving word that he would not return. He came back, however, when the money was exhausted.

In discussing her earlier attitudes toward the boy, it appeared that she had been very over-solicitous. There were certain traits in her husband which she disliked, and she had determined to bring up her boy in such a manner that he would not acquire them. To this end she had instituted a rather rigid type of training and had given him little freedom. When the natural restlessness of adolescence asserted itself, she tried to meet it by redoubling her restrictions. The boy's response was that described above. When met differently by the mother,

acting under the guidance of a social worker, the boy's
behavior became more acceptable.

Sex adjustments of adolescence.   Besides all the
other adjustments that adolescence is called upon to make,
it is at this time of life, too, that one must become accustomed to the increasing strength of the sex impulses and
work out patterns and standards of sex behavior.   To be
sure, we no longer think of sex problems as having their
inception only at adolescence.   We have learned that
certain types of sex play may be a part of the child's
experience even in very early years, and we know, also,
that curiosity about reproduction makes an early appearance.   But the physical maturation of puberty transforms
this childish curiosity and experimental attitude toward
sex into a definite drive.

Here, again, we shall find that the attitude of parents
has had much to do with making adjustment easy or
difficult.   As was described in the preceding chapter, the
manner in which the child's first questions about the birth
process were received, or the way in which his first experience with masturbation or other forms of sex play
was greeted, may color all subsequent reactions to sex.
If questions have always been answered honestly and sex
experiences met with wholesome candor instead of punishment or horror, then the adolescent is able to turn to the
parents who have dealt with him frankly and reasonably
as a child with his later problems in the field of sex.

But many parents evade childish questions on the
grounds that the child is not old enough to understand.
"We will tell you later on, when you are older."   But by
the time he is older, he will have acquired information—
or misinformation—from other sources, and when the
parent attempts to give the long delayed enlightenment

at the beginning of adolescence there is little response. If the parents have done more than evade the earlier issues, if they repeated the threadbare stories of stork, or cabbage-patch or doctor's bag, then they may be almost certain that any subsequent information they proffer will be skeptically received by the adolescent son or daughter. Outside sources have previously proven more reliable than the word of the parents, and will very probably be considered so still. Thus attempts to correct misinformation will be largely unsuccessful.

Even in this enlightened day there are boys who attain puberty without being prepared for the normal experience of sex dreams and nocturnal emissions, just as there are girls who are totally unprepared for the onset of menstruation. Both boys and girls, if thus unprepared, may be puzzled and dismayed by these unexpected happenings to their bodies which all too frequently are interpreted by them as disease processes and become a source of grave anxiety. It is not entirely the fault of parents that this condition of affairs exists. Many of them are anxious to have sex education for their children, but feel completely inadequate to give it themselves. Sometimes they ask the family physician to act as a substitute; sometimes they let the matter drift, vaguely hoping that the school will give whatever instruction is needed. If the latter is their hope, it is doomed to disappointment, so far as most schools are concerned. Here and there courses in physiology and hygiene in secondary schools include material on sex, but ordinarily text books are used which carefully refrain from mentioning the existence of the reproductive system.

Sex as a substitute for other emotional satisfactions. The proper control of the sex impulses is not decided entirely upon the basis of education. To a large extent the sex behavior of the adolescent boy or girl is determined by the whole emotional adjustment. If their contacts with parents and friends are satisfactory in other ways, it is more than likely that they will be able to meet the problems of sex adequately in spite of incorrect or meager information, and even in the face of unfortunate childhood conditionings. It is the emotionally starved boy or girl who plunges into adolescent experimentation with sex. The girl who feels that she is not wanted or not loved at home, whose parents are faultfinding and critical, turns to friendships with boys for the petting and admiration which she craves. Through sex alliances, she tries to find the security of affection that she lacks in her relations with her parents. That she is usually disappointed goes without saying, for these companionships based on sex are apt to be fleeting. On the other hand, the girl who feels secure in the affection of her parents has less need of finding love outside her home, and her friendships and flirtations with boys are apt to be less intense and not so likely to eventuate in actual sex experience. In every case which comes to the attention of a psychiatrist, psychologist or social worker because of maladjustment in the field of sex, unsatisfactory parent-child relationships are to be found as a fundamental factor.

Even when other emotional outlets are denied, the adolescent does not embark so lightly on sexual adventures as popular essayists who write of "flaming youth" would have us believe. There is struggle against temptation and repentance for yielding to it. One boy, discussing his special sex problem, which is masturbation, remarks, "If you could see my diary you would understand how hard I have tried to overcome my bad habits." Yet this boy has for years lacked any other emotional satisfactions. His parents are divorced, he has been sent to one boarding school after another, but has never remained anywhere long enough to form any real ties. His removals are through no fault of his own, but are a part of his desire to keep in touch with both his parents, who are widely separated, and constantly traveling. He has been accustomed to spend a half year or a year in a school near first one and then the other, but has had too little time with either parent to form any intimate association. At one of his schools he was taught to masturbate. His lack of any parental affection and the constant adjustment to new sets of schoolmates have tended to throw him back upon his own resources. His isolation has fostered the continuation of his habit of masturbating.

Although it has been continued, his emotional conflicts about it are far more harmful to him than the habit itself. He feels that he is different from other boys, that his difficulty with school work (despite his superior intelligence) and inability to make friends readily are both results of this failing. He cannot see that his frequent changes of school and his lack of parental love are enough to explain all his difficulties. He fears that if he continues to masturbate he will either become insane or be unable to adjust to a normal married life in later years. Fortunately, in his present school, he has the help of a psychiatrist in working out his problems of sex adjustment, and it is to be hoped that he will ultimately be reassured and relieved of his present anxiety.

Sublimations for sex. If the adolescent finds his emotional adjustments satisfactory in other ways, the sex energy can find plenty of sublimated outlets. Participation in games and sports uses up some of the physical energy that might otherwise be concentrated into the sex drive. Dancing offers both a physical and an emotional outlet. Creative effort, whether it takes the form of drawing or painting, literary endeavor, or some other line furnishes a sublimation for considerable sex feeling. It does not matter so much about the quality of the work as that it provides an absorbing interest into which sex energy may be drained. For parents or teachers to discourage interests merely because they do not point to any vocational aptitude is exceedingly unwise.

Recently a high school girl remarked upon the fact that she had passed in a love story when the students in her class had been permitted to select their own subject for English composition. She added that she should never dare to repeat the episode, because her teacher had ridiculed her product, ending with the remark that she was too young to know about love and should write of things with which she was familiar. The teacher in question may have been well versed in standards of literary criticism, but she was totally ignorant of mental hygiene and of the psychology of adolescence. Nothing could be more natural than a seventeen year old girl's interest in love or her impulse to write a love story. She was finding a wholesome outlet for her sex interests, and should have been encouraged for the sake of her mental health. Surely it would have been possible to correct her errors in English without holding her particular choice of subject up to severe criticism.

Religious problems. As has been stated in the preceding chapter, there was a period of society when the experience of religious conversion, preferably accompanied by feelings of guilt and the desire to be purified of sin, was held to be a function of normal adolescence. Although the social pressure at this point has been greatly reduced, feelings of guilt still arise in many adolescents because of sex or other experiences and undoubtedly play a part in the tendency to turn to religion at this age.

Repenting behavior which he has learned to consider sinful, the adolescent turns to religious teachings for forgiveness and for a source of strength which may be of aid in struggles to resist further temptations.

At this time, too, the religious beliefs acquired in childhood must be reinterpreted. The concept of God changes and becomes more abstract; instead of the child's vision of a mighty personage the adolescent is able to grasp the idea of a disembodied spiritual force or power. The ritual of the church may take on a new meaning and beauty to the stimulated imagination. In certain cases, the adolescent breaks away from the family church and seeks one of another denomination, where the teachings are more in accord with his own inner need for humility and repentance or the service appeals to strivings for the esthetic. The wise parent does not make these religious differences an occasion of conflict but leaves the adolescent free to work out his own problems in this field.

In the later years of adolescence, particularly if the individual reads widely or comes into contact with the subject matter of higher education, there is the possibility that religious doubts will arise. But even if early teachings are abandoned, this does not mean that the emotional and idealistic strivings which characterize the religious feeling of the adolescent have been lost. Rather they are translated into other terms, such as the longing to be of service to humanity. And, after all, humanitarian principles have always characterized the great religious faiths, so that the inner meaning remains even if the outer forms are no longer accepted. Actually, it is perhaps a matter for congratulation if the youth takes religion generously and interprets it as the will to service instead of adopting the narrow concern with precepts of living to assure his own entry into heavenly rewards regardless of the fate of others.

Adolescent response to social stimuli. Ordinarily, the adolescent spends much more time outside the home than is permitted to the younger child. Therefore, as the high school age is reached, the influence of the family begins to decrease somewhat and external stimuli are multiplied. To parents the most disconcerting result of this situation is the development of standards of conduct and ways of thinking which are alien to those of the family. It is popularly believed that the new ideas taken on from companions outside the home are always radical, but as a matter of fact they are just as apt to be conservative. It depends entirely upon the group of companions with whom the adolescent is thrown and upon the attitudes of the family group as compared with theirs.

Thus, one girl is found practicing the art of smoking and meets her mother's dismay with the statement that "all the girls in school do it." But another girl comes home from high school and tries to dissuade her mother from indulging in cigarettes because none of her friends have mothers that smoke and she is afraid of losing caste with them if they discover that her own mother has this habit.[2] In order to be happy, the adolescent must have his place within a group of friends of about the same age and this can be secured only by conforming to the standards of conduct which prevail in that particular group, however much these may differ from the rules of behavior in the home.

While this susceptibility to social stimuli may be somewhat conducive to family conflicts, it is nevertheless an

[2] G. H. Pearson, "What the Adolescent Girl Needs in Her Home," *Mental Hygiene,* 1930, Vol. XIV, pp. 40-53.

excellent thing in many ways. It insures the adolescent from remaining a complete replica of his parents' prejudices and enables him to come into contact with other points of view. Eventually, after he has established himself as an independent person, he will be able to strike a final balance between home and extra-familial influences.

Conflict in obligations. The conflict between outside stimuli and duty toward parents should not be too much minimized, however. It is not always easy for the adolescent to decide whether he shall cling to the ideals of the family or sacrifice these to the preservation of his position in his own age-group. Thus he often finds himself pulled in one direction by his own wishes and in an opposite way by the commands of his parents.

Still deeper conflicts may arise with the coming of increased freedom. Some of the adolescent desires have the characteristics of an ought and there is a feeling of obligation to carry them out to success. They may still be contrary to the teaching of parents or even to their direct orders. In such a case, the inner life of the boy or girl is torn by antagonistic duties. If personal inclination is followed, the adolescent may be accused of selfishness and indeed fears that this may be the true explanation. On the other hand, merely to coalesce with the parents' ideas means repudiating his own best thought or sacrificing values in which he has confidence for a course of action that seems prejudiced and unfair.

Such conflicts are inevitable to the adolescent who is seeking to direct his own life and to justify his decisions to himself and to those whose approval he desires to retain. There is hardly anything that happens in the family circle that may not lead to a difference of opinion involving for the younger person the question of what is the right thing to do. Hence these conflicts are very common in adolescence, and there is continually arising the question, "Should I do what my parents think is right or what I believe I ought to do?"

The parents may easily use force to coerce the child's judgment or exploit him by an appeal to his affection for them. The adolescent who decides to follow out his duty to himself is likely to feel exceedingly guilty toward his parents. Rather than experience this feeling of self-blame, he may yield to unwise family pressure. While this may give immediate relief it will eventually bring bitter regret and resentment toward the family. The psychiatrist often finds these family conflicts at the basis of maladjustments in later life. A typical example is that of a young woman who broke her engagement because the young man she wished to marry met with the disapproval of her parents. She revealed a resentment and hostility toward them which she had been trying to conceal, even from herself, but which was the chief cause of her unhappiness and neurotic behavior. She could not retrieve her mistake, but her protest against a decision which seemed to her to have come from weakness of character found an outlet through her illness which was, at least in part, a revenge upon the parents whom she had never forgiven for their interference.

It is the temper of our age that these disputes in the family life of most normal adolescents are sooner or later settled in accord with the thought and feeling of the young. Decisions are not, however, easy to make, and when made they may lead to unnecessary estrangement from the parents or to feelings of guilt that are carried on into maturity. When Dr. Samuel Johnson went back to Litchfield and stood in the market place to atone for the time when he disobeyed his parents and ran away from his task, he showed how strong and lasting the adolescent feeling of guilt may be, particularly for the neurotic personality. It is fortunate that contemporaneous social philosophy dwells less upon duty to parents and more upon the rights of youth to happiness, for this attitude helps to diminish the feelings of guilt which would otherwise oppress every individual who in order to achieve his own life control has had to break somewhat with the prejudices and traditions of his parents.

Adolescence and personality readjustment. While it is true that life patterns are determined very early in childhood, it is probable that later experiences may act to reënforce or mitigate these patterns. One of the most hopeful aspects of adolescence is that some individuals, at this age, begin to acquire insight into their own reactions. They size themselves up in comparison with others and classify certain of their habits and personality traits as desirable or undesirable. If they strike too unfavorable a balance, there is the possibility that this self-survey may only increase feelings of inferiority and produce discouragement which prevents any attempts at readjustment. But many persons during the time of adolescence set out to remold themselves in harmony with newly acquired ideals. If their efforts at reëducation cannot be entirely successful at least they may hope to bring about some improvement.

One sixteen year old girl, consulting a psychologist for vocational advice, voluntarily remarked that she had a quick temper but that she was trying to control it because she realized that it would be a handicap in her business and social relationships. An eighteen year old boy discussed his violent temper with considerable insight, tracing its origin to temper tantrums in early childhood and saying that he had just begun to understand that he must overcome his tendency to give way to rage whenever anyone annoyed him.

The danger in the acquisition of such insight is that it is likely to carry with it an understanding of the part parents have played in creating difficulties. Then the adolescent may feel resentful toward them and blame them for his maladjustments rather than trying to work things out for himself. It is necessary, therefore, that insight be more complete; that the parents be seen as suffering from their own personal problems and making mistakes with their children because they were unable to do otherwise. Resentment toward the parents must be replaced by understanding and acceptance of the relationship at a more mature affectional level before the individual is truly free from dependence upon them and in a position to solve his own problems and overcome his own handicaps.

Unless the emotional reactions to the family can be readjusted at this adult level, the individual will find it difficult to adjust in a grown-up fashion to other people. It is this kind of emotional growth which determines whether the person remains adolescent in his attitudes toward life or whether he becomes sufficiently mature to meet its testing of his personality.

ILLUSTRATIVE CASE

Harry is a seventeen year old boy who has been having many difficulties in making his adjustments to life. His childhood was an unhappy one, because his parents were separated and he spent most of his years in different boarding schools. He has never known a normal home life with happy parents, and has never been able to compensate by forming any lasting attachments to teachers or friends of his own age, because he was changed from one school to another so frequently. In the course of his boarding school experiences, he was taught to masturbate, and this habit has been prolonged with him over a number of years, largely because of the continual changes of environment which have cut him off from making satisfactory social contacts and forced him back upon himself for emotional satisfactions.

His father and several of his teachers, learning of his practice of masturbation, lectured him severely about it. They warned him that it would cause him to go insane and that it would sap his physical vitality. This is a point of view generally held but having no foundation in fact. Harry naturally believed it, however, and his anxiety over his habit of masturbation has been a source of considerable emotional disturbance to him. He tells how he has struggled to overcome it, and how he has sought help in prayer about it.

Another difficulty with Harry is his inability to make friends readily. Because he has had so little real affection in his life, he is pathetically eager to be liked, but his feelings of insecurity and inferiority make him ill at ease with boys and girls of his own age as well as with older people. His very need of friendship renders it difficult for him to obtain it, for he is sensitive to slights and unable to meet other people without a great deal of self-consciousness and stiffness.

Because of his emotional conflicts over masturbation and about his parents, he found the adjustment to educational requirements hard to fulfill. It was impossible for him to concentrate on his studies because his mind was so preoccupied with his troubles. In the classroom, he would frequently lose himself in daydreams of a wish-fulfillment type, in which he pictured his parents as reunited and himself living with them. At other times, he would find it impossible to work because of repentance for having lapsed once more into the habit of masturbation, and preoccupation with regrets and resolves to do better.

After Harry had failed the first year of high school work because of these emotional conflicts, his father refused to pay for his continuation in school. Although the boy has superior intellectual capacities, he has had insufficient educational preparation for any kind of skilled job, and he has had to find work of a monotonous sort in a factory. He is still living away from home, and as yet he has not succeeded in making very many friends. However, he is entering into athletics and clubs through the Y.M.C.A. In spite of the fact that he does not like the kind of work he is doing, he has stayed in the same place over a period of several months, and this argues well for his increasing emotional stability. Some of his conflicts over sex matters have been relieved by talks with a psychiatrist, who has given him a better perspective about these things. He has thus lost some of his feelings of guilt over his habit of masturbation.

His present anxiety is largely over the problem of his future. He feels, quite correctly, that he is in a blind alley job, but he sensibly says that he believes he must keep it until he can see a way to securing something better. He is also concerned over the more adult aspects of sex adjustment. He has met a girl in whom he is interested, but he knows that it will be many years before he can afford to marry. Both these problems, that of vocation and marriage, are ones that frequently emerge in adolescence to complicate the adjustment of the individual.

SUGGESTIONS FOR CLASSROOM DISCUSSION

1. Why does adolescence carry with it the emergence of problems of adjustment?

2. How do the ambitions of parents affect the adolescent?

3. What purpose would high school classes in vocational orientation serve?

4. What effects do early parent-child relationships have upon adolescence?

5. What does adolescent rebellion against the authority of parents mean?

6. How do the sex experiences of childhood affect adolescent sex adjustments?

7. What is the relation between maladjustments in other fields and sex behavior?

8. How does the adolescent react to social stimuli?

9. Can the adolescent make any personality readjustments?

SUGGESTIONS FOR WRITTEN REPORTS

1. Religious Experience in Adolescence.
2. Adolescent Problems of Sex Adjustment.
3. Achieving Emancipation from Family Bonds.
4. Vocational Guidance for High School Pupils.
5. Adolescent Idealism.

SELECTED BIBLIOGRAPHY

BEELEY, ARTHUR L. "Juvenile Suicide." *Social Service Review*, 3, March, 1929, pp. 35-49.

BLANCHARD, PHYLLIS. "Sex in the Adolescent Girl." *In Sex in Civilization.* New York, 1929.

—— *The Adolescent Girl.* New York, 1924.

—— *The Child and Society,* Chaps. VI, XI and XII. New York, 1928.

GROVES, ERNEST R. "Adolescent Strain and Social Pressure." *Social Forces,* March, 1929, Vol. VII, pp. 343-350.

GROVES, E. R. and GROVES, G. H. *Parents and Children,* Chap. XII. Philadelphia, 1928.

HOLLINGWORTH, H. L. *Mental Growth and Decline,* Chap. XII. New York, 1927.

HOLLINGWORTH, LETA. *The Psychology of the Adolescent.* New York, 1928.

HALL, G. S. *Adolescence.* New York, 1904.

KUPKY, OSKAR. *The Religious Development of Adolescents.* New York, 1928.

MEAD, MARGARET. *Coming of Age in Samoa.* New York, 1928.

NIMKOFF, MEYER F. "Parent-Child Conflict." *Sociology and Social Research,* 13:446-458, May-June, 1929; and 14:135-150, November-December, 1929.

PRUETTE, LORINE. *Women and Leisure.* New York, 1924.

RICHMOND, WINIFRED. *The Adolescent Girl.* New York, 1925.

SANDS and BLANCHARD. *Abnormal Behavior,* Chap. X. New York, 1923.

STEDMAN, H. R. *Mental Pitfalls of Adolescence.* National Committee for Mental Hygiene, 370 Seventh Ave., New York.

STOPES, M. C. *Sex and the Young.* Dublin, 1926.

TAFT, JESSIE. "Mental Hygiene Problems of Normal Adolescence." *National Committee for Mental Hygiene,* 370 Seventh Ave., New York.

THOMAS, W. I. *The Unadjusted Girl.* Boston, 1923.

TRACY, F. *The Psychology of Adolescence.* New York, 1920.

TRUITT, R. P. "Adolescent Instability." *Hospital Social Service,* September, 1925.

VAN WATERS, MIRIAM. *Youth in Conflict.* New York, 1925.

CHAPTER VII

MENTAL HYGIENE AND MARRIAGE

Since mental hygiene represents an effort of science to assist men and women in their behavior so as to increase human happiness and efficiency, it is necessarily concerned with all eventful experiences. Although these occurrences are particular in their significance to each individual career, they cluster about various centers of interests and naturally can be grouped. Among these consolidations is marriage. Whether looked upon as a source of satisfaction or a means of efficient adjustment, it has large importance. Indeed, for many individuals it represents the supremely significant event of their life. For this reason marriage in the large sense, including its innumerable ramifications, occupies a large place in mental hygiene. This is, of course, a larger matter than the marriage experience narrowed to fit that time period following the wedding. From the point of view of mental hygiene, the marriage interest covers a long line of experience antedating marriage and having some of its most forceful influences starting in early childhood. It means not so much definite occurrences as a growth of personality. Emotions are experienced, habits are formed, actions are constructed along the line of marriage values that come to be fundamental parts of personality make-up. When the marriage interest is dissected in the effort to discover its salient features, three groupings appear: One represents sex, another the contact experience, and the third reaction to reality. Each of these constitute important

154

problems in mental hygiene, but as they appear in the marriage setting they deserve specific treatment.

The importance of sex is generally recognized both in and out of science and it is necessarily discussed from different viewpoints throughout this book. As related to marriage, however, sex has a special meaning which mental hygiene recognizes. The contact element in marriage includes all the difficulties that naturally arise in human association with some in addition due to the intimacy and emotionalism that gather about matrimonial experiences. Mental hygiene is also much occupied with the problems that arise from human hesitancy to accept actual conditions less inviting often than the creations of the imagination that the individual, if he pleases, may substitute for the facts of his situation. Since romance feeds upon the love element that figures so largely in marriage, matrimony becomes a supreme test for many individuals in their temptation to evade life as it is in order to obtain their wishes through fiction constructed by their own thinking.

Mental hygiene deals with marriage as a culmination rather than as an episode. Just as water in certain rock formations of the earth's crust sinks underneath and travels far before it finally escapes through the outlet provided by the spring or the Artesian well, so behavior-characteristics of long standing are, according to mental hygiene, given free expression in marriage and come forth with all their intensity. No individual seeks marriage in order to be supremely tested, but whether he wills it or not, matrimony becomes for him a searching experience that brings to fruitage his most consequential personality traits.

Sex strain. It is an axiom that every normal child has curiosity concerning what the adult calls "sex." These matters to the child are not in any degree different from other experiences until they have been made peculiar because of the reaction of the father and mother to the child's interest in them. Even yet unfortunately it is rare to have parents meet the child's first questioning with reference to sex in such a natural manner, utterly free from emotion, as to prevent the child from receiving any unusual impression. Ordinarily the treatment he receives turns his original curiosity into a quest for the mysterious and makes it difficult for him to meet sex in any of its aspects with the freedom from emotion that is characteristic of his other adjustments to life. It is true that a great change has taken place in the attitude of intelligent people toward sex, but the strength of taboo that, in the past, society's fear of sex lawlessness made necessary still persists and easily starts trouble in early childhood not to be fully revealed until marriage has been consummated. In no other fundamental life interest is so much taboo common. Nowhere else has conventional thinking expected a mere change of legal status to perform such a miracle of adaptation. The wedding ceremony has been treated as if it were a magical influence that could wipe out all the effects of a taboo policy and permit the two people mating to start a sex union free from all the influences of past experience.

The wedding may succeed in bringing about a decided change in attitude as far as conscious thinking is concerned, but this by no means destroys the multitude of impressions, desires, and reactions that constitute the sex development which has taken place in the life of the individual before marriage. Moreover, only on the lowest levels or in pathological deviations do we find in human sex experience the simplicity that is characteristic of animal life. In the normal man and woman an enormous amount of emotion and thought has become affixed to sex, making its final physical expression extremely complicated and attended with hazards that would not occur if its successful functioning depended merely upon appropriate stimuli, physical soundness, and normal structure. It is in the psychic accompaniments rather than in the physiological condition that most sex disappointment and incompatibility arises. The wedding provides a new testing and requires a reconstruction of the life program but it cannot give a pristine start nor can it eliminate the risk of failure born of earlier conditioning.

The two mates obviously do not bring to their experience the same background. Not only must they face their beginning of marriage with diversities of experience, but they also lack the easy frankness which leads to free exchange of attitudes and thinking. They are seldom even conscious of the need of discussion since they do not appreciate the differences that have become characteristic because their pre-marriage sex careers have been unlike. To this must be added the contrast between them because one is male and the other female, and aside from different impulses born of unlike structures, they have assumed the diverse rôles that society has insisted upon their playing.

Even where there is an impulse to be open and cooperative and to keep the sex union from the beginning, however impetuous it may be, upon the level of entire frankness there is great difficulty in carrying out this high purpose. The emotions involved are not easily discussed nor can they quickly be adequately interpreted. Usually they are not even clearly perceived by the person who wishes to bring them to complete expression. This problem is complicated of course all the more where there has been, especially in the early years of childhood, a very strong taboo. By mere will, underground thinking cannot be immediately drawn to the surface and interpreted to the mate. It must not be forgotten that fear often accompanies these early days of marriage. General inferiority built out of pre-marriage experience stands ready to take possession whenever any dramatic occurrence permits strong emotions to flow. This feeling of inadequacy, accumulated largely outside the realm of sex, quickly rushes into the new territory provided by the beginning of matrimony.

Neither member of the mating can entirely avoid looking forward and asking whether he or she is adequately prepared to play the rôle that is pictured as necessary for the successful marriage. This does not entirely relate itself to physical sex, but as a rule sex elements are included. The very effort of friends and relatives and of society, through its preachment, to create a sense of responsibility in those who enter marriage may leave the individuals overstrained, especially the conscientious and analytic type, who wonder whether they are equal to the task expected of them or who exaggerate the difficulties of matrimony and become anxious lest somewhere they fail or reveal inherent weakness. Commonly this is associated only with women, but the student of mental hygiene is familiar with the fact that the man may be even more strained than the woman.

The risk of the early days of marriage would be much less were it possible in some way to bring help to the newly wed. This is by no means easy even when it is tried, and ordinarily little substantial effort is made to give assistance of practical value. The emotional situation creates a difficulty that makes wise counsel well nigh impossible to give. Exaggeration is the danger that some men and women encounter when they seriously concentrate upon the counseling of friends who try to prepare them for the ordeals of marriage. In contrast to this type are those who are so thoroughly in the grasp of the new emotion that they fail to apprehend whatever is said to them by those who are trying to give counsel out of their experience. What is said does not sink in. It is also true that the adviser frequently assumes his self-appointed rôle without adequate emotional preparation. If marriage has been hard for him or her a morbid theme is usually present in the counsels given. Not so rarely as one might suppose the impulse to give advice is prompted by an infantile or morbid curiosity about sex which usurps the opportunity that a contemplated marriage presents.

If the counsel is presented in the manner of a specialist giving instruction as to diet or if the consummation of marriage is treated as if it were something like a major operation the reaction is bound to be unfavorable since it takes away that flavor of romance which alone makes early sex beginnings satisfactory. Thus the giving of instruction in all its various aspects reveals the risk of two extremes, a peculiar sort of emotional ambivalency. Sex is both commonplace, needing ordinary treatment in practical form, and it is something special, highly colored by the psychic features that have been annexed to it, so that it requires peculiar delicacy and a sensing of the emotional meaning it has for the individual. To neglect the one leads to the dangers of ignorance, to discard the second removes esthetic values and drops the mating into coarseness that easily turns to disgust.

Contact strain. The environmental contacts that try the temper of modern man and create the necessity of mental hygiene are primarily social. It is in association with his fellows that he mainly reveals personality defects and originates various types of maladjustment. Since it is a matter of subjective reaction there can be no rule as to what particular grouping will carry for any person greatest strain, but, as one would expect who understands the significance of intimacy and privacy, the family is for most people the most intense association and the one most liable to gather stress. Within the family there is normally less reticence than anywhere else; it is also within the home that the most exacting demands are made by one person upon another.

It is not possible to turn the contacts in the family to a mere routine as is so often done in business or professional life, since even neutral attitudes are positive in their stirring of irritation. Opposition in the family may as often be aroused by what is not expressed as by what is. A mere indifferent attitude is impossible. As a consequence everything that happens has its significance and the minor events may stir up emotions and create disturbances out of all proportion to their real importance. Upon no other association are such demands made for personal satisfaction, and, at the same time, in no other contacts is it possible to be so selfish in deciding what one will give. The family because of its privacy is denied the advantage of the pressure of public opinion which so largely regulates relationships in other fields. There is no family code of conduct which expresses a general standard and curbs individualism as is true everywhere else where people are thrown together. The family stands by itself and in the interplay of its own members it constructs standards that become representative.

To their union come the husband and wife each with his own ideas as to how to obtain the supreme satisfactions that are expected from family enterprise. Desires run high in early years and at the same time tolerance and patience are, through lack of experience, feeble. These conditions inherent in home life explain why it is that marriage so quickly brings out the best or the worst of the personality that embarks upon matrimony. Individuals who have fair success as they meet with others in the ordinary walks of life easily develop incompatibility when thrown in the intimate and unremitting contact characteristic of family association.

Because marriage issues from the deepest cravings of human nature and ordinarily affords the freest opportunity for emotional expression, it more than any other association uncovers personality defects that call for self-discipline if it is to furnish in any degree the satisfactions that impel people to enter it. It is a supremely soul-stirring contact and nowhere else do the principles of mental hygiene have for most people a greater utility.

The strain of reality. The experience of marriage is peculiar in that events that preceded it, even when not definitely related, have so much to do with its success. This is especially seen in the long line of fancy-making that starts in childhood, becomes vigorous in adolescence, and shapes itself into concrete expectations in courtship. In no territory given over to man's imagination is there commonly such a quantity of romantic creations as in the daydreaming that anticipates marriage. Every fundamental craving is made to contribute ideals for marriage to achieve. Clearly under such circumstances the temptation to overdraw the capital which experience can finally furnish is almost irresistible.

The most prosaic persons face the necessity of turning from fancy to fact when finally they find themselves actually entered upon marriage. It is high tribute to the association that so often it maintains its integrity and appeal for those who rapidly go through adjustments volcanic in the upheaval they force upon the individuals.

Much that fancy pictured has to be discarded, while limitations and obligations not even dreamed of are put upon the newly married. The temptation to refuse to leave the paradise of daydreams to accept the stern reality of actual life is strong in marriage as in every undertaking where actual conditions threaten to crush the creations of imagination.

The psychology of attraction. The meeting of people is seldom a neutral experience. In our first associations with strangers we are nearly always attracted or repelled. This is especially true when members of opposite sex meet, and most especially when they are young, with sex cravings thoroughly awakened. It is obvious that these reactions which lead toward or away from people with whom contact has been made are not mere happenings devoid of preparation. Behind each attitude is a history which may stretch back into the very early years of childhood. For example, contact with parents and with older brothers and sisters influences the preferences that young men and women feel for their acquaintances of the other sex. These influences may be either physical or psychical. They are not always favorable, for sometimes the individual reacts with hostility whenever he meets someone of the opposite sex who suggests a certain member of his own family. Usually, however, these resemblances lead to an attraction. They are but an illustration of a host of impressions gathered as one travels out of childhood, that predispose toward favorable or hostile reactions upon first acquaintanceship.

It is evident that sex impulse is featured in these early attitudes toward members of the opposite sex, especially when they are potential candidates for mating. It does not do violence to the facts to think of the sex history of the individual as providing a reservoir of influence ready for discharge by any stimulation that opens up opportunity for its flowing forth. In other words, the individual has been conditioned into a predilection that operates automatically whenever the stimulating person appears. This explains what is popularly known as love at first sight, but includes much more since even when the reaction does not start with overwhelming violence it is nevertheless predetermined by earlier conditioning.

The strength of the attitude does not guarantee a successful mating, for it is common knowledge that even where there is genuine love at first sight it is easily dissipated in the wear and tear of ordinary domestic experience. Indeed, investigation discloses that the strong appeals or deep antagonisms come primarily out of the past and do not in themselves prove either that the acquaintance can be continued over a length of time successfully, or that there is a deficiency of interest for the establishment of a permanent comradeship.

Although sex is involved usually in such occurrences, it must not be conceived of in narrow terms. It is not restricted to the physiological sphere, but represents an emotional cluster that deserves the term "complex." The physical lends its force to the total reaction, but the entrance to its awakening is through the psychological wrappings that time has placed about the original instinct. The individual has developed a personality that invites stimulus from a definite sort of person. In these reactions we discover both identification and differentiation, sometimes conscious but more often not fully recognized by the reacting individual. The literature of sex experience, especially in its pathological expression, is full of illustrations of the power that early happenings in the life of the child have in determining personality trends of the greatest significance both for sex and love attraction.

It is necessary to separate these two elements, sex and love, since sometimes it is clear that the impulse of attraction is predominantly physical and cannot be conceived of as including what is known as affection. In certain cases where the two have not been fused but remain separated because of a fundamental dissociation of personal development, sex passion separates itself from affection and is stimulated by conditions and persons who are utterly unrelated to the love life of the individual. Wherever prostitution is common many men feel the difference between an appeal which, however strong, is predominantly physical and one that incorporates love response. No normal individual could mistake one reaction for the other. Mental hygiene, therefore, has to recognize this difference or it falls into the confusion so evident in the discussions of pathological sex. The fetish that has become necessary for sex stimulation in the badly adjusted person is quite a different thing from early conditioning that operates upon the complexity of sex in persons who are well unified and who have woven together passion and love.

It is not too much to say that no part of the body and no personality trait is without a stimulating power in the contact reactions of individuals. Some persons strongly respond to one thing, some to another. These reactions in certain individuals are restricted to the realm of physical passion, while in others they are love stimuli. The face predominates as the source of such stimulation. For most people it is the most complete reflection of the personality—the mouth, the teeth, the chin, cheeks, eyes, nose, and ears appear often in cases known to the psychiatrist. Probably the voice is an influence that is likely not to receive full credit, one's reaction to it is so thoroughly automatic and unconscious. In like manner the hair, including quantity, texture, and color, forcefully appeals to some, acting either as a mere sex stimulus or as incitement toward or away from intimate relationship, with sex attraction or repulsion included.[1]

In numerous cases, for therapeutic purposes, an analysis has been made of the personal history when individuals have been drawn to or repelled from others because of the influence of some physical or psychic characteristic, and it has been found that these compulsion attitudes can become tied to all sorts of bodily and mental features as a result of vivid experiences in childhood or in youth. The exaggeration of such experiences in pathological cases reveals how very superficial characteristics may dominate in bringing about or forbidding intimate relationship. When the reactions are positive and the two individuals are irresistibly drawn toward one another, it does not follow that their association will necessarily be a happy one. On the other hand, there are illustrations not a few that show clearly that where these attractions are absent incompatibility easily comes about and even so substantial a matter as sex impulse is rendered ineffective or impotent. Characteristics so slight as mannerisms may tyrannize over associations, drawing the captivated person toward one individual and forcing him away from another. With motivations so trivial in real value operating upon human conduct, mistakes in mating are not strange. Even when the union has genuine promise it is not infrequently true that these underground, peculiar stimulations bring forth incompatibilities that strangle happiness.

[1] William Stekel, *Frigidity in Woman in Relation to Her Love Life,* Vol. I, Chap. 2.

Childhood as a source of conditioning influences. The determining influences that arise in childhood and operate upon the matrimonial career naturally fall into four groups. One has to do with sex. Either because of the suggestions that come out of his contacts with other children, or because of the attitude of his parents, who show an emotionalism that is common in the parent-child relationship as it involves sex matters, and which appears nowhere else, the child begins his sex career badly. The adult by voice, mannerism, and even punishment forces the child to take an excessive interest in sex and to conceive of it as something inherently unwholesome. The curiosity of the growing child sooner or later expresses itself in regard to sex matters as it does in regard to everything else. It is met with evasion, deception, and even punishment. What otherwise would be a mere matter of fact becomes a thing of mystery persistently inciting the interest of the child. The parent's reaction to the play of his offspring just as soon as it includes anything to which the adult has given a sex interpretation is even more violent and is fearfully upsetting to sensitive children.

The parent attempts to substitute punishment, mild or severe, for guidance. The expensiveness of this bad preparation becomes impressive when the question is asked, What would become of the appetite of hunger if it were commonly treated as is the sex impulse? There are many differences between the two, but they have in common a sensitiveness to suggestion which makes it easy for the adult to establish habit-reactions. If the child in his eating were constantly made to feel fear, shame, the necessity of concealment, penance, and continuous conflict, what would happen to so relatively stable an appetite as hunger and what idiosyncrasies of diet and table manners would necessarily follow?

It is a tribute to the fundamental soundness of the sex impulse that even wretched conditions of early childhood do not always operate to the extent that reasonably could be expected, but that individuals through experience or later enlightenment achieve a normality in sex comparable to their successes along their other interests. Necessarily, however, many fail to reach so happy a goal and their maladjustments bring out in strong light the mischievous conditioning that they received in early childhood.

Another group of conditioning experiences has to do with parental fixation. This is so common a problem that it looms large in the literature of mental hygiene. For various motives, either conscious or through self-deception, one or both parents attempt to continue the infantile habits of the child, retarding his growth and undermining his sense of confidence. The fixation becomes a personality trend, and if for any reason the adult afflicted with this immaturity of emotion loses the support to which he has long clung, as, perhaps, by the death of the parent, he tries to find the same sort of relationship by transferring to someone who can substitute for her who has been giving emotional succor. Recently I had a letter from a woman who wished assistance in breaking the dominance that she realized her mother had long exercised over her, and which was crushing her personality. She stated her age and that of her mother—she was fifty, her parent eighty. A writer in mental hygiene gives a case in which the child was sixty-three, her mother eighty-four. Finally, the daughter was set free by the death of the mother who had maintained her control until the end. In spite of her marriage the daughter had never escaped from this fixation and, after floundering around in her effort to manage herself, she developed a depression, thus bringing about her entrance into the shelter of an institution.[2]

Along another line the child is conditioned so that an uncertain attitude toward marriage becomes firmly fixed in the growing personality. Parents in their family interplay are constantly giving expression to their feelings toward one another and toward the institution of matrimony, expressions which are more clearly recognized by children and youth than older people imagine. The child is always sensitive to irritation, suspicion, and disappointment, and, although at first these reactions may be definitely related to his mother or his father who is receiving criticism from the other parent, the suggestions powerfully affect the child. In most cases, as the individual travels toward maturity, these impressions color his thoughts regarding marriage so that even if he finally mates he does this with an element of doubt or even suspicion which, although unconscious, provides the basis for harsh judgment and at times serious disturbances. Long before a child understands at all what marriage means he is given a favorable or unfavorable feeling about the definite relationship of his father and mother, and when the little one desires affection from and confidence in both parents, these early experiences sink deeply into his life.

Still more powerful impression is made upon the child when the home is broken by divorce or desertion. Not only is the child deprived of one of the two parents that he needs, but with that necessarily goes a tremendous inner conflict as he tries to disconnect the ties that hold

[2] C. P. Obendorf, "Sex Education in the Light of Analytic Experience," *Mental Hygiene*, Vol. 7, No. 4, p. 742.

him to the father or mother from whom he is separated. If he goes back and forth from one parent to the other, he finds himself coming into intermittent contact with a situation that is organized to win his allegiance and to lead him inwardly to repudiate the love of the other parent. When suspicion is created it does not cling merely to the individual father and mother involved, but issues in disordered behavior of the child at school and in play, and the emotion once generated passes into an attitude which sooner or later concerns marriage itself. The handicap this brings to children who have lived in the atmosphere of a mutilated family is often revealed by cases of juvenile delinquency treated in our child guidance clinics.

Another sort of conditioning which largely influences the later career is not the result of any suggestion from father or mother, but represents an accident of childhood from which every parent tries to save his offspring. From some older playmate, or even from an adult, and more often than one would suspect from a near relative, the child may be initiated early into some sort of sex experience that precociously awakens sex development and turns the awakened interest into perverted or unsocial forms. Such an early tragedy in the life proves an overwhelming episode that is distinctly influential in marriage. This is brought out by many pathological sex problems that come to the attention of the psychiatrist. Even in such cases it is generally clear that a wise parental attitude toward the occurrence could have easily drained out from the little child the vicious influence that started. It is not, therefore, the happening itself that is disastrous, as is commonly thought, for even in the extreme misfortune of attempted rape with all its fear sequences an intelligent parental attitude may make it possible for the child to rid herself of any serious permanent injury in her attitude toward sex. It is the unfortunate way the problem is handled as well as what has occurred that brings tragedy to the growing personality of the child.

Modern conditions that affect marriage. Marriage adjustment has to be made under prevailing social conditions. In no class or section do these conditions remain constant so that the hazards of matrimony may be numerically stated. They vary according to circumstances, but there is every reason to suppose that at the present time in the United States, and particularly in our cities, there are many influences that adversely affect marriage. The prevailing civilization has done much to encourage marriage discontentment and to increase matrimonial failure. Changing conditions, especially as the predominance of rural habits of life turns to that of urban habits, operate upon marriage in all its aspects, and the literature that attempts to interpret our present situation is enormous.

It is, of course, unfair to think that all these changes are adverse, or that any must permanently remain harmful. At a time when industry is passing through rapid changes because of new inventions, different methods of organization and changing demands of the consumer, disturbances that mean trouble for both worker and employer necessarily follow. Marriage at present is in a parallel situation. All sorts of changes in the manner of living, in the ideals of people, and in expressions of fundamental human desires are complicating the mating problem and originating dissatisfaction and incompatibility that attract the attention of mental hygiene.

It is not that changes have occurred to which matrimony now has to adjust itself, but rather that changes are occurring to which the life of the married must be constantly adapting itself. Individual families may attempt to protect themselves against these changes and erect barriers to keep out as far as possible the influences that originate from the newer ways of living, but one of the great departures from the past is that this very isolation is practically impossible to maintain. Not only will the family that makes an effort to keep itself anchored to the past fail, but in the effort it is bound to suffer excessively sooner or later from its retardation. This commonly appears in the child more than in the adults who are responsible for the family policy. Not only has the American family lost heavily in its privacy, but it has utterly sacrificed the power to remain separated from the surging life characteristic of the time.

One of the most disturbing changes has been the emergence of the sex element in marriage so that it occupies a more self-conscious, independent position than was true until recently, during the period we know as civilization. Once in the very earliest stages of simple society the sex element in human mating predominated in the same way. Birth control, making possible the family that does not go beyond the intimacy of husband and wife, magnifies the sex element, and gives it an independence once characteristic in primitive society. In the recent past the coming of the child has lifted the earlier stage of matrimony in which sex is predominant to a relationship that is at least more complicated, and by this process sex has relatively lost its importance.

It would be an error to regard these social changes as necessarily an attack upon the family, but for the most part they do antagonize family life in its present expression and demand readjustment. Thus, their first result often seems destructive, but we can expect now as always in the past that society will build up defenses against the evil effects of these changes and eventually turn most of them into influences that will elevate the family to higher standards. Whatever may be their final effect, the general trend of recent changes has been toward demoralizing many families and creating for the newly married additional strain.

Marriage and contraception. Since the latter part of the nineteenth century the idea of voluntary parenthood has been gradually spreading through the American population. During the last fifteen years knowledge of birth control has been extensively popularized until to-day it is both largely known and practiced in all classes except that of the lowest economic status, where ignorance of contraception still largely persists and where hostility to efforts to prevent birth is strongest among those who know of the existence of contraceptive methods.

This popularizing of birth control is, of course, of the greatest significance for marriage. Contraception permits the separation of reproduction and sex. Contraception permits the marriage of the conscientious, who, although thoroughly fitted for matrimony do not feel that they have the right to bring offspring into the world. For example, a college student some years ago, unusually successful in her scholarship and an impressive physical specimen, sought counsel with reference to her marriage, because her mother was a moron, and possibly her father, and her sister had been pronounced by competent authority both feeble-minded and insane and committed to a state institution. This young girl recognized that in spite of her apparent soundness of body and mind, the family heredity made questionable her right to reproduce. She was counseled to marry provided she and her husband were willing to abstain from parenthood. This advice was given with confidence that it could be worked out without strain because of effective methods of contraception.

A study of the birth rate of various classes makes clear that at present contraception is being most widely practiced by the wealthy and middle classes, leading to a relatively higher birth rate among those socially inferior, although those economically disadvantaged are not necessarily biologically inferior. The practice of birth control is, therefore, acting exactly opposite to what the eugenists desire. It is widely practiced among those who should contribute more offspring, and is only lessening in slight degree the reproduction of those already disproportionately contributing to the population.

Contraception has a great significance for the individual in the mental hygiene program, since it makes possible earlier marriage when the economic burden of children would discourage matrimony. It permits smaller families when many children would bring about excessive strain for mother or father or both, and enables the spacing of children, so that childbirth will not by its frequency break the health or spirits of the mother. On the other hand, the ever widening knowledge of contraception is becoming a temptation to those who by separating sex from reproduction are led to circumvent marriage or who, entering upon legal alliance, escape parenthood for motives that are not socially justified, and by their decision not to have children lessen their own development and decrease the social value of their marriage.

First matrimonial experiences. In nearly all enterprises, the danger of serious mistake is greatest at the beginning through lack of experience. It is doubtful, however, whether man enters upon any undertaking in which the occurrences at the start are so consequential in determining the final outcome of the enterprise as in marriage. Here as elsewhere first mistakes can be retrieved, but as a general rule what happens at the start of marriage has a decided emotional significance throughout the union. Feelings run so strongly and expectations are so compelling that even trivial events are greatly magnified and misinterpreted.

The central feature in this is sex, for it is with reference to sex that awkwardness, misunderstanding, fear, shame, and nervousness, the products of inexperience and taboo, are most likely to appear. Even greater risks come to those who discover or suspect in the mate a sophistication that originates from experience. Only the well-informed, perfectly frank, and mutually confident individuals enter upon early sex experience without misgivings. These first days of marriage have such significance that we find the psychiatrists speaking of the honeymoon trauma. Often it is true that the emotional results of these first experiences in marriage are the final culmination of a neurotic trend that has had a long history, but, on the other hand, they may start an original complex growth or may add vigor to one already in operation. Mental and social hygiene, by helping to establish a more healthy attitude towards matters of sex and by distributing information of genuine help to the newly wedded, are attempting to minimize these risks of early marriage, but under no circumstances can they be entirely eliminated.

Habit changes. The early problems of marriage are not merely those of sex adjustment. Each partner has to reconstruct his habit life since there is a decided difference between single and married life. This is not adequately expressed by thinking of one as a state of freedom in contrast with the responsibilities of the other. Both have their freedoms and their responsibilities. As one passes from the first to the second, many long-continued habits have to be modified because every important aspect of the new relationship has a double significance.

As the two lives are fused into one, the individual who passes out of a large family where he has had many intimate contacts may have an advantage in making this adjustment, but his previous training does not relieve him of the need of new adaptation. This is strikingly revealed by those who attempt the hazardous solution of remaining after marriage in the childhood home of one of the couple. The wife or the husband is not just an addition to the old family. The really significant thing is that a new attitude has been created in the bride or groom, which makes it impossible for him in his association with his former family members to be as he has been. He is different on account of the new meaning that has come into his life. Whenever a habit mass is dislodged and new construction in conduct takes place, favorable conditions spring up for inner stress and emotional conflict.

The coming of the child. The coming of the first child is for every family a momentous event. Parenthood is not merely a physiological occurrence. It is saturated with romance and demands are laid upon it in the same way that we have found marriage called upon to yield expected satisfaction. This also requires somewhat new relationships between husband and wife since a new interest has been developed and usually a new and strong affection. Jealousy easily shows itself in a stubborn reluctance to accept new responsibilities or to change from familiar ways in order to take proper care of the new life. Here also the critical period is often at the start and it frequently seems to one of the partners that unreasonable demands are being made or that the old husband-wife relationship has been entirely pushed aside.

Motherhood frequently awakens with an impetuosity that startles the husband and makes him feel that the values he has been enjoying are forever to pass from him. More frequently than many would suppose this exaggeration of parental reaction is made by the man rather than the woman. In many cases it is deeply resented and an emotionalism comes forward at a time when there is great need of using all the resources of intelligence to make the readjustment called for by the coming of the child.

The adjustments of contacts. Mention has already been made of the fact that even though after marriage one remains with his previous family, it is nevertheless necessary for him to change in his relationship. This readjustment is normally felt with reference to all of one's contacts, whether with relatives or friends. For one thing, the individual crosses the line between the single and the married and finds himself committed to a group from which he was formerly estranged. There also has to be a consolidation of husband-wife attitude toward the friends of each, which eventually means the elimination of some friendships and the establishment of new ones. If the husband finds that some of his former acquaintances are decidedly distasteful to his wife he must either get rid of them, conceal his intimacies, or allow them to become a bone of contention between him and his spouse.

Often this problem of former associations has not been anticipated, while sometimes a foolish but heroic effort has been made to strip oneself of all former acquaintances upon entrance into marriage. This policy proves dangerous because it creates after a little time restlessness, perhaps even a sense of loneliness. It is, however, only traveling too far along the roadway that all well-married individuals must take. If the husband or wife persists in holding former associations as if nothing had occurred to change the status of things, the marriage, however legal, is emotionally aborted.

Vocational adjustments. The changes in habits that have to be made in early marriage are likely to have an economic and vocational aspect. Disturbances because of this are much more common now than under the simpler family régime of the rural culture. The building of new habits is a more serious ordeal for the woman who previously has had no household responsibility and who suddenly undertakes to finance and manage her own home, or for the woman who, after having for several years earned her own living as a wage worker, now finds herself dependent upon the husband's income. How greatly this will clash with deep-seated desires no one can tell until she has learned from experience. It represents a more fundamentally disturbing situation than faces the youth who leaves a country environment for city employment, but it may not carry with it the understanding of what is happening which naturally goes with the more spectacular change of physical environment.

Convention and the pressure of public opinion add their complications, especially when the wife abstains from working in her former vocation because it will bring criticism from those who disapprove of such a procedure or will lessen the self-respect of the husband who has been made to feel that it is the masculine prerogative to earn and manage the finances of the family. It is the testimony of persons experienced in dealing with family maladjustments that a common cause of trouble is the restlessness of the wife who has withdrawn from the work she enjoyed to undertake housekeeping which she detests, or the difference of opinion, unsuspected before marriage, between husband and wife with regard to the propriety of the woman's working outside the home.

Marriage as a revealer of character. As mental hygiene views marriage, it is an experience that brings out the personality in all its delicate shadings of character, including both unconscious antipathies and concealed cravings. As one writer has suggestively said, matrimony is a sort of psychic litmus paper. It discloses, however, not only the general color of the personality, but markings previously hidden. In this respect it resembles the sensitive plate of X-ray photography. The personality, however, is not pictured once and for all, but again and again; under different conditions the innermost life is made to record itself through speech, manner, and inner thought. It matters not what emphasis is given to marriage by those who enter upon it; it is a testing, and what it reveals is personality. The tests that are put upon the individual who marries are not general but particular and cover the whole range of intimate associations.

Marriage is thus a bit of life which carries insistence upon adaptation if success is to be achieved, but it is life intensified by being shot through with emotional meaning that seldom appears in other relationships with equal intensity. For the majority of men and women marriage represents the last port of call in their sailing toward the elusive goal of complete happiness. As the meeting place of reality and idealism, it stops the ongoing of some who lose confidence in a goal still evasive, while others are encouraged in their determination to continue their confident voyage.

Until there have been most radical changes in the motives of men and women, no amount of cynicism born of the disappointment of others will prevent youth from starting toward a permanent life union, for marriage has

come about as a social means of satisfying desires that
have become native to both men and women. It can, however, never provide more than an opportunity for two
lives to fuse into affection, and by offering this it necessarily tests the individuals who make use of their opportunity, with the consequence that every element in either
person that has significance for the intimate fellowship
acts to promote or block happiness.

Conserving marriage. Marriage is never a thing
apart from the general social situation. It is, therefore,
immediately influenced by favorable and antagonistic
changes in every department of human activity. Legislation has a forceful influence upon marriage as an institution and it is a favorite choice of reformers who wish
at once to operate upon matrimony. They choose law-
making because it seems so immediate and effective. It
is seldom, however, that it has had much influence on the
more fundamental interests of the intimate union of man
and woman. From the mental hygiene viewpoint too
much confidence is put in legislation, such as laws that
require publicity of a contemplated marriage or that
regulate the kind of ceremony needed to make marriage
legal or even that determine conditions by which the marriage can be put aside. Familiarity with the concrete
family situation casts doubt upon the ability of any sort
of legislation to do much to increase the family happiness
which in the last analysis must be the security of the
union.

Public opinion even more than legislation regulates the
externals of marriage. It is made up of influences from
many sources, but is obviously open to the influence of
both propaganda and leadership. There are some evidences at present that the great amount of family incompatibility revealed by the increasing divorce rate is

leading educators and public-spirited people who direct
social attitudes to seek methods by which more favorable
conditions may be presented to those who marry. This
effort is leading toward various sorts of experiments along
the line of instruction in preparation for marriage and
for parenthood. These in turn are creating need for more
reliable knowledge regarding marriage experience and a
better technique and greater frankness in the giving of
information that has proven itself of value for those who
marry.

Teaching and investigation, however, are still decidedly
pioneering in character and by no means adequate to
meet the expectations of those who assume that the mere
will to educate candidates for matrimony is all that we
now need to make most marriages successful. We have
made progress in providing means by which those encountering difficulty in marriage can obtain expert counsel.
Upon the psychiatrist, however, for the most part falls
the burden of giving this assistance. Family courts, even
though they meet their problems late in the matrimonial
career, also make their contribution. The child guidance
clinics likewise do their part since in dealing with child
difficulties, more often than one might suppose, they are
obliged eventually to deal with a family or marriage situation.

Already there is experimentation in establishing some
sort of organized service for the married or for those
about to enter wedlock comparable with the preventive
work carried on by certain kinds of medical clinics.
This when it is worked out will have the advantage of
giving a wider outlook than any one counselor ever can
bring to matrimonial difficulties.[3] Until such service is

[3] E. R. Groves, *The Marriage Crisis,* pp. 199-209.

within the reach of everyone, expert advice must be sought from doctors, lawyers, ministers, or psychiatrists, according to whether the problem is physical, legal, moral, or in the wide sense a matter of personality adjustment.

ILLUSTRATIVE CASE

J. M. met a young woman of wealth on ship board on a trip to Europe one year after his entering upon the profession of teaching. It is whispered that the woman from the beginning took the lead in their courtship, and that she led him somewhat reluctantly to the wedding altar. Whether this was true or not it soon appeared after the marriage that she was determined to dominate and that he resented this. Although of cheerful disposition before marriage he gradually developed a pessimistic attitude toward life and a quarrelsome and suspicious attitude toward others. He was constantly having trouble with his students in the high school where he taught, especially at the beginning of the day. He also became interested in radical thought along various lines, soon winning for himself the reputation of being both touchy and cranky. He was finally dismissed from the high school in the city where he lived for having in a fit of anger struck a student in the presence of his class, under such circumstances that his continuing as an instructor was clearly impossible. Not being able to get another teaching position he became extremely restless and depressed. Now that he was at home so much of the time, he began quarreling constantly with his wife, who, under the suggestion of relatives, eventually applied for a divorce. Once this was granted her the man removed to a distant city, entered graduate study, and after obtaining an advanced degree, returned to high school teaching where during the last two years he has continued to enjoy the approval and support of the principal who regards him as one of his best teachers.

SUGGESTIONS FOR CLASSROOM DISCUSSION

1. How do childhood experiences influence marriage happiness?
2. What are the common mistakes of parents in dealing with their children's interest in sex?
3. What influences built up the taboo of sex?
4. Are family relations more or less difficult than those of business and profession?
5. What is meant by the term affection as used in this chapter?
6. What are the causes of parent fixation?
7. What makes people in these days so conscious of sex problems?

SUGGESTIONS FOR WRITTEN REPORTS

1. Influences decreasing the sex taboo.
2. Freud's contribution to our knowledge of sex.
3. The conditioning of sex in childhood.
4. Influence of divorce of parents upon the marriage attitudes of children.
5. Mental hygiene in the family court.
6. A program for a family clinic.

SELECTED BIBLIOGRAPHY

ABRAHAM, KARL. *Dreams and Myths.*

FREUD, SIGMUND. *Three Contributions to the Sexual Theory.* Nervous and Mental Diseases Publishing Co.

EMERY, E. VAN NORMAN. "Revising Our Attitude Toward Sex." *Mental Hygiene,* April, 1927, pp. 324-38.

FLINN, HELEN and JACOBY, ARNOLD L. "One Hundred Domestic-Relations Problems." *Mental Hygiene,* October, 1926, pp. 732-42.

GALLICHAN, WALTER M. *The Psychology of Marriage.* New York, 1918.

GRAY, A. HERBERT. *Men, Women, and God,* Chap X. New York, 1922.

GROVES, E. R. *The Drifting Home,* Chaps. VII and VIII. Boston, 1926.

GROVES, E. R.   *The Marriage Crisis,* Chap. X.
—— *Social Problems of the Family,* Chap. XII.   Philadelphia, 1927.
—— and G. H.   *Wholesome Marriage,* Chap. I.   Boston, 1927.
HAMILTON, G. V.   *A Research in Marriage,* Chaps. XI, XII, XIV, XV.
KEMPF, EDWARD J.   *Psychopathology,* Chap. II.   St. Louis, 1920.
MEAGHER, JOHN F. W.   "Homosexuality; its Psychobiological and Psychopathological Significance."   *Urologic and Cutaneous Review,* 33:505-18, August, 1929.
—— "Marriage and Love: A Psychiatric Problem."   *Long Island Medical Journal,* 23:354-62, June, 1929.
MYERSON, ABRAHAM.   *The Nervous Housewife,* Chap. VII.
OBERNDORF, C. P.   "Sex Education in the Light of Analytic Experience."   *Mental Hygiene,* October, 1923, pp. 734-43.
OWENSBY, NEWDIGATE M.   "Sexual Fridigity."   *Urologic and Cutaneous Review,* 33:534-37, August, 1929.
POPENOE, PAUL.   *Modern Marriage,* Chap. V.   New York, 1925.
ROBINSON, WILLIAM J.   *America's Sex and Marriage Problems,* Part I.   New York, 1928.
WELLS, F. L.   "The General Personality and Certain Features of the Sex Life."   *Mental Hygiene,* April, 1926, pp. 345-54.
WILE, IRA S.   "The Dynamics of Marriage."   *Urologic and Cutaneous Review,* 33:537-42, August, 1929.
ZINN, EARL F.   "History, Purpose, and Policy of the National Research Council's Committee for Research on Sex Problems."   *Mental Hygiene,* January, 1924, pp. 94-105.

CHAPTER VIII

MENTAL HYGIENE AND THE SCHOOLS

A psychiatrist looks at school children. If a psychiatrist were surveying the children in our public and private schools, he would find many maladjusted individuals among them—so many that he might be tempted to speak of them in sadly prophetic strain. Of these maladjusted school children, Frankwood Williams writes thus:

"Several courses are open to the children who at this early age are already beginning to fail in making a proper adjustment. Which road they may take a psychiatrist may not be able to say, but he may say that, if left to find their own way out of the woods of their emotional difficulties, fifteen years will find them well along one of the following roads:

"1. Some will find an adjustment that will be excellent for *themselves* . . . but, in the process of finding their own purely personal salvation they will crush many of the rest of us.

"2. Some as they grow older will find of their own accord adjustments that will be more or less satisfactory. They will get along fairly well—as you and I get along— but distinctly handicapped as a result of the scars of their early combats. We like to think character is so made. Something is made, surely; one may call it character if one likes . . . Strong prejudices, unreasonable likes and dislikes, loves and hates, gusts of blind emotions that surge through us at critical moments and upset our carefully thoughtout judgments and plans of conduct—these are the rewards of our early blind combats . . .

184

"3. Probably the greatest number of these children, left alone to devise methods of warding off inroads upon their personalities, will curl up within themselves and thenceforth look out timidly upon the world. They will drift into quietly rebellious, dispirited, unhappy mediocrity . . . a mediocrity that is not expressive of inherent lack of capacity. . . . Excellent intellects there will be among them but intellects that cannot be freely used because of the imposed emotional handicaps. Among this group, too, there will be those who will meet similar problems with an opposite type of reaction; instead of with timidity, with boldness. But a boldness that is not courage but is fear. Fifteen years from now they will be the 'hard-boiled,' and become the bullies in the market place, or on court benches, or on commissions and boards of trusteeship.

"4. In the above groups there may be only unhappiness, frustration, waste of good material and no direct social damage . . . But in the group on this fourth road and in the next groups we are faced with a different situation: we are no longer dealing with a negative good but with a positive bad—bad in the social sense. Children born well who later contract tuberculosis of the spine or infantile paralysis come eventually to plaster casts or braces from which after a time they are relieved, many improved and helped; but children born well who later contract certain habits of emotional reaction come eventually to courts and reformatories from which after a time they are relieved, few of them improved or helped . . . And the number of delinquents becomes greater each year and the tolls more mountainous . . .

"5. Along this road there will be many. No one has ever dared even to estimate the number that crowd it but everyone who has come in contact with it has been seriously impressed. Into it pour thousands from homes and shops and offices. These were but recently, of course, in the schools, and there their adenoids and tonsils were carefully looked after and their intellects carefully trained, but . . . although they started out hopefully, they did not long remain efficient in the home, the shop and the office. It is odd, too, because they had been told not to worry about things, to control their tempers, always to be cheerful and to smile in spite of everything, to be brave and courageous and to believe in success and to keep themselves pure. [Yet they have become sufferers from] hysteria, neurasthenia, 'nervous prostration,' morbid fears and anxieties, and a variety of other 'nervous' [disorders].

"6. And finally we come to those who are to fail entirely . . . Some will drop out of school before the high school course is finished; some will finish well—as valedictorians, perhaps. On they will go to college, many of them, where, on entrance, they will be given a physical examination . . . and a psychological examination . . . but there will be no one present to notice some other minor matters. Some will drop out with many excuses, but the fact is, of course, that they simply were not of college caliber—some will finish little known and with modest grades, but others with honors and keys and the blessings of faculties who have daily nurtured them for four years but who have never for an hour understood them. And —as the world is—all of them, within the fifteen years, will have been gathered to their mattresses on the floors of hospitals for the insane." [1]

This, then, is what the psychiatrist sees when he looks

[1] Quoted from "Community Responsibility in Mental Hygiene," by Frankwood Williams, *Mental Hygiene*, July, 1923, Vol. VII, pp. 496-508.

at school children: a young army from which will be re-
cruited in the future the victims of mental diseases; the
vocational misfits; the individuals who will swell the divorce statistics because they cannot adapt themselves to
marriage relationships; the inmates of reformatories and
prisons; the partially adjusted who will get along in some
half tolerable fashion but with little chance for personal
happiness, and—in the minority—a small number of children who will be healthy, well-adapted adults. Yet our
leaders in the theory of education visualize the function
of the school as preparation for life, and mental hygiene
sees in the school a strategic center of attack where maladjustments fostered by unwholesome family life may be
ameliorated or where the handicaps already set up may
be intensified by unwise treatment. Thus a mental hygiene survey of the school system must see two sides, the
one which is an aid and the other which is an obstacle to
mental hygiene aims.

The teaching personnel. It may be stated axiomat-
ically that the possibilities of the school in the service of
mental hygiene cannot rise above the capacities or the
limitations of the teaching personnel. It is also true that
at present the limitations all too frequently outweigh the
capacities. Too often the teacher comes to her task of
molding the personalities of her pupils—for mold them
she will inevitably, whether she considers this as her task
or not—utterly unprepared for this high endeavor. Her
mind has been crowded, in her teacher-training classes,
with methods of pedagogy; she has been taught the ap-
proved ways of presenting the elementary subjects. But
of the psychology and mental hygiene of childhood she
has heard comparatively little. And what she has been
taught in this field has been so academic, so divorced
from contact with the living, individual child, that she

would be at a loss how to apply the principles she may have memorized in order to pass a required examination and to obtain the coveted teacher's certificate.

Moreover, the teacher may enter upon her work with her own problems of personality adjustment largely unsolved. Her own home and school experiences have been such, in many instances, as to deform her own personality. She then brings with her the fearfulness, the inferiority feelings, the emotional conflicts that have been unresolved in her own life. She brings with her also a goodly number of prejudices, built up through her own life experience; there are things which she believes to be so bad, when she sees them in her pupils, that she is horrified and condemnatory and totally unable to understand that here is her opportunity to be vitally concerned with the function of life preparation which she has heard mentioned in connection with the school but which is to her a vague and mystical ideal unrelated to the concrete, everyday occurrences in the classroom. If she interprets it at all, it is as a command to weave into her presentation of the different subjects little homilies on the moral virtues—truth, honesty, purity—and the qualities of good citizenship— patriotism, love of country, Americanization. Seldom indeed does she visualize it as concerned with the vital social relationship between teacher and pupil, between her own personality and the personalities in the making that are seated before her, quiet and respectful or wriggling and defiant, according to the way in which they have thus far been shaped.

In the educational system, as it exists to-day, the teacher's mind must be occupied with far different matters. She must hurry her whole class through a prescribed amount of work per semester; she must see that her

pedagogy, her discipline, her number of pupils doing satisfactory work, are sufficient to insure her the rating from
her principal or her superintendent that will bring her
promotion and increase in salary. She lives in the daily
fear lest one of these may fall below the standards arbi-
trarily set for her. She has enough of a struggle to coerce
the dull intelligences into a fragmentary grasp of the
educational material which she offers them; the breaking
point for her overworked nerves would be reached if she
had also to struggle with warped personalities and endeavor to set them straight.

Dangers inherent in the teacher-pupil relationship.
The very classroom situation carries with it its own special
dangers. The teacher is placed in a position of power
and authority which, if she conforms to the requirements
noted above, she may use as she desires. Few are the
personalities sufficiently well-integrated to withstand
using an accession of power to gratify their own thwarted
emotional needs. Too many of us have suffered from
inferiority feelings to be entrusted with power. We are
tempted to assert our authority just because it gives us a
pleasurable glow to make certain that at last we possess
it. The teacher is not immune to this compensatory drive.
It may even be, in more cases than we suspect, that the
unconscious motivation which led her to choose her profession was the need to compensate for an inferiority
which had been thrust upon her in her own home life or
school experiences.

The dignity of the teaching profession and the social
prestige it carries with it induce girls from middle-class
families to enter it. The salary is as good or better than
that for stenography, work in a department store, and
many other occupations, while it places the person in a

much higher class, socially. The teacher is respectable and respected, and the desire to be thus regarded motivates the vocational choice, in some instances, regardless of aptitude.

If in the beginning the teacher's motives were honest, if she sincerely believed in her ability to perform a real service, the profession imposes such a repressed mode of life that integrity of personality is difficult to maintain. The hours of work which must be put in outside of the classroom duties, if the teacher is at all conscientious, and the continual fear of being found inefficient in the production of results or not quite spotless as to reputation, combine to restrict her interests and to deny her opportunity for emotional expression. Then, too, due partly to prejudices of boards of education and their rulings on this point, the teaching profession is largely one of unmarried women; married women and men teachers form only a minority of the personnel.

Moreover, the attitude of society toward the teaching profession forces her into a thwarted life. The teacher must be a model person, in the eyes of parents, and this means that she must exemplify the conservatism of the older generation. Even in such intimate personal matters as dressing her hair, using rouge or lipstick, following the fashion in wearing apparel, she is not free. She must consider the criticism her slightest act may bring upon her, and the danger of losing her position if her behavior is criticized.

Thus we may picture the teacher as peculiarly unhappy in her situation; struggling with the tension of anxiety with regard to her economic security, which depends upon the approval of those higher up in the educational system, thwarted in self-expression and in her sex and love life. Small wonder that she finds relief from all these tensions in explosive outbursts of impatience toward her dull or disorderly pupils.

In all fairness, considering the conditions which her life imposes upon her, we should rather be surprised that even now and then we find a teacher who has been able to make her own emotional adjustments and can therefore be concerned, genuinely and objectively, with the welfare of her individual pupils. But only where there are such teachers—and such principals and superintendents—can mental hygiene really prosper in the schools. One of the fundamental needs of the educational system, from the mental hygiene point of view, is the better adjustment of the teachers, themselves. Release from fear, opportunity for the cultivation of diverse interests, freedom for self-expression, the privilege of continuing their profession after marriage, would go far toward re-creating the whole school personnel. And what a beneficent effect upon their pupils would be the contact with teachers who, living more fully under such changed conditions, would be able to help those in their charge to develop in more vital ways.

Teachers' attitudes toward maladjusted children. One of the most recent studies of teachers' attitudes toward problem children brings out some interesting facts as to the type of child generally recognized as suffering from maladjustments. On the whole it appears that little attention is bestowed upon pupils from this viewpoint unless their behavior is such as to interfere with the classroom routine. The pupil who is inattentive and disturbing is considered to be a problem, so also is the one who lies or steals. But the child who is quiet and amenable to discipline is looked upon graciously; he may be timid, withdrawn from his playmates, wholly lacking in initiative and independence, yet the teacher will manifest no concern.[2] To her mind, the child who is docile and does not interrupt her work is well adjusted, while the pupil who shows overt conduct disorders is facing serious difficulties.

The psychiatric viewpoint is radically different. The psychiatrist is deeply concerned about some of these quiet, well-behaved pupils, for he knows that withdrawal from playmates, timidity and dependency are symptoms of grave personality deviations. He may even suspect that from this group will be drawn a large number of the individuals who in later life will become the victims of mental disease, particularly dementia præcox or some psychoneurosis. Even if it be admitted that some of the children who openly misbehave display pre-delinquent tendencies, the very fact that they have broken into active rebellion is likely to indicate a better state of mental health than would a retreat from overt expression with its shut-in personality.

It is only natural, however, that the teacher should not be so well able to evaluate degrees of maladjustment as the psychiatrist, whose training is directed toward making him an expert in dealing with such problems. It is more pertinent, perhaps, to inquire what is her attitude toward concrete mental hygiene needs of the individual pupil when these are pointed out by the psychiatrist, psychologist or social worker. Here we find a variety of reactions, ranging all the way from absolute refusal to accept the expert's opinion to whole-hearted and intelligent coöperation. The individual differences in this respect may make all the difference toward helping to adjust the pupil or tending to prolong or increase his maladjustment.

[2] E. K. Wickman, *Children's Behavior and Teachers' Attitudes*. Commonwealth Fund, Division of Publications, Fuller Building, 57th St. and Madison Ave., New York, 1929.

Consider, for instance, the type of principal or teacher who sees the intervention of the expert as a threat to diminish authority. Immediately, the response is an assumption of superiority to whatever suggestion may be made. Take the case of a bright pupil, repeating his school grade and too discouraged or bored to put forth any effort to do his work. The authoritative principal replies to this explanation: "If he is capable of doing the work let him prove it," disregarding the evidence of intelligence and educational tests which testify to high achievement. Infrequently we find an open-minded principal who agrees to give the plan of incidental promotion a trial, although frankly skeptical as to results. Still more rare is the principal who, after seeing the pupil respond, announces voluntarily that the psychologist was right in sizing up the situation.

Occasionally—a bright spot to workers in mental hygiene—there is a principal in complete sympathy with efforts to improve the pupil's adjustment and ready to take an experimental point of view. Such a principal is willing to try not one but many innovations and does not let the matter drop if the first trial move brings no results. On the whole, the private school personnel is likely to be more sympathetic with mental hygiene aims than the public school, because the private school is less subject to arbitrary regulations imposed from above and there is less to fear from any departure from the regular routine.

Teachers' prejudices and pupil adjustment. Like ordinary folk, the members of the teaching profession have their prejudices. There are certain forms of childhood misconduct which are particularly apt to rouse these. Dishonesty and sex behavior are perhaps the most likely to provoke a condemnatory attitude. Unless the

teacher has had considerable contact with the newer views
on child behavior she sees in such conduct proof that the
child is hopelessly delinquent or morally bad. From this
viewpoint, the only solution is to exile the child from her
classroom and to send him to a special school for behavior problems or to an institution for delinquents. If
for some reason this solution is impracticable and the
child remains in school, his reputation precedes him from
one class to the next.

"You will have Jimmy Smith next year," says the third
grade teacher to the fourth grade teacher. "Look out for
him; he is a terrible little thief," or "You'll have to watch
him or you will find him writing notes with bad words in
them."

Jimmy goes on to the next grade, to a teacher on the
alert for his misdemeanors. If a dime is missing from
her purse or an obscene note is found on the floor, there
is no doubt in her mind as to the culprit. Jimmy is accused—usually—and if he denies the fault he is just a
plain liar. In a children's clinic we see tragic instances
where a child who has committed no offense is accused and
punished for another's guilt just because he has been
given a bad reputation. To have the blame if one has
the name is a rather human reaction, and some children
revert to misbehavior on just these grounds.

It is interesting also to note the misuse of the special
class for mentally deficient children to satisfy the teacher's prejudices against certain types of behavior. In one
such class a bright girl (intelligence quotient 112) had
been kept from the age of nine to twelve years. When
she was nine years old the teacher had discovered that
she was masturbating, a habit which she had learned
from an older child. The matter was reported to the
principal, who immediately transferred her to the special

class where she was placed with low grade mentally defective children. Meanwhile, the habit had ceased entirely, but when the principal was approached with the suggestion that she might well be restored to the regular grade she replied that she could not have an immoral child in contact with normal children. It was necessary to have the child placed in another school, where the principal was more modern in her attitudes, in order to remedy the situation.

By way of more cheerful contrast let us consider the attitude taken toward such problems by principals and teachers who have become informed of the scientific viewpoint toward behavior deviations. In a certain school, a principal and some of her teachers attended a summer school course which was based on methods of child guidance. As a part of the course, they did actual work for three months in the child guidance clinic. In the fall, a new method of handling problem cases was instituted at that school. When misbehavior was reported, the principal and teachers conferred, tried to understand the causes of the behavior deviation in the particular child in question, and formulated a plan of treatment calculated to deal with the cause rather than the symptomatic behavior pattern. If the case was bafflingly obscure or if their plan of treatment was unsuccessful, they then referred the child to the clinic for more intensive study. They had achieved a distinctively mental hygiene point of view which had far-reaching effect upon the lives of their pupils.

New methods in education. It is only fair to review briefly some of the ways which the school itself has devised to meet the needs of the child. One of the most common is the effort to construct a differentiated curriculum to meet the individual variations in intelligence found among school children. As an outgrowth of this, we have the special class in which mentally deficient children are taught by highly specialized pedagogical methods; the three-fold division of the regular class to create separate sections for pupils of dull, average and superior intelligence (carried to such a degree that in some of the large junior high schools there are as many as seven or eight sections based on ability); the opportunity classes for highly gifted children, which are still all too few and confined to a very small number of school systems. Then there are the nutrition classes with their mid-morning and mid-afternoon glasses of milk and their rest periods for improving the condition of the undernourished child; open air classes for pre-tubercular pupils; adjustment or restoration classes for the child who is deficient in some one subject in which there is need of intensive teaching; sight-saving classes for the child threatened with loss of vision; classes for the correction of speech defects, and all the other many new departures. Every one of these makes for better mental adjustment.

The older pupil has not been neglected. The modern city high school offers a wide variety of courses; college preparatory, business, general, art, retail selling, mechanical and other vocational courses. These courses do not, however, take care of the pupils not sufficiently endowed intellectually to reach high school, yet far above the level of the mentally deficient. Compulsory education laws, in most communities, insure that these children remain in school whether or not it has anything to offer them above the sixth grade. As a result, these duller pupils are found clogging the classrooms and repeating the sixth and seventh grades interminably until age brings a welcome release from legally enforced school attendance.

The problem of the dull normal pupil has been recognized by educators, and there has been some attempt to meet his needs. The most hopeful is the vocational school, with the courses for boys emphasizing manual training and preparation for the simpler mechanical trades, and for girls shaped closely around the domestic arts of cooking and sewing. Theoretically, these vocational schools should have entrance requirements which would permit them to serve those pupils who are unable to advance beyond the sixth grade in academic work. This would mean the acceptance of pupils with an intelligence quotient as low as 80 on psychological examinations. Where these schools are functioning for the dull normal child, these are the requirements actually in force. But sometimes the entrance requirements defeat the very purpose for which the schools were created. In one city, for example, in order to limit the number of admissions, the applications being far more numerous than the capacity of the vocational school building, an intelligence quotient of 100 is required; in another city, also for the purpose of reducing the number of applicants, the pupil must have completed the low eighth grade instead of only the sixth, as was the original intention.

It may be that this perversion of equipment intended to meet a certain problem to quite different ends is merely an indication of the stress which the educational system places upon the possession of good intelligence. But this is not a far-sighted policy. Investigations of the educational status of the general population show that only a small percentage of people attend high school, a still smaller percentage reaching college; psychological studies suggest that the bulk of the population is not endowed with the type of intelligence enabling them to attain to high school and college standards. If this is true, our neglect of the pupil with low average intelligence (to use psychological terminology, for actually this is the statistical average) is doubly reprehensible. It is the solid citizenship of a democratic country that we are leaving unprovided for by our schools. We are not training it in any practical way for self-support nor for the duties of participating in a government by the people. Instead we are placing these young citizens of to-morrow in a situation which is so unsuitable that it creates very definite maladjustments: a feeling of inferiority and failure induced by grade repetition, or recourse to truancy, with its tendency to build up habits of idleness and vagrancy, as a way of escape.

Mental hygiene and the nursery school. The nursery school movement has many points of contact with mental hygiene. Its primary purpose is not the inculcation of book learning but training in habit formation and the development of desirable personality and behavior patterns. One of the chief features is the program of co-operation between parents and nursery school personnel, so that home and nursery shall supplement one another wisely. Unless there is this intimate relationship, all that the nursery school strives to build up in its short day may be torn down in the hours spent at home.

The nursery school studies both the physical and mental health needs of the pre-school child. It is interested not only in his intellectual aptitudes but also in his emotional responses, his habit patterns, and his early personality trends. Its whole aim is to bring about better adjustment and to lay a foundation for physical and mental health in the years to come.

It is unfortunate, in some nursery schools, that the advice given to parents is offered at a somewhat superficial level. As we have seen in Chapter V, the bringing up of the child depends very largely upon the parents' attitude, and parental attitudes are fundamentally determined by their reactions to their own problems. It is insufficient to instruct a mother (or a father) in the rudiments of child training. There are too many parents who, although able to appreciate this instruction intellectually, are so maladjusted emotionally that they can not possibly align their behavior with this intellectual apperception. For example, a psychologist at a nursery school discussed with an over-anxious mother the dangers of her methods of child training. The mother was constantly questioning the child as to how she felt, what she had been doing, what she would like to eat, whether she had missed mother while at school. The child, subjected to such a flood of verbal stimuli, took refuge in silence or a negativistic attitude. She would not answer when questioned as to how she felt or whether she had missed her mother; she refused whatever was offered her in the way of food. In vain was the mother told that she was provoking these very reactions from the child by her own unwise behavior. She agreed that this was true, but she was unable to restrain herself.

As a matter of fact, the mother's absorption in the child grew out of her emotional dissatisfactions in her home life. She had little in common with her husband; her marriage had failed to provide her with satisfactory emotional outlets, and she had not developed any broadening interests outside the home. The basis of her marital disharmonies was unknown; a psychologist giving part time service to a nursery school and otherwise occupied with teaching duties, was in no position to enter into the problems of the parents—especially since parental maladjustment was not limited to one or two of the mothers. Yet the need for work with the parents, in the interest of the child's proper personality development, was very apparent.

What the nursery school needs most, in addition to its present personnel of trained teachers, physicians, and psychologists, is the service of the psychiatric social worker. There should be some one person, trained for that particular job, who can give a large share of time to the problems of the parents and help them to a better adjustment. Without some such program with the parents, their coöperation with nursery school methods and ideals will inevitably be superficial. They will have the best intentions of carrying out suggestions regarding their children, but they will be emotionally incapable of doing so in more than a partial fashion.

Relationship between school and home. Earlier in the present chapter, it was stated that the school is a strategic center for the application of mental hygiene. This does not imply, however, that the school can secure the mental health of the child by the attention which is given him there regardless of the influences to which he is subjected in his home. All our clinical studies of maladjusted children point to the family as the most potent influences in the child's life. A liaison between the school and the home is therefore imperative when the school makes any attempt to improve the social adjustments of its pupils.

The visiting teacher plan offers one of the best methods for effecting a closer relationship between school and home in the interests of the pupil's mental hygiene needs. If a child shows signs of maladjustment, the visiting teacher studies the family situation and assists the parents in working out the problem. Her technique is very similar to that of the social worker, which will be described in some detail in Chapter XIV. She helps the parents to make better adjustments in their own lives, and to understand the effect of their own attitudes upon the child's personality and behavior. She gives them the encouragement and support which they need in carrying out a long time plan for the readjustment of their way of handling their family problems.

At the school, the visiting teacher interprets the child to the classroom teacher so that the latter may understand the origin of his difficulties. She also interests the teacher in devising modifications of the school régime which may be helpful in producing a better integration of the pupil's personality. Thus she manipulates both home and school situations in order to call out new reaction patterns on the part of the child.

The work of the visiting teacher radiates beyond the immediate cases which come to her attention. The classroom teachers who are in close contact with her methods gradually absorb mental hygiene principles which can be applied to other than just problem children. Thus the whole tone of pupil-teacher relationships may be improved so that minor difficulties are often adjusted without her direct intervention and before they develop into serious cases.

Parent-teacher associations. Parent-teacher organizations, which have been in existence for some time, furnish a ready-made medium for educating parents. Some of the more progressive parent-teachers associations are converting their meetings into child study groups. Leadership may be assumed by the principal of the school or by a mother who has had training in child psychology and hygiene. Occasionally the services of a professional can be secured, and if no personal guidance is available there are always the carefully selected reading lists issued by such organizations as the National Committee for

Mental Hygiene and the Child Study Associations. Using these bibliographies, the parent-teachers meeting can resolve itself into a class for reading and discussion without encountering too many obstacles.

In some schools, the parent-teachers associations are building up libraries of child study literature from which individual parents may borrow books and magazines. This coöperative purchasing and sharing gives accessibility to a wider range of literature than most individuals can afford. In communities where child welfare work is well developed at the hands of a personnel with professional training, these experts may be persuaded to lecture and lead discussions at parent-teachers meetings.

The child study purpose is of comparatively recent introduction into the parent-teachers program and for the most part exists only in neighborhoods where there is a distinctly progressive spirit. It has the usual dangers of parent education schemes in that it appeals to the more conscientious parents who take their responsibilities to their children very seriously. It is not unusual for these parents to react to new information with a feeling of guilt over errors which they perceive they have made in bringing up their children. Nevertheless, even at the risk of stirring up some such emotions, it is necessary that efforts at parent education should be continued in the interests of childhood mental health.

The school task and mental hygiene. Aside from the other effects which the school may have on the individual child, there is also the matter of adaptation to the educational task. The pupil who is successful in his work finds a satisfaction therein which may help to compensate for inferiorities he may have felt in other situations—at home or on the playground. Success is a wholesome tonic to the personality, increasing self-respect and self-reliance and producing interest which stimulates to further endeavor. On the other hand, the effects of failure are just the opposite. The child who does not succeed in the assigned tasks of the school day becomes discouraged, experiences a sense of inferiority, and loses interest. This makes demotions and repetitions of a grade destructive to personality formation, and the injurious results are intensified, usually, by the criticism which is evoked from parents. Very often the parental attitude implies that such occurrences are a source of family disgrace, and all too frequently the child is blamed for laziness or for deliberate refusal to do his work.

Few parents know how numerous are the causes of failure in school. It may be the child started at too early an age and has been pushed beyond his limits; in many instances intellectual dullness or subnormality interferes with regular progress through the grades; sometimes disabilities for one of the fundamental subjects, ordinarily for reading or arithmetic, handicap a child; intellectual superiority even may be a cause of failure, the child who is far too bright for his grade escaping the boredom of tasks which are over-simplified by a retreat into daydreaming or surreptitious reading, paying little attention to the classroom routine.

The drive for college entrance. The classes for gifted children, for mentally deficient pupils, and for those physically handicapped or backward in some one subject, have been introduced to prevent the child from having an experience of repeated failure. But not all school systems are provided with such facilities, nor are they always efficiently utilized when they exist. Moreover, there are still numbers of pupils whose needs are not met by these special classes.

There is present, within the educational system itself,

a force which is working directly against the aims for which these special classes were created. On the one hand, we have a realization of the necessity of fitting the school curriculum to the individual child; on the other there is pressure from above, particularly in the secondary schools, to meet the requirements for college entrance. The preparation for college board examinations is especially the goal of the private schools. And this pressure is often exerted to the point where it seriously injures the physical or mental health of the child. The fatigue and anxiety occasioned by the drive to meet college entrance standards can hardly be overestimated.

This unhealthy situation is not fostered by the schools alone. It is an outcome of the American attitude toward education. College is no longer regarded as a place for those of exceptional ability where they may prepare for a profession. Rather, it is regarded as an insignia of social status. One business man frankly stated that the reason he wished his son to attend college was so that he might feel at ease when asked in after years, "What was your college?" or "What was your fraternity?" College has become the accepted thing for certain economic classes, regardless of vocational aims.

As a result, the applications for college enrollment are too numerous for the relatively scanty accommodations of these institutions. The applicants increase more rapidly than dormitories can be built to house them or classrooms enlarged to receive them. Also the number of applicants intellectually unsuited for college work has grown exceedingly as a result of this social attitude. The raising of entrance standards and·the stiffening of the college board examinations represents an attempt on the part of the institutions of higher learning to limit this eager throng and to preserve the colleges and universities for those who are intellectually able to profit from what they have to offer. Unfortunately, the pupils in secondary schools meet this demand for increased effort at a time when their adolescent bodies and minds need security and leisure and protection from undue nervous strain.

Character education programs. Influenced by the modern concern for the development of character, educators have attempted to arrive at some way of educating the child in order to impress desirable character traits. One popular method is the "Children's Morality Code for Elementary Schools," which formulates in elaborate terminology a series of resolutions upon the ideals of self-control, responsibility, honesty, courtesy, obedience, patriotism and similar virtues. The pupils memorize these resolutions, and are taught to associate with the code material from the different academic subjects. They are also asked to find illustrations of the code in poetry, proverbs and slogans. This program lays undue stress upon verbalized affirmations of ideals, with a naïve faith that the verbalization will affect behavior.

Realizing that the superimposition of such ideals of conduct cannot be entirely successful in modifying behavior patterns, there have been other plans which attempt to relate character education more directly to pupil activities. For example, there is the "Knighthood of Youth," in which the pupils advance in rank in proportion to the nicety with which they perform everyday duties such as putting away their books carefully, being polite and helpful at home, etcetera. The duties are listed on charts, a daily record of success and failure to be filled in at home under the supervision of the parents. Discussing this plan for character education, W. I. Thomas and D. S. Thomas comment that the situation is one which offers a temptation to falsification, and that both parents and children sometimes make dishonest reports on the charts.[3]

A more vital attempt to influence character is the organization of the school in some form of student government project. This can be instituted in junior high schools. Under this plan, problems which arise are discussed in a conference in which teachers and pupils participate, the leading rôle being left to the pupils, as far as possible. Different points of view are freely presented, and each pupil thinks his way into new knowledge and new attitudes towards everyday problems by virtue of this interchange of ideas.

The case for and against the different character education programs is ably summed up by the Thomases: "In many of the programs there is an overanxiety to associate a moral lesson with all the subjects taught, as if the materials of study were designed to substantiate the virtues of the moral code. . . . With regard to the project method, its superiority over the preceptual is obvious. Virtues are in part evolved unconsciously, and if exposure is made to situations which develop desirable behavior patterns the plan is to that extent good. . . . The superiority of the visiting teacher work . . . over programs of the type described is apparent. The former emphasizes the production of adjustment, the latter the development of virtues. The visiting teacher deals directly with situations and the development of activities, which become the basis for whatever preceptual teaching is necessary. The amount of moralizing is kept at a minimum. As a system of character education the preceptual method is inadequate in the school as it has proved

[3] W. I. and D. S. Thomas, *The Child in America,* p. 283. New York, 1928.

itself inadequate in the family and the church. The mere multiplication of precepts is like the creation of more laws when the old ones have failed to work." [4]

It would perhaps be erroneous to consider these character education programs futile. But when this is the only force opposed to the powerful social pressures which (as we saw in Chapter IV) are among the fundamental causes of undesirable behavior, we may well be skeptical of its success.

Mental hygiene and the home economics curriculum. While courses in mental hygiene have been introduced into colleges and universities and into teacher training institutions, they have not penetrated very far into the secondary school curriculum. The one exception to this statement is the interest in mental hygiene which is beginning to permeate the department of home economics. In some of the colleges, we find that the nursery schools are maintained as a home economics project, with cooperation from the schools of education. More recently, courses in child care and child training have been introduced into the home economics curriculum of the junior and senior high schools. While the physical care of the child is prominent in these courses, some attention is also given to the problems of habit formation and mental health needs. As the teaching personnel acquires training in these last two subjects, we may perhaps expect to see more emphasis bestowed upon them. Even the present rudimentary beginnings, limited to a few school systems and with mental hygiene playing a minor part in the instruction, are of importance as showing the trend of modern pedagogy. It will indeed be interesting to see what the future brings forth in this field. Since only a

[4] *The Child in America,* pp. 291 and 294.

small percentage of the population is destined to reach the college, it is necessary that the teaching of mental hygiene principles be extended to the lower schools if we hope to have the next generation of mothers better prepared for their duties than has been true in the past. There is another reason, also, for this early instruction, since it reaches the individual before habits of thinking and prejudices are quite so strongly entrenched as they become in later years, and it may thus prove more effective.

The school and the clinic. In at least two cities in this country, the child guidance clinic has been instituted as an integral part of the school system. This is probably one of the most vital moves for making mental hygiene a concrete part of the educational plan. These clinics within the school system provide a center for the study and treatment of the maladjusted child, whether the problem be one of failure at the school task, personality disorders or misbehavior. The clinic personnel provides medical examiners who study the child's physical condition much more thoroughly than is done in the routine medical inspection of pupils; psychiatric service for the child who needs expert aid in making personality readjustments; psychological examiners to furnish skilled diagnosis of educational disabilities and plan remedial methods, and also to insure the proper use of special classes; and a corps of social workers and visiting teachers in order that the home influences may be thoroughly understood and, in so far as possible, improved.

The need of so many different types of service can be clearly understood in the light of some actual facts concerning the school children referred to community child guidance clinics in two different cities. Medical examination of these children, for instance, revealed the fol-

lowing physical conditions, which had either been passed
over by the routine medical inspection or not been corrected thereafter:

PHYSICAL CONDITIONS FOUND IN SCHOOL CHILDREN STUDIED
BY TWO CHILD GUIDANCE CLINICS [5]

Physical Condition	*167* *Los Angeles* *Cases*	*163* *Philadelphia* *Cases*
Nose and throat conditions...	41.3 per cent	47.3 per cent
Undernourished	39.6	28.8
Dental defects or diseases....	26.4	46.0
Eye defects or diseases......	26.9	33.8
Defects of posture.........	24.5	27.6
Endocrine symptomatology...	19.7	9.2
Cardiac conditions.........	13.2	4.9
Overweight	12.6	7.3
Defects or diseases of ear....	6.6	13.5
Pulmonary conditions.......	5.4	2.4
Anemia	5.4	1.8
No physical defects.........	4.7	9.8

The need for a thorough physical examination is apparent from these figures, which show that less than ten
per cent of the children are entirely free from physical
defects or disease. Perhaps some indication of the value
of the psychological study can be gained if we mention
the fact that not more than forty per cent proved to be
correctly graded in relation to their mental ability. The
importance of the social worker's task in helping to adjust the children is very clear from the following tabulation of the data with reference to home and other environmental conditions:

[5] The figures in this and the following tables are taken from
Educational Achievement of Problem Children, by Paynter and
Blanchard. Commonwealth Fund, *Division of Publications,* Fuller
Building, 57th St. and Madison Ave., New York, 1929.

UNDESIRABLE SOCIAL CONDITIONS IN CASES OF SCHOOL
CHILDREN REFERRED TO TWO CHILD GUIDANCE CLINICS

Social Conditions	167 Los Angeles Children	163 Philadelphia Children
Poor training and discipline..	87.4 per cent	92.7 per cent
Recreation lacking or improper	32.4	68.7
Broken home..............	29.3	47.9
Undesirable companions.....	27.5	38.7
Parental disharmony........	12.6	13.5
Poverty	11.8	38.0
Neurotic or psychotic parent..	10.8	39.9
Alcoholic parent.............		20.3

The personality and behavior maladjustments for which
these children were referred for clinical study and treatment may also be of interest as indicating the wide range
of problems and the desirability of psychiatric and psychological service.

PERSONALITY MALADJUSTMENTS

Personality	167 Los Angeles Children	163 Philadelphia Children
Mental conflicts............	44.9 per cent	22.1 per cent
Hyperactive	22.8	10.5
Inferiority feelings..........	19.1	54.0
Over-emotional	15.6	3.7
Fearful	13.2	14.7
Daydreaming (excessively)...	8.4	17.2
Adolescent instability........	7.8	6.1
Functional nervous disease...	7.8	3.0
Seclusive	5.4	5.3
Neurotic	3.0	7.9

BEHAVIOR SYMPTOMATIC OF MALADJUSTMENT

Behavior	167 Los Angeles Children	163 Philadelphia Children
Stealing	36.5 per cent	38.7 per cent
Lying	28.7	37.4
Sex experiences	23.4	9.8
Truancy	21.6	28.2
Disobedience	21.6	19.7
Running away from home	17.9	16.0
Enuresis	13.8	8.5
Temper tantrums	12.6	27.0
Fighting (excessively)	7.8	12.9

It should be emphasized that, from the viewpoint of child guidance, such personality and behavior traits as are listed in the above tables are to be regarded as symptoms of maladjustment. Through the coöperative studies from the medical, psychiatric, psychological and social angles, the causes of maladjustment are sought out. The treatment plan is aimed at the removal or correction of these causes, and not at the symptomatic personality or behavior trait *per se*. If the fundamental influences which lead to maladjustment can be modified, the symptoms will disappear without any especial attention being directed toward them, in most instances. The tabulation of undesirable social conditions should be especially suggestive as to causation and the lines of treatment to be followed.

The personnel of the Newark Public Schools Department of Child Guidance indicates the relative amount of work carried by the three professional groups. In 1928, the staff consisted of one psychiatrist, four psychologists and eight social workers, the proportion experimentally found to give most efficient service. The unit for the small school system should be composed of a full time psychologist and two or three social workers or visiting teachers, with psychiatric service available for consultation in certain types of cases. The modern swing of clinical psychology beyond the narrow limit of mental testing to a broad conception of human adjustments and interest in treatment techniques insures that the adequately trained psychologist and visiting teacher could carry a considerable burden of the school adjustment service. This plan would further mental hygiene aims in communities where the maintenance of all three professions on a full time basis would be financially impractical.

ILLUSTRATIVE CASE

Gerald's mother was ambitious for him to make a success in school. When he came home in tears from the first grade one morning, and stated that he was never going back to school, she was considerably disturbed. She made him return to school, but went with him to interview the teacher. She found that the teacher had shaken him because he made the figure three backwards. Thereupon she made up her mind to help Gerald with his arithmetic, so that there would be no need for the teacher to punish him again. Unfortunately, in trying to teach him at home, she duplicated the teacher's method. If Gerald did not know the answer to a problem, she threatened to whip him, and sometimes actually did so.

By the time Gerald was in the third grade, his mind seemed to become a blank at the sight of an arithmetic problem. His teacher complained that he was inattentive, and seemed to be lost in daydreams much of the time. His mother stated that no matter how often she punished him he would not say his tables right. It was probable that he would have to repeat the third grade. This crisis caused the mother to ask help from a child guidance clinic.

Gerald became a clinic case shortly before school closed for the summer vacation. During the summer, he was given help with arithmetic by a tutor especially selected because of her youthfulness and attractive appearance. The teaching methods were planned with a view to building up pleasant associations with arithmetic to take the place of the former unpleasant ones. Almost all the teaching was accomplished by playing games. When thinking of it as incidental to play, Gerald could do arithmetic very well, but when the same processes were presented in the form of problems, he became panic-stricken and confused and made many errors. However, by the end of the summer he was able to do fourth grade arithmetic with his tutor or with the psychologist at the clinic.

When school opened in the fall, a report of Gerald's progress was made to the principal with a request that the boy be given a trial in the fourth grade. The principal refused to accept this suggestion, and Gerald's mother was very much upset that he would have to repeat the third grade, despite the summer's work. Her attitude reacted upon the child and caused him to feel very much discouraged. All his old hatred and fear of arithmetic returned.

The only recourse was to persuade Gerald and his mother to adjust to this unfortunate situation. Intensive psychiatric work was undertaken with the mother, and it was found that her insistence on regular school progress for Gerald was tied up with personal problems of her own life. As she was helped in working these out and in reaching a better adjustment, her attitude toward the grade repetition altered considerably. With this relaxation on her part, it was possible to initiate direct treatment for Gerald.

By this time the boy was on sufficiently friendly terms with the clinic psychologist to be able to discuss his difficulties with her. For the first time, he began to reveal the content of his daydreams, and to verbalize his feelings about his situation. His descriptions of his attitudes and daydreams were illuminating. "I am not afraid of the teachers," he said, one day. "I could cover my face with a big red handkerchief and make

them think I was a pirate and scare them." In class he day-
dreamed of how he would like to get a big club and kill all
the teachers. At another time, discussing arithmetic, he said:
"When my teacher puts all those hard examples on the board
I feel like jumping out of the window and running home. I
would like to get my father's revolver and shoot her. All the
teachers in that school deserve to be shot, anyway. The only
kind teacher I ever had was in the kindergarten." He also
described other daydreams which came to him when he was
supposed to be working on arithmetic, saying that he often
thought he would like to go up on the roof and jump off and
kill himself so that he would never have to do it any more. If
he had a million dollars, he would buy a farm and never go to
school.

The open expression of thoughts and feelings which he had
hitherto repressed except for daydreaming, seemed to bring
some relief of itself. But Gerald was encouraged to go further,
and to try to understand why he found arithmetic so difficult.
At last, he worked out the connection between his attitudes and
his difficulties in school. "I think I just get nervous when I
see any arithmetic, I am so afraid I can't do it."

From this time, Gerald's work began to improve. In part
this was due to his new insight, but also it was largely conditioned by his mother's altered attitude. Where formerly she
had made him stay in after school and work with her on arithmetic, she had now begun to encourage him to go out to play,
had permitted him to join a boys' club at the church, a swimming class at the Y.M.C.A., and a group of boys at the
neighborhood recreation center. From concentrating all her
energy on the aim of having him succeed in school, she saw
that he needed a wholesome, active childhood in order that he
might develop a happy, socialized personality.

At the end of the school term, Gerald was promoted to the
fourth grade, in which he seems to be making a satisfactory
adjustment. The teacher has praised him for the improvement in his work, and he says that he likes her and that he can
go to the board and do arithmetic as well as anyone. These re-

sults in school could not have been obtained without the fundamental change which took place in Gerald's attitudes and those of his mother. Had his mother continued to make success in arithmetic so vital a factor in bestowing approval or disapproval upon the boy, he could not have overcome his feelings about it. Instead he would have been forced to continue to retreat from an unhappy situation into daydreams, and would have kept on regarding teachers as the natural enemies who were causing all his troubles and estranging him from his mother's approval.

SUGGESTIONS FOR CLASSROOM DISCUSSION

1. What motives operate in the choice of teaching as a profession?
2. What restrictions of personal liberty must the teacher accept?
3. What are the mental hygiene needs of the teaching personnel?
4. What provision does the school make for the adjustment of atypical pupils?
5. Why is the pupil of low average intelligence peculiarly a problem?
6. What attitudes may the teachers assume toward misconduct of pupils?
7. What are some of the signs of maladjustment in school children?
8. What are the relationships between home and school?
9. What services can the clinic offer the school child?

SUGGESTIONS FOR WRITTEN REPORTS

1. Nursery School Methods.
2. The Work of the Visiting Teacher.
3. The Education of the Gifted Child.
4. Reading Disabilities as a Cause of Maladjustment.
5. A Mental Hygiene Program for Schools.

Select some school system with which you are familiar and study its administration from the mental hygiene point of view. What mental hygiene facilities already exist in this educational system? What other facilities for pupil adjustment are needed?

SELECTED BIBLIOGRAPHY

AIKINS, HERBERT AUSTIN. "The Gifted Child and His Teachers." *Mental Hygiene,* October, 1929, Chap. XIII, pp. 719-39.

ALLEN, ELIZABETH. "A Mental Hygiene Program in Grade Schools." *Mental Hygiene,* 1929, Vol. XIII, pp. 289-297.

ANDERSON, ROSE G. "The Problem of the Dull-Normal Child." *Mental Hygiene,* 1927, Vol. XI, pp. 272-286.

AVERILL, L. A. *The Hygiene of Instruction.* Boston, 1928.

BLANCHARD, P. "Attitudes and Educational Disabilities." *Mental Hygiene,* 1929, Vol. XIII, pp. 550-563.

—— "Reading Disabilities in Relation to Maladjustment." *Mental Hygiene,* 1928, Vol. XII, pp. 772-788.

—— *The Child and Society,* Chap. IV. New York, 1928.

BURNHAM, W. H. *The Normal Mind,* Chaps. VIII and XV. New York, 1924.

CHAMBERLAIN, H. E. "Mental Hygiene in the Public Schools." *Minnesota Public Health Nurse,* 2:4-6, 8, July, 1929.

CLARKE, E. DEV. "Mental Health in the School." *Canadian Nurse,* Winnipeg, 25:422-25, August, 1929.

ELLIS, MABEL. *The Visiting Teacher in Rochester.* Commonwealth Fund, Division of Publications, 1925.

GATES, A. I. *The Improvement of Reading,* Chaps. I and II. New York, 1927.

HARDY, RUTH. "The Freeing of the Teacher." *Mental Hygiene,* 1929, Vol. XIII, pp. 33-44.

HINCKS, ELIZABETH. *Disability in Reading in Relation to Personality.* Harvard University Press, 1926.

HOLLINGWORTH, LETA. *The Psychology of the Adolescent,* Chap. IV. New York, 1928.

HORN, J. S. *The Education of Exceptional Children,* Chaps. VI-XIII. New York, 1924.

JOHNSON, H. M. *Children in the Nursery School.* New York, 1928.

LOW, BARBARA. "A Note on the Influence of Psycho-analysis upon English Education During the Last Eighteen Years."

International   Journal   of   Psycho-analysis,   London,
    10:314-20, April-July, 1929.
MEEK, LOIS H.   "The Preschool Movement."   *Progressive
    Education*, 1929, Vol. VI, pp. 3-10.
MILLER, H. C.   *The New Psychology and the Teacher*.   New
    York, 1922.
MYERS, GARRY C.   "Schoolroom Hazards to the Mental Health
    of Children."   *Mental Hygiene*, 1928, Vol. XII, pp. 18-24.
MORGAN, J. J. B.   *The Psychology of the Unadjusted School
    Child*.   New York, 1924.
OPPENHEIMER, S. D.   *The Visiting Teacher Movement*.   Com-
    monwealth Fund, 1929.
PAYNTER and BLANCHARD.   *Educational Achievement of Prob-
    lem Children*.   Commonwealth Fund, 1929.
PLATNER, M. M.   "A High School Demonstration Clinic."
    Mental Hygiene, 1929, Vol. XIII, pp. 278-288.
RADEMACHER, GRACE C.   "The Psychiatric Social Worker and
    the Nursery School."   *Mental Hygiene*, 1929, Vol. XIII,
    pp. 298-308.
REAVIS, WILLIAM C.   *Pupil Adjustment in Junior and Senior
    High Schools*.   Boston, 1926.
SCHMALHAUSEN, S. D.   *Humanizing Education*.   New Educa-
    tion Publishing Co., 1924.   Especially pp. 23-42.
TAFT, JESSIE.   "The Relation of the School to the Mental
    Health of the Average Child."   *Mental Hygiene*, 1923,
    Vol. VII, pp. 673-687.
TERMAN, L. M.   *Suggestions for the Education and Training
    of Gifted Children*.   Stanford University Press, 1921.
THOMAS, W. I. and D. S.   *The Child in America*, Chaps. V and
    VI.   New York, 1928.
TRUITT, RALPH P.   "Mental Hygiene and the Public Schools."
    Mental Hygiene, 1927, Vol. XI, pp. 261-271.
WALLACE, DOROTHY.   "Problem of the Quasi-delinquent in
    the School."   *Mental Hygiene*, 1924, Vol. VIII, pp. 115-
    165.
WICKMAN, E. K.   *Children's Behavior and Teachers' Attitudes*.
    Commonwealth Fund, 1928.
WILE, I. S.   "Mental Hygiene in the Public Schools."   *Mental
    Hygiene*, 1929, Vol. XIII, pp. 70-80.
ZELENY, L. D.   "Pupil-teacher Relationships."   *Sociology and
    Social Research*, 1929, Vol. XIII, pp. 265-275.

CHAPTER IX

MENTAL HYGIENE IN THE COLLEGE AND THE UNIVERSITY

Mental hygiene has a large place in the modern college and university. This is not because mental disease is rampant among the students in the institutions of higher learning, but on account of the responsibility that the college and university have as possible distributors of mental hygiene principles. Such institutions may rightly be expected to practice in their administration and instruction the principles of mental hygiene. To a large extent also they have under their guidance during four or more impressionable years potential leaders who need to be, both for their own happiness and welfare and for the good of those whom they are likely to influence in later life, familiar with the teachings of mental hygiene.

Although the records show that mental disease is uncommon in the college population and breakdown rare, when serious mental abnormalities do appear they often prove costly experiences for the institution, which obtains much undeserved notoriety and frequently serious criticism. In no place is mental disorder so likely to be misinterpreted. The press still insists on holding over-study responsible for suicide and the onset of insanity, although the scientist knows that there is no connection. The situation in the colleges is similar to that in industry. Young men and women who are basically unsound, when transferred from the relatively easier environment of the secondary school, because of the new demands put upon them and also because of their advancement in age, are brought to a testing which causes their basic unsoundness to appear in a serious form that announces the onset of some sort of nervous malady. Such students are unequal to the competition and pressure of a college environment, just as they would be marked for disaster were they to enter some other undertaking where greater maturity and application than that of their high school period would be demanded of them. Since the college represents a high selection of desirable types and an environment unusually wholesome, it furnishes as favorable a situation for youth as can be found, but it cannot give to the basically unsound the special treatment and consideration they need.

Mental hygiene and preparation for life. The college and university assume the task of preparing the student for life. They are more than lecture halls. Youth comes to them with the expectation that he shall be better prepared to cope with life as a result of his investment of precious years. The college takes its intellectual responsibilities seriously. It is concerned with standards and insists upon the student's progress in the accumulation of credits. Unfortunately this emphasis upon the passing of courses often leads to neglect of the emotional life of the student. Only the unusual teacher gives much thought to the inner life of his students, and the administration also is apt to neglect the emotional aspect of the student's life until some outward conduct that involves discipline forces attention.

There is an exaggerated emphasis upon the value of intellectual achievement in the college as a method of preparing for life. As a consequence students drift through the college and even the university without gaining any substantial insight into personal problems. If the instructor notices idiosyncrasy in the student he seldom brings it to the latter's attention and more rarely does he make any constructive effort to straighten out what may be a serious kink in the personality of the young man or woman. When the time for graduation appears the multitude of youth have made little substantial emotional growth and almost none as the result of any intentional help from the institution. Nevertheless, education of the right sort does lead to emotional maturity and does become a protecting influence against psychopathic trends. This fact is well brought out by a term we use for the special treatment given those suffering from a mild type of mental disorder. In the vocabulary of the psychiatrist this treatment is known as "reëducation." Had there been in such cases proper education at the start, a reconstruction of character would seldom have become necessary. Anyone who has served on college administration committees knows how often troublesome or peculiar students are discussed and reference is made to characteristics that the mental hygienist would recognize as neurotic trends. Pity is expressed, but seldom does anyone suggest that the college has an obligation to assist the student in ridding himself of qualities that are bound to limit his success as soon as he graduates from the institution.

More is involved in the task of emotionally maturing the student than merely his own happiness. Intellectual achievement means power, but it does not insure judgment, or, by itself, establish wholesome attitudes toward one's fellows. Unless the emotions are disciplined, intellectual power like any other may be turned to unsocial ends, driven by the force of abnormal cravings, the results of a childish character. Perhaps nothing at present so limits the usefulness of the colleges as their neglect of the emotional life of their students.

The need of mental hygiene in the college. The college has need of mental hygiene because its various activities require every help science can give that will increase success. Since the institution brings youth together in close contact, attempts to instruct them, and assumes a responsibility for their discipline, it especially needs the contributions that mental hygiene can make to these different interests. It is, however, only when we think of the final product of the college, its graduates, that we see fully the importance of mental hygiene. This was forcefully brought out by an anonymous article entitled "Mental Hygiene and the College Student Twenty Years After." [1] In the effort to discover just how much mental hygiene is needed in the American College, a graduate investigated the careers of his classmates a generation after leaving the institution. Of one-fourth he knew practically nothing, so he left them out of the investigation. Of the three-fourths whose careers he had been able to follow in detail he discovered that about forty per cent had since graduation shown signs of neurotic, psychoneurotic, or even psychotic difficulties. Among this number were two-thirds of those who were admitted to Phi Beta Kappa and this group included also the most serious cases of mental and nervous diseases. Of the seventeen per cent that had died, two thirds gave evidence of some degree of neurotic difficulties. One death was a suicide. There was nothing in the college history of this class to indicate that it was a particularly psychopathic group of young people, indeed its reputation was that of a rather commonplace class. The author briefly sum-

[1] See *Mental Hygiene,* October, 1921, pp. 736-40.

marizes the careers of some of those who met with disaster after graduation, and the following examples are impressive:

A. One of the ablest members of the class, who received not only the highest marks for scholarship, but also the highest office in the gift of the student body. This individual, an only child of New England extraction, was, it appeared later, of a markedly, though long latent, manic-depressive constitution, and after achieving considerable success in a professional field, succumbed some fifteen years after graduation to this increasingly emerging and menacing type of disease. A long course of psychoanalysis resulted in marked improvement and the diminution of the frequency and severity of the alternations of the emotional states, but the prognosis has never been considered very favorable by the psychiatrist in charge of the case.

B. Perhaps the most brilliant member of the class, who subsequently attained to the rank of a college professor. The patient's career in two colleges was terminated by the onset of depressions, the first mild and lasting for only about six months, the second severe and involving two years of treatment in hospitals for nervous and mental diseases. Since the latest episode a few years ago, the uncongenial profession of teaching, in which success was attained at such immense cost of vitality, has been succeeded by research work, for which this individual is eminently adapted.[2]

Of course there is no way of telling just how much mental hygiene could have done for these individuals when they were in college, but if preventive work is possible in the field of mental disease surely such a record as this justifies the mental hygiene program in the college.

Opportunity for mental hygiene. The colleges and universities offer an unusually favorable opportunity for mental hygiene. Not only are the students highly se-

[2] *Op. cit.*

lected, representing, on the whole, the more promising graduates of the high schools, but the situation on the college campus gives the mental hygienist an advantage over those who work in industry or in private practice. Ordinarily the patient scatters his life over many contacts of which the specialist can, for the most part, have little information. It is true that to meet this difficulty the psychiatric social worker is called upon and she frequently can supply the needed data. Even with this information the complete picture of the individual is usually not so easy to make as it is when the college student is being investigated. His life is largely expressed on the campus where it can be observed in its various aspects in detail and with a definiteness difficult to obtain elsewhere. The specialist if he so desires can have easy conference with other men or women who intimately know the student in the classroom, in sport, or in the lighter social experiences.

In most up-to-date colleges also the medical department can be called upon to supply necessary information regarding the physical condition of the patient who appears to be in need of psychiatric assistance. A better opportunity to know the patient intimately without bringing him into the atmosphere of an institution devoted entirely to the handling of psychopathic disorder can hardly be imagined. Thus the college and university setting not only challenges mental hygiene, but provides an experiment station and an opportunity for demonstration exceeded only by the possibilities of the family and the grade schools where the earlier age of the child gives preventive work greater promise.

Forms of adjustment difficulty. The college furnishes its own peculiar types of social strain. It helps in the understanding of the problems of mental hygiene in the college to distinguish these, but they must not be thought of as unrelated, for it is seldom that any one alone is the explanation of a personal maladjustment.

1. The Environment. Many college students have not been away from home for any length of time before they enter college. Possibly this is a mistaken policy on the part of parents who might well prepare for the ordeal by permitting the child to have a few days away from home, spent in travel or in visiting relatives. But only the thoughtful parent is likely to see the need of this, and thus it happens that most young people when they go to college experience for the first time the pangs of homesickness.

Not only must the ties of home be broken, but the environment itself requires new adaptation. It is larger than the high school from which the student has come and less personal. For the first time the young man or woman may be thrown among strangers. The instruction is different and the standards are higher and may seem more exacting than they really are to the new student.

It is true that at present most colleges make special effort to help the freshmen at the beginning of their courses. This very effort, unless wisely handled, often adds to the bewilderment of the student, who is rapidly introduced to many features of college life in the effort to help him get adjusted, and makes him feel less secure than if he were given a more gradual approach to his new activities. Whether he is labored with at the beginning by a special faculty organization created to orient him to college life or left alone, he must change some of his habits and become conscious of others as has never been true before. He may, for example, for the first time have to become accustomed to cooking very different from that of his mother. He may be surprisingly disturbed by the boarding-house fare. Although there is frequent rationalization in regard to this, those experienced with college students realize how difficult the new food adjustment often is.

2. Demands are put upon the young person for self-direction to an extent that makes college experience something unique. Of course, the more responsibility he has been given by his parents and former teachers, the easier it is for him to make the adjustment. The mere fact that he changes from living with his family to a dormitory existence throws upon him the necessity of making decisions that were previously merely a part of household routine. If he seeks advice regarding the more important decisions he has to make, he must turn to persons whom he has not long known, of whose interest he may not be so confident as he was of his parents' and former friends'.

It is found in practice that the time schedule is a very persistent problem that comes up when the mental hygienist deals with concrete difficulties. The student is not trained to make proper use of time which appears so abundant when he first comes in contact with what seems to be a widespread leisure. It is folly for the faculty to complain when the freshman does not know how to study or to use his time with profit. Just because of these immaturities has he come to college; this training in the use of time it is the business of the college to provide.

3. Competition and self-esteem are sources of much trouble among college youth. No one deals much with youth in any environment without appreciating how significant in their life is the problem of self-esteem. The very fact that the student has entered college proves that he has had a degree of success in his high school. Frequently he has been an outstanding student and has re-

ceived a good deal of distinction, in sports, in study, or in general popularity. Thrown into the new environment, one of the first efforts of the young person is to estimate his standing and if possible to win back the position that he had in the high school, and which he feels he has lost. His ambition may concentrate on any one of four interests: scholarship, athletics, fraternities, and, in case of the girl especially, popularity expressed in dates. Along whatever line he struggles for self-esteem he finds new competition. Not only must he contend against his own classmates, but under the overshadowing of the upper classes.

The prestige of the fraternity is not only great but maintained by having a portion of the student body left out of membership. This immediately creates for the fraternity, in addition to its actual usefulness, an artificial value which the student easily exaggerates. There is hardly any place about which more tragedy centers for the freshman than the question, Will he make a fraternity? Social popularity, as expressed in dates with members of the opposite sex, also has a prominent place in the problems of the college student. Lacking such concrete evidence of popularity, he or she may come to have a sense of inferiority. On the other hand, if bids are plentiful, the temptation to accept them all results not merely from the strength of sex attraction, but may come even more from the desire to build up social reputation and satisfy self-esteem.

4. Growth also brings for the college student a great deal of difficulty. The college environment often forces rapid growth where gradual change would bring little disturbance. When the student has come from a narrow religious home or community the difficulties of adjustment are multiplied and the immediate effect of growth may

be painful. The trouble is usually rooted in the fact that parents have not made possible the child's growth beyond their own ideas without a moral struggle due to the feeling of the young person that any departure from what has been taught him is a treason against love and a letting down of standards. These unnecessary struggles, due to faulty preparation in the family, create a moral risk and explain the sudden change in characteristics sometimes found in college students. The mental hygienist is interested in such an experience because it represents an emotional crisis. Many colleges, in the effort to help freshmen, have orientation courses designed especially to meet the needs of the new students.

5. Sex. The problem of sex comes to the adolescent whatever his environment and cannot be prevented from entering the college campus. Indeed there are many circumstances which bring it to the front. The freedom that the new environment permits, the contacts which lead to the rehearsal of experiences by the more sophisticated, the new instruction which frequently seems to the student to be sapping his moral ideas because they have been built upon traditions out of accord with the ideas he is given in his college courses, all add to his confusion in dealing with personal problems of sex. If the college is one that is exclusively for men or for women the very artificiality of such a segregation during the late adolescent period stimulates and distorts sex. The co-educational institution, however, does not escape its problem. Although the constant contact of the young men and women provides a more normal environment, the very freedom of association makes it all the more irksome for some to give proper attention to study, the value of which seems remote in comparison with the immediate and compelling interest that the young man or

woman takes in some member of the opposite sex. Since success in college demands self-discipline, the opportunity for maladjustment is present. Even the most healthy association of young men and women cannot eliminate problems that are caused by the postponement of marriage for the purpose of getting an education.

The program of mental hygiene. The chief purpose of the mental hygiene movement in the college is prevention. It undertakes to lessen the failures of the college students, especially in meeting the tests of their environment. It also of course attempts to do everything possible to detect those who are candidates for later neurotic experiences and if possible to keep them from developing their morbid tendencies.

Next to the preventive part of the program comes the handling of adjustment difficulties. Mental hygiene takes over the emotional problems so largely neglected by conventional college courses and endeavors to help the student develop wholesomeness in his own inner reactions to life. This involves more than merely showing the student how he can more wisely meet any present difficulty, for effort is made also to help the student get the insight which not only will assist him in correcting immediate maladjustments, but will enable him also to have that understanding of himself which will insure a happy and useful life. This part of the mental hygiene movement is directly concerned with the growth of the student who must go forward and bring into accord his intellectual advance and his emotional attitude. Mental hygiene, by giving insight to the student, also enables him to estimate more correctly the resources he has for his undertakings in life. This makes possible greater success in his life after graduation. It also contributes to his later happiness since misinterpretation of one's own equipment for life is a prolific root of trouble for most people.

If it is thought of as an annex rather than an integral part of the institution, the mental hygiene program is more difficult to carry out successfully. Surely nothing in college has a better right to be considered educational than the use of science in dealing with problems of personality. It is merely its newness that makes it seem to some an addition rather than an organic part of the function of the institution.

Mental hygiene and admission to college. Since the college can give no one an adequate preparation for life if it stresses only intellectual achievements, admission to college should never be based entirely upon the credits obtained at the high school. There are always among those who present themselves for entrance some who, in spite of good grades, are unfit to enter upon a college career. Others there are who have chosen the wrong institution and for them there must be loss of time and energy if they are not directed to the kind of college that can serve them best. Still others need special counsel if their college career is to prove successful. Thus at the very time of entrance, problems that are essentially related to mental hygiene often arise and therefore admission to college should never be a mere mechanical routine. Questions can be asked and information gathered of great value to the psychiatrist who wishes to discover as early as possible those whom he can especially help. If the emotional preparation were entered upon in somewhat the same fashion that the colleges now concern themselves with intellectual attainments, mental hygiene would be able to prevent a considerable number of the tragedies that result from students going to college when they should not, or entering the wrong college, or starting a career that without proper insight they cannot prosecute successfully. Mental hygiene will not eliminate at the start all the problems that the college brings forth, but it will reduce them to the minimum.

Mental hygiene lectures. There is a consensus of opinion at present that one of the most useful undertakings of the department of mental hygiene in college has to do with lectures which bring to the students in an understandable form the principles they need in mapping out their college course so as to get from it the greatest values possible. Regarding the questions, when these lectures ought to be given and what should be their content, there is not the same unanimity of judgment. Some believe that the lectures should come early, at least during the freshman year, that the student may have the benefit of them from the start, while others would depend more upon conferences as a means of helping the freshmen and would develop more serious and mature courses best adapted to seniors who are just about to leave the institution. Probably the most efficient program combines these two, giving an introductory course early in the freshman year, while later, preferably in the senior year, a more substantial and advanced course is offered. The first surely should be required of all students; in order to maintain a sympathetic interest among students it might be preferable to have the latter course elective. In determining this, however, consideration must be made of the general policy of the institution, since requiring the advanced course would not seem coercive to seniors accustomed to little freedom of selection.

There appears to be general agreement among those who have had experience in giving courses in mental hygiene in colleges, that the first course especially should center about the common problems of the students. They should be interested first in difficulties near at hand and through these experiences should come to have a grasp of the principles of the science. It has been found by many teachers an advantage to have the student write out his life history. This not only helps the student to get greater insight and an ability to treat more objectively his own personal difficulties, but it also brings to the notice of the instructor individuals who seem most to need special counsel. The instructor of experience is quick to detect those who show morbid trends.

It is most important that the elementary course in mental hygiene be protected from the stigma of dealing essentially with mental diseases. It is not difficult for the instructor to appeal to a morbid interest in a certain type of student to the disgust of the more healthy minded members of his class. I have seen this perversion brought about by an instructor who thought himself in accord with mental hygiene. It is only fair to say that he was not a psychiatrist. Indeed, he had come to have a psychopathic reputation himself among psychiatrists of the city, because they had in several instances treated patients who had been hurt by the teaching received in his classes. The well-qualified instructor will steer clearly away from any emphasis of the morbid, especially in the first course in mental hygiene. In the more advanced work the student can be expected to have the background which will make it safe to use clinic cases, if such can be had, to illustrate various types of mental abnormality.

In no instruction does more depend upon the character and good sense of the teacher. Mental hygiene courses are worse than useless if they are impractical or presented in such a form as to make it next to impossible for the uninitiated student to understand what is being talked about. The instructor must have the gift of transferring highly technical material to a simple vocabulary. Nothing will spoil the mental hygiene program sooner than instruction teeming with technical jargon.

The institution that is not prepared to organize a mental hygiene program with a full-time psychiatric specialist is not justified in not offering any mental hygiene instruction. Some institutions that are not in a position to employ a full-time worker—and indeed if all colleges were ready for such psychiatric work their demands at present could not be met because of lack of competent instructors—have with good results brought to the student body outside lecturers especially gifted in presenting in a popular way the principles of mental hygiene. In other institutions someone connected with the psychological department or with biology has built up an efficient course that has been essentially instruction in mental hygiene. Rarely the same work has been done by someone connected with the department of sociology. Sometimes there has been a combination of outside lecturers and an allied course taught by some member of the faculty whose specialty was intimately related to the field of mental hygiene.

Personal conferences. The most important part of mental hygiene work in the colleges centers about the personal conferences with students. Young people are quick to realize that their difficulties need to be treated concretely, and they are surprisingly eager to get assistance. Whether there is a definite mental hygiene program or not, in all colleges the students seek counsel and naturally gravitate toward some member of the faculty from whom they get sympathy and understanding. It is extremely important that this counseling be done by those who have the experience and background that justifies the giving of advice.

The present policy of many institutions of higher learning, to distribute students so that each member of the faculty becomes an adviser for several young people, is utterly formal and fruitless and even at times mischievous. College instructors are not trained counselors and it is not criticism to say of many of them that they are not well prepared to counsel young people except with regard to the most trivial matters. No one can give good counsel who is not well acquainted with modern science in its application to problems of human nature. He needs familiarity with the usable materials of psychology, sociology, and psychiatry. He especially needs the background which will make it possible to detect problems outside his province and to know to whom they rightly belong. It is true that the majority of problems presented by young people to those from whom they choose to take counsel belong within the field of what we would call normal social life, and it is a pity from the point of view of the welfare of his science that the sociologist so rarely takes an interest in the concrete maladjustments that would be brought to him in quantity were he prepared to deal with them. Many psychologists also are neglectful of their opportunity, but in every sizable department of psychology there is usually someone whom the students seek for insight and advice.

However competent the psychiatrist may be, and however responsive the students to his offer of counsel, it must be recognized that students always seek other faculty members as well as the psychiatrist. If this relieves the latter of minor problems, it proves an advantage that is exceedingly necessary to anyone who gives serious counsel, but the faculty advisers must be ready to steer immediately to the specialist in mental hygiene students who seem to need expert assistance. When intimate contact is maintained between these faculty members to whom students go for first aid and the department of mental hygiene, the latter deals not only with the cases that come directly to it for help, but also with those that are sent to the specialist for counsel adequate to their needs. Were it possible to force all students to go to the mental hygiene specialist for advice, the burden presented by such a conference program would be excessive, for the social problems that arise in the college environment are many, ranging from the most trivial to the most serious, but it is imperative that any faculty member to whom students have easy access shall be thoroughly in sympathy with the mental hygiene movement and eager to turn over to the specialist any problem that appears to be serious in character.

Conference topics. During the winter of 1926-1927, the members of the mental hygiene staff at Yale met a small group of freshmen every night in the week. These conferences were held before the open fire and were informal, bringing about discussion by the students. The general purpose of the Department of Mental Hygiene was briefly outlined to the group and then questions were encouraged. The following are some of the questions that were asked, revealing the interest of the students and the practical counsel they sought. These questions issued from the campus life, emphasizing both personal and group problems.

What causes lack of confidence?
Why does a boy change his girl about once a month?
What is the soul?
What causes a nervous breakdown?
How do you cure an inferiority complex?
What are vocational-guidance tests?
Why does a man go to sleep while studying?

How do emotions motivate conduct?

What would you do for a man who is failing in studies due to being in love?

Would you tell him to get rid of the girl?

Can you tell by our questions and general reactions at this conference what our problems are and what our attitude is to your talk?

What is a complex?

Are mental disorders inherited?

In choosing a vocation or profession should one be guided by his natural inclinations?

Is present civilization increasing nervous disorders?

Do you ever cure any of these problems?

Don't you find students very reluctant to consult you about their problems by talking them over?

Does fear of disease cause the disease?

Will you cite some specific examples of life failures that might have been prevented by proper mental hygiene in college?

Is there any sexual basis for friendships between people of the same sex?

Does a restrained sex life offer greater chance of success and achievement?

What has this got to do with psychoanalysis?

Will there be any talks on sex? [3]

Mental hygiene and the faculty. To make mental hygiene successful in college and university there is need of the faculty's coöperation, and this means that the administrative and teaching staffs have sympathy with the purposes of mental hygiene. They must also have some understanding of its methods and a confidence that will make them quick to take advantage of its resources just as soon as they come in contact with a case that needs

[3] Harry N. Kerns, "Experiences of a Mental Hygienist in a University," *Mental Hygiene,* July, 1927, pp. 489-95.

the expert. To bring about this working arrangement some educational effort must be made to enlighten the faculty as to the value of mental hygiene. It is unreasonable to assume that the teaching force made up of specialists in fields far away from the science of human affairs will all have understanding of or interest in the mental hygiene movement. Most of them have spent nearly all their life in scholarship which has taken them away from familiar problems of everyday life and given them to some extent a detached attitude toward personal problems. Indeed some of them are definitely psychopathic themselves and their entire career including their profession has been influenced by morbid trends which from time to time appear even in their instruction.

Speaking from experience, I know that some of the difficulties that appear in the student body are actually brought about by morbid suggestions of psychopathic teachers or result from the unbalanced behavior of such instructors who have authority without discretion. Probably every college administrator has persistent problems arising as a consequence of the unadjusted life of some professor whose brilliancy has carried him on to a life appointment but who has never been well adapted to the teaching of young people on account of his emotional handicaps. It is seldom that such a personality can be changed, since any suggestion that would lead to better adjustment is usually resented as unwarranted criticism. Fortunately the great majority of any faculty are healthy-minded men and women, who, although busy with their own affairs, are willing to take a reasonable interest in any effort to conserve the welfare of their students. It is from these instructors that the mental hygiene specialist must expect his greatest assistance in discovering the problems of students and also in handling them with success.

One of the best ways of interesting the faculty is to invite men of national reputation gifted in the interpretation of the principles of mental hygiene to speak at a faculty meeting. In the past I have been so fortunate as to make it possible for the faculties of which I was a member to hear such national leaders in mental hygiene as Frankwood Williams, William A. White, Abraham Myerson, George K. Pratt, and others. The response in each instance was immediate and direct. Again and again members of the faculty told me in confidence that they had dealt differently with a student problem in their class on account of what they had heard at the lecture. Requests were also made for reading material, the more progressive instructors realizing that familiarity with mental hygiene would prove an aid to them in dealing with their classes in the ordinary routine of instruction.

These requests often came from scientists in other fields who wanted to gain familiarity with mental hygiene for its advantage in their own work. In my consultation service I have had many requests from my colleagues who felt the need of assistance in dealing either with their own personal problems or that of members of their family, and I have in certain instances been able to direct these individuals, when their problems were clearly outside the field of ordinary social adjustment, to the mental hygiene specialist who seemed best fitted to help them.

As mental hygiene makes greater progress in letting its resources be known there is every reason to suppose that persons who are well trained will seek the specialist in mental and social problems just as now they have become accustomed to go to the doctor as soon as they realize the need of information regarding problems of health. Dr. Frankwood Williams tells of a faculty member of national reputation who was convinced of his mental abnormality, and was persuaded to go quietly to a sanitarium for treatment. As a result he came back to his institution to go on with his work which otherwise would have been spoiled by a nervous breakdown, clearly inevitable unless he obtained outside assistance. Since the faculty exercises authority, it is extremely important that it be made as wholesome-minded as possible, for even one badly adjusted faculty member can stir up an enormous amount of trouble in any college.

The problems of the college student. What are the problems that the college students bring to the department of mental hygiene? This question can be answered from experience. Dr. Riggs and Dr. Terhune report that from their record the following have been the most common problems among the Vassar women.

. . . discouragement, depression, living on a poor schedule or none at all, below par physically, bored, dissatisfied, pain, love affair, infringements of rules or good taste, fear, too dependent, homesickness, low intelligence, acute grief, low cultural level, narrow interests, poor work, cheating, lack of purpose, suicidal or talked-of suicide, sex difficulties, difficult home life, fear of mental disorder, carrying too heavy an academic schedule, working long hours, religious difficulties, financial strain, sleep-walking, nightmares, and stammering.[4]

Dr. Thompson gives us a general classification that brings out the type of problem experienced by the Yale student.

[4] "The Mental Health of College Women," *Mental Hygiene,* July, 1928.

Per cent

Frank mental disorder which includes mostly
   depression and neurotic reactions......... 45
Scholastic difficulties.................... 25
Sex problems............................ 15
Personality problems.................... 15 [5]

Some interesting statistics come to us as a result of the
work of Dr. S. J. Smith at the University of California.
From 1924 to 1926 three hundred male students sought
assistance. They came from the following sources:

General dispensary...................... 198
Infirmary wards......................... 21
President's office........................ 3
Dean of men............................ 14
Other deans............................. 5
Heads of departments.................... 5
Berkeley police......................... 3
Voluntarily 51
                        ——————
                        300 [6]

These three hundred men represented the following
classes:

Freshmen 81
Sophomores 82
Juniors 68
Seniors 49
Postgraduates .... 20 [7]

[5] Dr. L. J. Thompson, "Mental Hygiene in a University," *American Journal of Psychiatry,* May, 1929, p. 1051.

[6] "Psychiatry and University Men," *Mental Hygiene,* January, 1928, p. 40.

[7] *Ibid.,* p. 41.

Their problems roughly classified were as follows:

	Number of Cases	Average Age
Maladjustment	84	22
Sex	58	21
Hysteria	15	23
Neurasthenia	21	24
Psychasthenia	12	22
Anxiety neurosis	5	23
Traumatic psychoneurosis	11	21
Intellectual inferiority	11	21
Psychopathic personality	10	22
Disorder of ductless gland	15	19
Neurological disorder	24	20
Psychosis	24	23
Unclassified	10	22
Total	300	21.7 [8]

In this work of Dr. Smith at the University of California, twenty-four neurological cases were given the following diagnoses:

Diagnosis	Cases
Epilepsy	10
Brain tumor	1*
Multiple sclerosis	2
Progressive muscular atrophy	1
Friedreich's ataxia	1
Peripheral neuritis	2
Migraine	4
Encephalitis	3

* Diagnosis questionable.[9]

[8] "Psychiatry and University Men," *Mental Hygiene,* January, 1928, p. 41.

[9] *Ibid.,* p. 45.

The following table permits us to see the physical condition of these men:

CONCOMITANT PHYSICAL DEFECTS IN 300 MALE STUDENTS EXAMINED ON THE PSYCHIATRIC SERVICE, UNIVERSITY OF CALIFORNIA

Problem	Cases	Total	Disorder of heart	Disorder of lungs	Anemia	Gastro-intestinal disorder	Defective teeth	Defective tonsils	Other foci of infection	Faulty posture
Maladjustment	84	64	4	1	24	6	18	5	2	4
Sex	58	35	1	0	11	2	14	3	3	1
Hysteria	15	19	3	0	7	2	1	2	1	3
Neurasthenia	21	34	2	2	13	3	4	1	5	4
Psychasthenia	12	12	0	0	1	2	7	0	0	2
Anxiety neurosis	5	10	1	1	3	1	0	2	1	1
Traumatic psychoneurosis	11	7	0	0	2	1	3	1	0	0
Intellectual inferiority.	11	18	3	1	8	2	1	2	1	0
Psychopathic personality	10	8	0	0	2	0	2	2	1	1
Disorder of ductless glands	15	19	5	0	4	1	5	2	1	1
Neurological disorder..	24	14	2	0	2	1	6	3	0	0
Psychosis	24	21	5	1	8	2	4	1	0	0
Unclassified	10	13	1	0	6	1	3	2	0	0
Total	300	274	27	6	91	24	68	26	15	17 [10]

Problems of sex. The average college student is in the period when sex most often creates mental disturbance. As already suggested, this is due in part to the postponement of marriage and in part to the segregation characteristic of the institution that is exclusively for men or for women. The environment, however, does not account for the appearance of sex difficulties, since in many cases, the individual was destined to have trouble in his late adolescence. In these instances the trouble harks back to the family training. Moralizing proves to be an

[10] *Ibid.,* p. 46.

ineffective way of helping the average college student who faces concrete sex difficulties. The usual result of forcing a moral issue without giving insight is concealment and mental conflict and despair on the part of the student who needs help. In no experience is it so important that simple, definite, and constructive information be furnished the student in a way that will instill confidence which will help him to use all his energy in straightening out his difficulty.

As would be expected, masturbation, at least in the male college, is one of the common problems of sex. Kerns reports that at West Point autoeroticism is the one sex problem that stands out above all the others. This is probably in part, as he suggests, the result of the limited social contacts possible at the military academy.[11] Smith also finds at the University of California that masturbation is a common sex problem. He reports that the improvement of the student concerned with this difficulty is usually reassuring, but, on the other hand, the distinctly homosexual problems are much more difficult to bring to a successful issue.[12] Unquestionably the students now at college are better prepared to cope with sex than their predecessors, due to franker attitudes, clearer understanding, and for many a better preparation in their early life than was generally true a generation ago. Nevertheless, it is one thing to understand sex, and another to cope with it. It is the artificiality of the student's life, his removal from his family, and his postponement of marriage that explain in large measure the various types of sex strain that are felt by the students who are free from psychopathic trends.

[11] Harry N. Kerns, "Management of Acute Mental-Hygiene Problems Found Among College Men," *Mental Hygiene,* April, 1925.
[12] *Op. cit.,* p. 44.

Problems of self-esteem. The atmosphere of the college is one that challenges self-esteem. From every quarter the student has hurled at him preachment, warning, and inspiration designed to stir up his ambitions and make him feel the need of exerting himself to the uttermost. Much of this is standardized to the requirement of the loafer—the irresponsible and insensitive type of student. Its effect upon the more imaginative and sensitive is often to exaggerate wholesome ambition, leading to over-confidence in one's equipment or a discounting of one's actual resources. Parents urge the student to maintain the same standard in the college that he did in the high school, while from the administrative office suggestions often come to the faculty members that they conform in their grades to a standardized curve that assumes a certain proportion of low marks and even possibly of failures. Thus the student is urged to maintain good scholarship and the faculty is expected to restrict high marks to a small proportion of all the marks given to students in the course. Sometimes the institution even goes so far as to demand that the instructor report his grades according to a pre-determined distribution of credit. Thus instead of emphasizing efficiency in instruction, the institution mechanizes the entire procedure and the student is asked to struggle for what only a limited proportion of the students can actually attain. The orator who visits the campus is forever inciting students to distinction by making it appear that it is a moral fault not to obtain high places of authority and reputation. The average student if he is at all sensitive, especially if he has had marked success in the smaller environment of the high school, has everything set to develop inferiority feeling leading to depression and even at times to thoughts of suicide.

Suicide problems. The suicide of a college student is always first page news. There is hardly any social occurrence that the general public is more likely to misinterpret. Nearly always there is an underground feeling among those who know of the suicide that the institution was in some way at fault; that it was putting too much strain upon the young life. This belief is encouraged often by the letters that the suicide leaves behind in which he puts upon something other than his own emotion the responsibility for his contemplated act. The scientist knows that most suicides are not the result of an objective situation, but a product of the distorted personality. The desire to end everything by self-imposed death is usually a fleeting, although while it lasts an almost irresistible, obsession. Thus it follows that if the person contemplating suicide comes under the oversight of an experienced psychiatrist he may be led out of the gloom into which he will never again retreat. This, of course, is not true of those who are chronically depressed as the victims of some serious mental disease. Although many of the threats of suicide have no significance, since they represent mere talk, it is never safe to assume that this will be the case, for sometimes the student who has again and again announced his intention of committing suicide, without anything happening, finally under sudden impulse ends his life.

The pity of many college suicides is the ease with which the student could have been brought out of his depression, if only at the right time he had come in contact with some discerning person. Once the black curtain that seems entirely to surround him is thrown back he becomes free. A college suicide has not only pathos, but usually a great quantity of morbid suggestion. Frequently the very atmosphere of the college life seems suddenly to change and a thick shadow spreads itself over all the activities of the institution. In addition to the suffering and morbid reactions that accompany the suicide, appears the distressing notoriety which the institution receives from the undiscriminating. It follows that, although the suicide is not a major problem for mental hygiene in college, every time an incipient suicide is detected and wisely handled much has been done for college welfare.

Mental hygiene and vocational guidance. The more seriously colleges undertake to give the necessary guidance that the students have a right to expect in the shaping of their future careers, the more stress it is found necessary to put upon the emotional life of the students seeking counsel. Thus mental hygiene aids in the intelligent choosing of one's life profession. When the institution supports a bureau for vocational counseling it is important that it function in close fellowship with the department of mental hygiene.

College discipline. A large proportion of the discipline problems that are carried to administrative committees or handled by deans issue from mental or social maladjustment. The college radical and the individual who is always heckling against authority are frequently the product of inferiority feeling produced by an autocratic parent who made the child hostile to every thought of regulation. Chronic disturbers of the college peace as these individuals are, they often have much promise if only they can become free from emotional conflict and able to make constructive use of their opportunities. Even stealing, lying, and cheating, when dealt with by the specialist in mental hygiene, have been found not to be so much an expression of immorality as the coming forth through a subterranean channel of disorganized impulses, the product of an emotional conflict. It is doubtful whether any serious case of discipline should ever be treated without the final decision being made in the light of mental hygiene. Although the college psychiatrist cannot wisely be made the institutional judge, rendering verdicts when offenders come up for discipline, there are many reasons why his assistance should be sought whenever any serious case for discipline arises on the campus.

The limits of mental hygiene. Indispensable as mental hygiene is in the modern progressive institution of higher learning, it is disastrous when the value of its work is exaggerated. The mental hygiene department cannot afford to crusade or promise too much. Immodesty on the part of those who direct such activities in the college shows a lack of judgment that is a bad prophecy for a long-time successful program. No mental hygiene department, however efficient, can prevent all occurrences of maladjustment. Sometimes those in charge of mental hygiene work in the colleges feel the need of being saved from the exaggerations of enthusiasts. Sentiment is always ready to gather about any new thing, and the American easily turns to fads. Mental hygiene represents a serious effort of preventive science. It necessarily works with caution and puts forth modest claims for itself. The greatest exaggeration of its service comes not from those in charge of the work but from the supporters who find in mental hygiene something resembling a new religion.

Mental hygiene progress in the college. Mental hygiene offers the college a much needed resource, and as time reveals more clearly the value of its contribution it will surely come to be a necessary part of every well-equipped institution for higher learning. It is the only constructive effort made to deal with the emotional life of the youth who are seeking superior training for the responsibilities of life. It is too early to lay down in any rigid fashion the line of progress that mental hygiene will follow in its attempt to serve young life. The American is more inclined than ever to look to education as the efficient means of advancing social life. As soon as science cut underneath the intellectual level, it began to deal with the emotional content of personality. It was inevitable that a movement should develop to apply such information as we have for increasing the happiness of both the individual and the group. Once such an undertaking started it enlisted the interest of those responsible for college management, who, of all people, have the best reason for realizing the seriousness of emotional maladjustment. Mental hygiene is so needed in the college that it has only to demonstrate its usefulness to be widely welcomed as a modern educational asset.

ILLUSTRATIVE CASE

W. L., who had previously maintained average scholarship, began in his junior year to draw such low grades that it was clear to all interested that he was gradually failing and would probably be dismissed from college. In addition he was reported several times to the dean for discipline, particularly by the instructor with whom he was doing his poorest work. The dean talked the situation over with W. L. and advised his leaving college. Also two faculty members of W. L.'s fraternity thought he had better give up college. The members of his fraternity, however, protested against this, and while W. L. was arranging to leave the campus, the officers of his fraternity went to a member of the faculty who was known to be especially interested in problems of mental hygiene and who had assisted many students in becoming well adjusted to college life. From this visit a clew was obtained as to the difficulty that had changed W. L. and made his college career unsuccessful. During his senior year at high school he had acquired the habit of drinking and at the beginning of the junior year of college had sworn off and kept to his vow. He found abstinence more difficult than he had expected and had become restless and discontented. His mood had betrayed him in one of his classes into an offense, which, although trivial in character, was strongly resented by the instructor. This member of the faculty was highly vindictive and he began to irritate the boy and from time to time reported him to the dean for discipline, suggesting that he was the kind of student who ought not to be in college.

It was agreed by the officers of the fraternity and the faculty adviser, J. K., that it would be most disastrous for W. L. to leave college with a sense of failure and it was decided to appeal to his sense of pluck and change his determination to withdraw. Meanwhile, J. K., through the dean, got the boy changed from the section where he was having trouble with the instructor and getting his lowest marks to another section where the instructor was a more sympathetic and penetrating man. The fraternity promised to coöperate by absolutely keeping out of their building alcoholic liquor and as far as possible preventing any temptation from reaching W. L. J. K. also succeeded in getting the boy elected to a club made up of students interested in the line of study that had always appealed most to W. L. Gradually the boy's scholarship improved until in his senior year he was the highest-standing student in the department. At graduation he was offered a fellowship which permitted him to remain at the institution and go on with his favorite study. He eventually took his doctor's degree and now has a reputation as one of the most promising specialists in one of the eastern universities.

SUGGESTIONS FOR CLASSROOM DISCUSSION

1. What conditions in college are favorable to mental hygiene? Unfavorable?

2. Do purely intellectual courses contribute to the training of the emotional life of the students?

3. Are students of Phi Beta Kappa rank more or less likely to have personal maladjustments?

4. Is it an advantage for freshmen to start college life before the registration of the older students?

5. Should colleges give sex instruction?

6. What qualities in the teacher lead students to bring to him their personal problems?

7. Do college women have more or greater personal problems than men?

8. Should courses in mental hygiene be elective or required in college?

SUGGESTIONS FOR WRITTEN REPORTS

1. Scholarship as a sublimation of personality conflicts.
2. Inferiority feeling as expressed in college experiences.
3. Topics for college lectures in mental hygiene.
4. Mental hygiene at Vassar.
5. Mental hygiene at Yale.
6. Mental hygiene at Dartmouth.
7. College experiments in mental hygiene consultation.

SELECTED BIBLIOGRAPHY

BLANTON, SMILEY. "A Mental-Hygiene Program for Colleges." *Mental Hygiene*, July, 1925, pp. 478-88.

CHAMBERS, OTHNIEL R. "Character Trait Tests and the Prognosis of College Achievement." *The Journal of Abnormal and Social Psychology*, October, 1925, pp. 303-11.

"College Administration and Mental Hygiene." Editorial, *The Journal of Abnormal and Social Psychology*, October, 1925, p. 227.

CORSON, H. T. "Factors in the Development of Psychoses in College Men," *Mental Hygiene*, July, 1927.

GARDNER, GEORGE E. "The Psychology Professor and Student Mental Hygiene." *Mental Hygiene*, October, 1928, pp. 789-93.

—— and PIERCE, HELEN D. "The Inferiority Feelings of College Students." *The Journal of Abnormal and Social Psychology*, April-June, 1929, pp. 8-13.

HARRINGTON, MILTON A. "The Development of a Mental Hygiene Program in a College or University." *The Jour-*

nal of Abnormal and Social Psychology, October-December, 1926, pp. 245-49.

HARRINGTON, MILTON A. "The Problem of Mental Hygiene Courses for the College Student." *Mental Hygiene,* July, 1927.

HOUSE, S. DAVIES. "Educational Psychiatry." *The Journal of Abnormal and Social Psychology,* April 6, 1928, pp. 94-100.

KERNS, HARRY N. "Management of Acute Mental-Hygiene Problems Found Among College Men." *Mental Hygiene,* April, 1925, pp. 273-81.

—— "Experiences of a Mental Hygienist in a University." *Mental Hygiene,* July, 1927.

MacCRACKEN, HENRY N. "Mental Hygiene in the College Curriculum." *Mental Hygiene,* July, 1925, pp. 469-77.

McNUTT, LILA. "Psychiatric Social Work in the LaSalle-Peru-Oglesby Junior College." *Mental Hygiene,* April, 1929, pp. 271-77.

MENNINGER, K. A. "Adaptation Difficulties in College Students." *Mental Hygiene,* July, 1927.

—— "College Blues." *Survey Graphic,* September 1, 1929, Vol. LXII, p. 549.

—— "Psychoanalytic Observations on the Mental Hygiene Problems of College Students." *Journal of Nervous and Mental Diseases,* 1929, Vol. 69, pp. 642-50.

"Mental Hygiene and the College Student." Anonymous. *Mental Hygiene,* October, 1921, pp. 736-40.

MEREDITH, FLORENCE. "The Administration of Mental Hygiene in Colleges." *Mental Hygiene,* April, 1927, pp. 241-52.

MORRISON, ANGUS W. "Mental Hygiene and Our Universities." *Mental Hygiene,* April, 1923, pp. 258-70.

—— "A Further Discussion of College Mental Hygiene." *Mental Hygiene,* January, 1928, pp. 48-54.

MUENZINGER, KARL F. and FLORENCE W. "The Psychology of Readjustment with Special Reference to Mental Hygiene Work in College." *Mental Hygiene,* April, 1929, pp. 250-62.

PECK, MARTIN W. "Mental Examinations of College Men." *Mental Hygiene,* April, 1925, pp. 282-99.

PECK, MARTIN W. and WELLS, F. L. "On the Psycho-Sexuality of College Graduate Men." *Mental Hygiene,* October, 1923, pp. 697-714.

—— and WELLS, F. L. "Further Studies in the Psycho-Sexuality of College Graduate Men." *Mental Hygiene,* July, 1925, pp. 502-20.

PRESSEY, L. C. *Some College Students and Their Problems.* Columbus, Ohio, 1929.

RICHMOND, WINIFRED. "Mental Hygiene in the Colleges." *Journal of the American Medical Association,* December 21, 1929, Vol. 93, pp. 1936-39.

RIGGS, A. F., and TERHUNE, W. B. "The Mental Health of College Women." *Mental Hygiene,* 1928, Vol. XII, pp. 559-68.

RUGGLES, ARTHUR H. "Mental Hygiene and the College Student." *Mental Hygiene of Normal Childhood,* a series of lectures published by The Buffalo Mental Hygiene Council.

—— "College Mental Hygiene Problems." *Mental Hygiene,* April, 1925, pp. 261-72.

SMITH, SYDNEY KINNEAR. "Psychiatry and University Men." *Mental Hygiene,* January, 1928, pp. 38-47.

THOMPSON, LLOYD J. "Mental Hygiene in a University." *The American Journal of Psychiatry,* May, 1929, pp. 1045-52.

THOMPSON, C. MILDRED. "The Value of Mental Hygiene in the College." *Mental Hygiene,* April, 1927, pp. 225-40.

TRUITT, RALPH P. "The Child and the Community." *Mental Hygiene of Normal Childhood,* a series of lectures published by The Buffalo Mental Hygiene Council.

WELLS, F. L. "Report on a Questionnaire Study of Personality Traits with a College Graduate Group." *Mental Hygiene,* January, 1925, pp. 113-27.

WILLIAMS, FRANKWOOD E. "Mental Hygiene and the College Student," reprinted from *Mental Hygiene,* April, 1921, pp. 283-301 and April, 1925, pp. 225-60.

YOUNG, KIMBALL. "Mental Hygiene and Personality Guidance in Colleges." *Mental Hygiene,* July, 1925, pp. 489-501.

CHAPTER X

MENTAL HYGIENE IN BUSINESS AND INDUSTRY

The demand for mental hygiene in business and industry. Modern business has profited immensely from applied science. This has been particularly true of industry devoted to production and transportation. Many modern enterprises have their foundations in experiment. The research laboratory contributes enormously and increasingly to every sort of modern business and industry. Those who manage such undertakings have long since come to recognize the value of objective information regarding their operations.

Even in industry where automatic machine processes have been carried to the greatest efficiency and where organization is highly specialized and systematized there has been felt the need of scientific information regarding the human factors comparable to the contributions science has made to the mechanical part of the undertaking. This quest for applied science in its human aspect has come from two directions. On the one side there has been a desire to make more use of objective facts in dealing with problems of management, especially in the selection of higher officials. It has been recognized that adjustment difficulties arising in men who control the workers, from the shop foreman to the general manager, are largely problems of personality such as are always revealed when contact between people is constantly taking place. On the other hand, there has been equal need of

252

dealing with the worker himself on a more understanding basis. It has been recognized that the inherent weakness of modern business is the lack of individuality allowed the worker, whose status in so complex and impersonal an organization submerges personality into a mere "hand." Such an impersonal relationship makes it difficult to develop the interest and loyalty which even the largest organization finds of great value in its successful operation.

Progressive businesses have grown more and more eager to use any practical contributions made possible by advancement in the sciences of psychology and sociology. One of the first applications of science has been regarding the employment of workers. This has come primarily from psychology and has mostly consisted in the finding of methods by which the specific industry could test its candidates for employment so as to discover the fitness of those who applied for work and the special kind of labor they could best perform.

At the same time that industry was trying to work out some scheme by which it could more efficiently choose its workers, education, in its various forms, also became interested in vocational guidance as a means of helping the individual get well started in life. It is evident now, after considerable experience, that at the beginning too much confidence was placed in laboratory methods as a means of giving guidance in vocation, and for the purpose of weeding out undesirable candidates for employment. Experience has revealed that any testing has its inherent limitations, since no man can be reduced to a mathematical formula. This does not by any means discount the value of testing, but rather shows the need of a more complete study of the personality than that made possible by any set of tests. Personality in its entirety is involved in any activity that the person carries out, whether he deals with people as a manager or with automatic machines as a wage earner.

In industry as elsewhere the progress of mental hygiene also has demonstrated that the failures of persons cannot be entirely charged to their lack of intellectual capacity. From such discoveries there has arisen a wider outlook upon the mental side of industrial operation, and it is this that is meant when we speak of mental hygiene in industry. It would be unfair to think that this had originated entirely from the demand for greater efficiency in dealing with the workers in the effort to make them more productive and therefore more profitable to the company. The persons responsible for modern industry have also shown a sincere desire to lessen the maladjustments that are inherent in so impersonal and highly organized a form of activity as modern business has become. Many of these men and women have been thoroughly convinced of the value of mental hygiene when it has been carried on in other departments of life, and they have desired to build up a humane and conserving policy which would assist the worker as an individual as well as a unit in the enterprise.

This movement in mental hygiene has gone along with the health service that has become characteristic of many of our largest and most progressive kinds of industry. The doctor in charge of physical health work has come to realize the need of assistance from the specialist in mental and social problems. Thus far in this practical application of science, the psychologists and psychiatrists have both contributed immeasurably more than the sociologists; in part, perhaps, because they have been more thoroughly awakened to the need of practical contribution. In practice it has not been possible in mental hygiene artificially to separate the physical, the psychic, and the social when the personality has presented problems involving in unison these three aspects between which science makes a distinction.

The mental hygiene program. Although mental hygiene as applied to industry is still in the experimental stage, there have developed certain trends that permit us to emphasize three distinct activities. The best way to give this emphasis is perhaps to distinguish the work of the psychologist, the psychiatrist, and the psychiatric social worker. The psychologist has developed his part farther than the others, because he has been longer connected with industry. He has especially taken over the problems of the examination and testing of the applicant for employment and for promotion. He has also worked out practical means for discovering the kind of work best fitted for the candidate accepted. Where there has been dissatisfaction or failure, he likewise has taken over the problem of finding some other type of work that might be more suitable. Thus the psychologist has been a vocational expert—a student of the job and of the worker.

The psychiatrist has made his chief contribution with reference to difficulties that have arisen in the workers themselves. He has been called upon to deal with grievances, to handle peculiar personality types and to help formulate the policy of the business so as to create general happiness and a sense of loyalty. The psychiatrist has also been called upon to do his part in handling broader problems of health, especially in dealing with people who have a combination of physical and mental ailments.

The psychiatric social worker, in so far as she has appeared in industry and business, has taken over those aspects of the problem that are included in the life of the worker outside the factory or store. She has gathered

the material that the psychiatrist and psychologist and
medical doctor have desired in dealing with problems of
personality. She has attempted especially to become
acquainted with the family life and recreational habits of
those whom she has been asked to help or to investigate.
She has gone into the home and endeavored to bring about
more favorable conditions when the family experience
was clearly the cause of difficulty in the industrial career
of the worker. For the unsuccessful or discontented
worker she has done the same sort of service that she has
carried on when she has been a member of the child
guidance clinic or the juvenile delinquency clinic. She
has coöperated with the management in carrying out the
suggestions arrived at by the psychiatrist or by the
various interested persons in conference. Even in cases
where individuals have been discharged, she has frequently been permitted to attempt the straightening out
of difficulties that led to the unemployment.

The development of the program. The mental hygiene program has developed from experience. It has
come largely from the efforts of various organizations to
meet their special needs. Although mental hygiene has
grown up from these attempts to apply science concretely
to the specific needs of definite enterprises, it has not
been uninfluenced by the general interest shown by those
concerned with mental hygiene. The psychiatrist in his
general practice and in his responsibilities as a member
of the staff of a hospital for the mentally unsound has
seen the serious part industry plays in revealing or in
making personality difficulties. The business of getting
a living is second to no other influence, except that of the
family, as a source of maladjustment. Necessarily he
who has been interested in general mental health has been
forced to take account of the significance of its industrial

aspects. Psychology and psychiatry and to some lesser degree sociology have given thought to the possibility of better conditions for the worker in the effort to build up a mental hygiene program. This has led to the examination of modern industry from the psychiatric viewpoint and to insistence by the leaders in mental hygiene that industry as well as the family come to have a larger sense of its personality problems and a greater efficiency in handling them.

One of the first statements of a mental hygiene program in industry was made by Dr. Stanley Cobb, a member of the Harvard Medical School faculty.[1] In this discussion he stated that the following was a reasonable program for application of psychiatry to industry:

"1. Physical examination of all applicants for work.
"2. Mental examination by (a) a period of training and observation, or (b) through mental tests.
"3. Keeping in personal touch with employees' individual problems by means of (a) good foremen, (b) a system for watching individual efficiency, or (c) a sympathetic staff with a psychiatric point of view in the employment-management office, thus salvaging the men who might otherwise be fired.
"4. Training the industrial physician to a knowledge of how human nature is constituted, not in conventional terms, but in the light of a dynamic and living psychology."

This excellent program has not yet been generally achieved in industry. The following difficulties have hampered its coming. Many leaders in business and in industry have shown no serious interest in the mental hygiene movement. It is too new and experimental to

[1] "Applications of Psychiatry to Industrial Hygiene," *The Journal of Industrial Hygiene,* Vol. I, pp. 343-47.

have enlisted universal sympathy. Second, there is not
and for the present there cannot be a sufficient number
of competent and interested psychiatrists to make it possible for all industries to accept such a program as Dr.
Cobb suggests. Third, small stores and smaller manufacturing plants cannot finance professional psychiatric
service. They are not yet organized so as to get the advantages of this service by coöperating with other small
enterprises in carrying on psychiatric activities. There is
also, especially among workers and not infrequently
among lesser officials, a prejudice against mental hygiene,
in part because of its novelty and the difficulty they experience in making adaptation to something so new and
in part because their fundamental outlook upon industry
is inconsistent with the mental hygiene attitude. This
situation is not at all different from that found in the
court experiences of specialists dealing in a modern
way with juvenile delinquency.

Industry a relationship. To the mental hygienist industry is not merely a form of production or a method
of distribution, but a special type of human relationship.
The fact that the men are working for wages and are controlled by organizations must not conceal the social meaning of their activity as workers together in a common
enterprise. The significance of this working in concert
is brought out clearly in primitive society where the co-
operation of the savages in their struggle for maintenance
appears vividly in the more simple environment. Although the modern worker has a specialized activity assigned him, he does not work in isolation. Not only is he
associated with others but he has a special relationship
to the management of the industry, which he is wont to
personify even though his contact with higher officials
filters down through its subordinate representatives. Thus

the individual, as he earns his wages in industry, also carries on a distinct line of conduct which includes all the problems of personality adjustment that are found in any sort of behavior.

The chief concern of mental hygiene in industry is the laborer and behind him are conditions, physical, mental, and social, that have built in him a pattern of behavior and given him his unique personality. However automatic the operations given the worker may be, he is nevertheless a person in contact, making and expressing adjustments to life that are good, bad, or indifferent. Not only does the worker come to his task from an environment which has impressed itself deeply upon his character, he also, as he labors, constructs an underlying life-attitude which becomes a part of his general happiness or chronic dissatisfaction. In the long run, however it may be concealed for a time, industry is concerned with this deep-seated reaction to life, for, even in the narrow sense of profit, industry cannot be indifferent to discontent that is provocative of trouble. Between the industrial environment of the worker and his experience outside the factory or store there is a reciprocating influence. He brings to his home bitterness, trouble, and irritation and he carries back from his home the conflicts, suspicions, and discouragements that make his marriage life unsatisfying. In the same way happy conditions in either environment foster efficiency and content in the other. His industrial experience represents only a portion of his total life. Its influence spreads over the rest and, however he may attempt to separate the hours spent at work from those on the outside, emotionally the two experiences fuse and what happens in the one brings its results to the other.

The community itself has its stake in this industrial

relationship, since the worker is a unit in the group life of the town or city just as he is in the factory or the store. Because of this, even if mental hygiene were not interested in the welfare of the worker himself as an individual unit in the organization, it could not seriously conserve mental health without recognizing the significance of the industrial experience.

There are three special adjustment difficulties that appear in the industrial relationship which influence the emotional reaction of the individual worker. One is the attitude he takes toward the work itself. The fact that he can become expert in a particular operation does not by any means indicate that he enjoys the activity which he carries on with such skill. This problem of pleasurable reaction involves the lesser one of vocational choice. Most of our psychological interpretations of this have to do with professional experience. Even these higher levels of choice frequently involve serious disturbances due to emotional conflict. As Dr. White points out, a person's choice of life work is not, even when he attempts to do what he wants to do, as simple as it appears to be on the surface.[2] The personality sometimes is the battleground of conflicting desires so that any commitment to one type of employment carries the need of giving up satisfaction of a different sort. This condition with its emotional stress is not absent from the experience of wage earners who often covet intensely a different way of earning a living. In addition to the worker's attitude toward the kind of work he does, there is also emotional reaction to the conditions of his work and to the treatment which according to his own interpretation he receives from those who employ him.

[2] W. A. White, "Psychoanalysis and Vocational Guidance," *Psychoanalytic Review*, July, 1927, p. 243.

A second difficulty of adjustment is built upon the fear the worker frequently has of unemployment or discharge. The feeling of insecurity penetrates the personality and colors his outlook upon life. For a multitude of workers this dread of unemployment is the most uncomfortable element in their industrial situation, and therefore becomes a major problem for mental hygiene.

Industry also brings out personality defects, and the neurotic and mentally diseased reveal their symptoms in their behavior while at work just as they do in their other activities.

Choice of occupation. The college student who is given the advantages of higher education and knows from the start that he is headed for a profession often finds it difficult to make his choice of life work. If it is hard for him because of conflicting motives that lead him toward several different occupations, the matter is often otherwise with the wage worker. His need of getting early to work makes him the prey of irresistible forces that bring him to the occupation which he enters. Since the conditions which have determined his employment in life seem independent of his own wishes, we say his vocation is largely an accident.

The basic factor in his decision is the economic necessity of earning as quickly as possible. Sometimes the family is willing to sacrifice to give him the advantage of a superior preparation, but this means delaying satisfactions that he could have if only he could quickly get to work, and so he may refuse the training that would be decidedly for his advantage and make him less of a pawn in the industrial game. Often he starts work with no adequate idea of what he has to do, or of his opportunities for advancement, or of the hazards that normally belong to the occupation he has chosen. He happens upon a

chance to work through information he may get from the
paper or from some friend or relative, and frequently he
merely follows the line of least resistance and takes up the
kind of work his father or his brothers have been doing.

His choice is so automatic and free from any inner
conflict that it might seem at first thought that he escapes
the difficulties of those who debate as to what occupation
to enter. If, however, he starts more easily, conflict may
soon follow. His occupation may grow distasteful and
he may perpetually contrast what he has to do with what
he thinks he would like to do. The candidate for professional life is more likely to have his conflicts before he
starts his occupation, while the laborer in industry has
his afterwards. If he accepted his employment merely
as a means of getting money, all too often he finds that
it never becomes anything else. Being human with some
capacity for a sense of achievement and joy in work, the
predicament in which he finds himself, and from which
there seems never to be any hope of escape, acts as a constant irritant.

This irritation is felt most strongly by those who pre-
maturely went to work and sacrificed the opportunity to
develop some slight talent or skill which might have
given them greater security, more money, and larger
satisfaction in the doing of their life work. Although
there is of course enormous daydreaming on the part of
the wage workers who, without basis, believe that their
lack of opportunity forces them into positions of inferiority, it must not be forgotten that a proportion of these
discontented individuals did have a reasonable hope for
something better until they entered industry without adequate training. The more conscious they are of this and
the more fully persuaded that they have latent possibili-

ties that cannot be developed, the more restless and discontented they are apt to be.

Also, it must be remembered that many of the wage earners have drifted into their present occupations from other lines of work that were more difficult, in which they failed, and from which they were irresistibly drawn down to a lower level. Such an experience of being economically demoted, however justified, leaves its traces in the emotional attitude of the individual. He may have as a consequence of this experience a deep-seated inferiority feeling that is ever ready to burst out upon the slightest provocation. On the other hand, his general attitude may be more distinctly that of bitterness without the chronic sense of failure that the inferiority type have.

Selection of the worker. Industry has to draw its workers from the community in which it is established. This community, however, may be itself a reflection of the selecting process of the industry which has gradually assembled the type of individual most suited for the kind of work offered. In the community we necessarily find represented the various sorts of persons that make up the general population, and among them a considerable number of persons who are special problems of mental hygiene. We have the feeble-minded, the neurotically inclined, the mentally diseased, the chronically sick and those personally maladjusted to life. From this mass of persons industry selects its workers and, when modern and efficient, it tries to guide each worker to the job he can best do.

As a means of helping the individual find his life work, there have grown up efforts at vocational guidance which attempt to select for the candidate the life work most suitable for him and to give him assistance in finding the opportunity to start the kind of employment suggested. This work has been developed especially by psychology and at present in our large cities functions under various auspices: the college, the Y.M.C.A., civic organizations, and even at times churches stand behind a bureau organized for vocational guidance. On the other hand, the sizeable industries are taking over the same sort of problem from their own viewpoint and attempting to select from the various candidates that come to them for employment the individuals that can best enter their industry. Not only are such persons carefully selected from all who ask for employment, but when they are chosen, the effort is made to place them where they can best work, to assist them to start their new task well, and, when necessary, to remove them and place them in some other department of the industry. This vocational guidance involves the use of every resource known to science for judging people. It is not sufficient, for example, to make mental tests, since the intellect by itself does not constitute the entire problem. The principles of mental hygiene have to be drawn upon for guidance that will bring satisfaction to both the management and the worker. There has to be an understanding of personality defects and a recognition of emotional conflict and of the significance of family life as furnishing the emotional background of the worker. Especially in cases where the placement has proven unsatisfactory, mental hygiene is called upon to analyze the difficulty of the individual and give counsel as to how he can find within the industry a suitable place to work.

Mental hygiene and industrial policy. There are certain problems of policy that arise in the large corporation, to which mental hygiene is prepared to make a useful contribution. In an organization that is too large to

permit much personal contact between the higher officials
and the wage earner, general policies must take the place
of the individual decisions that used to be made by the
employer of labor when he had few workers and knew
them as persons. These policies cannot be adopted without due consideration of their influence upon the happiness and efficiency of the worker and they must all be
made with the realization that there are always some
neurotic individuals in a large assemblage of men and
women. To make regulations that affect the worker,
without giving attention to their possible influence upon
his mental health, is evidence of bad management. Some
of these important problems are policies with reference to
the retirement of the aged and incapacitated worker.
This affects not only those who receive an allowance but
also the contentment of all the workers, and as a result it
influences the labor turnover and the loyalty of the workers. The policy with reference to disability and accident
has a similar importance. Another problem intimately
related to mental health in industry has to do with vaca-
tions. Policies with respect to overtime work, absence
due to illness, and means of expressing grievances, real
or imaginary, have a mental health significance.[3]

Preventing failure. Modern industry in all its forms
is organized for profit, and we do not expect of the factory
or the store that it attempt to become a correcting institution. Nevertheless big business finds that it is profitable
as well as humane to undertake to discover the difficulties
that lead to the failure of workers. A rapid turnover is
expensive, but the only way to minimize the failures that
lead to discharge is careful selection of workers and alert-
ness in discovering their problems. Such a program is

[3] Augustus Scott, "Neuro-Psychiatric Work in Industry," *Mental
Hygiene*, July, 1923, p. 630.

not confined merely to the wage earner since the executive may also be a problem type who without the proper assistance is bound to fail. It is the task of mental hygiene in industry to discover early the difficulties of the worker and to study him as a maladjusted personality. Merely to find out that he is in trouble and to transfer him to some other department is an unscientific procedure. An understanding of the difficulties, which can come only through a careful diagnosis, is the first step in dealing with the unsuccessful worker.

These maladjustments that arise in industry range over the entire territory of applied psychology and psychiatry, and good practices in dealing with them involve all the principles of mental hygiene. Such problems require more than the experience of the employment manager, and the trend toward recognizing this gives promise of a larger contribution of mental hygiene to the practical problems of modern industry.

Industrial conflict and mental hygiene. Modern industry is prolific in its opportunities for antagonism and conflict. The mere fact that a wage earner accepts a position of subordination and is economically insecure is sufficient to bring about strain between employer and employee. Their relationship, however, is much more complicated than this and the opportunities for antipathy are many. In a good organization internal dissension and dissatisfaction will be reduced to the minimum. The best of management, however, cannot entirely eliminate personal grievances felt by individual employees, since dissatisfaction may arise from the most trivial of reasons or even on entirely imaginary grounds.

As has been previously said, any industry has to draw its workers from the adjacent territory, and, if it employs any considerable number, among them are bound to be some who are mentally peculiar and even unsound. For want of a better term to describe these workers who are to some degree mentally abnormal, the term, *industrial psychopaths*, has been used. They are individuals unstable in their outlook upon life, filled with suspicion, and ready to explode some complex upon the slightest provocation. Such individuals have been interpreted as persons expressing general protest against their inadequacy, and many clearly belong to this class. They are the trouble makers and, however frequently they may be weeded out, others of the same type enter from time to time and often create considerable disturbance before they are discovered. When these workers are protected from discharge by labor union regulations, they persist as disturbing factors constantly creating trouble for both the employer and the employee.

The chronically dissatisfied continuously provide problem cases for the mental hygienist, problems that often cannot be understood unless they are considered as deviations from normal mental life. The industrial psychopath may not be an employee, for occasionally among the higher officials in industry are found individuals who are constantly stirring up trouble by their brutal methods of handling the men. Frequently it is found that such individuals have changed in their disposition because of the onset of some mental malady which in its first stages is making it impossible for them to get on with their workers. Mental hygiene, therefore, has to be concerned both with the difficult worker and the unreasonable executive. In the history of American strikes there is abundant evidence of the contribution that has come from the industrial psychopath who has been a leader in discontent or who by his chronic grumbling has stirred up his fellow workers until the strike was the logical and inevitable result.

It would be an error to charge all industrial conflict to psychopathic individuals. Sometimes, as Dr. Fryer and Lorine Pruette have pointed out, the difficulty comes from a chronic protest against all authority, the product of some earlier experience, which the individual emotionally transfers to the adult occupation. Not infrequently this is a reaction against a domineering father who built up in his child hatred rather than affection. These individuals who cannot accept subordination or yield to authority are trouble-makers, because they fail in adjusting themselves to the practical demands of a large organization. Extreme in their individualism, they do not fit in, and although sometimes clever and intellectual they fail because they cannot work with others. The following case is a typical illustration:

"Age nineteen. Intelligence score 121, rating B. Clerical experience for five years, as timekeeper, pay-roll clerk, and brokerage clerk; always held positions paying twenty-five dollars or more. After a short period in the army, his parents secured his discharge because of youth. Conference with parents brought out the fact of their inability to influence or control son. Boy declared that he had no freedom at home, refused to tell parents anything, and insisted on doing whatever he wanted to do. Parents tried to make him contribute part of his salary to upkeep of home and he insisted that they would not leave him enough to get along on.

"Two counselors worked on this problem, trying to secure a meeting point between parents and son. Boy was placed several times, but showed himself entirely irresponsible about getting to work, asking for time off and so forth. In each place he was considered a good workman, but irresponsible. It seemed possible that the boy's attitude toward his father had been transferred to all authority. Although apparently desirous of a solution and showing at times a frank and pleasant manner, the boy also occasionally manifested resentment against the counselors whose advice he had sought and repeatedly told lies both to them and to his family." [4]

Not all conflict in industry comes from peculiar personalities, for the opportunity for conflict is inherent in the enterprise. Situations that lead to conflict are present in all human relationships, and industry as a special sort of activity does not escape the possibilities of tension always present where people are together. The clashing of personal desires, the antipathies that spontaneously arise in association, the obstacles to coöperative labor, all contribute opportunities for conflict. Nor is all of this necessarily bad either for the organization or for the individual. In so far as conflict exists in mild forms that may be termed rivalry or even competition, it may under wise guidance become a decided asset both to the worker and the management. Competitive struggle conserves energy, develops ambition and has been often used to stimulate achievement.

Such methods are especially common in businesses that develop salesmanship to the highest possible degree. It is easy, however, for the conflict to get out of hand and for groups to feel embittered against other groups in industry, and especially for the workers to set themselves against the management. In such cases a desire to dominate takes possession and the struggle becomes not a contest for superiority, but an attempt to drive the other group to abject surrender. Under these circumstances fear enters and makes the struggle more bitter. Neither party dares compromise because it feels that the slightest

[4] Lorine Pruette and Douglas Fryer, "Affective Factors in Vocational Maladjustment," *Mental Hygiene*, January, 1923, pp. 102-18.

evidence of any willingness to arbitrate will be interpreted as weakness, and that if it loses it can expect no mercy. This of course explains the seriousness of long-continued strikes which frequently never come to a settlement until the two warring parties are forced to give their problem over to disinterested outsiders who are free to find some sort of compromise. Behind these conflicts, whether between different sets of employees, or between management and laborers, we have, working as motives, the desire for satisfaction, the will-to-power, the fears, and the prejudices that are characteristic of human nature in all sorts of relationships. Industry merely furnishes an enormous stage for the exhibition of the mechanisms commonly expressed in the conduct of men and women, especially when they form crowds.

Mental hygiene and temper. Anyone of long experience in industry has seen many cases in which the expression of anger by either the executive or the worker has been a source of disturbance leading in time to the elimination of individuals who are constantly getting angry quickly. To the mental hygienist such a problem is not one of morality, but a case that calls for causal diagnosis. He has come to recognize the situations that encourage a breaking out in anger, realizing that often the individual has control of himself for a considerable period until at last the internal tension pours forth without warning and for the most part without deliberate intent. In such cases, the question which determines the proper policy of the industry toward the offending individual is, What are the causes behind the anger, and are they removable? Sometimes it is fatigue, ill-health, home conflicts, worry about finances, persistent endeavor by another worker to stir up irritation, or even misinterpretation of facts that is behind the explosive anger which cannot be tolerated. Not uncommonly there is a history of ill-temper in the conduct of the individual that carries back to early childhood. Then the problem is one of re-education if the industry is willing to make an effort to save the person from the consequences of his bad adjustment to life. If industry would attempt to handle such cases rather than merely discharge the offender, in the long run this course would be profitable to all, since discharging works out in the same manner that used to be true when towns got rid of their poor by paying their fare to a distant place. As each community was doing the same thing, the dependent individuals were constantly appearing and departing, and the cost was greater than if each community had taken its own burden. Especially when workmen are efficient or when executives are successful, it seems to mental hygienists a short-sighted policy merely to get rid of men who show ill temper, without making a genuine effort at scientific diagnosis and enlisting the individual in a reconstruction of his character.

Inferiority feeling in industry.   Dr. R. P. Truitt, in speaking on vocational guidance, once said: "One of the determining influences in the selection of a vocation is and should be the need of compensating for inferiority." [5] Unfortunately, for a host of workers, especially the unskilled, in industry there is no opportunity of carrying out this principle of mental hygiene. Their life work has often been forced upon them with no regard for their feeling toward it, and even if they have feelings of serious dissatisfaction, they are not in a position to change their occupation with any hope of advancing to something higher and more inviting.

[5] *Mental Hygiene*, January, 1926, p. 103.

The wage earner in industry who brings to it feelings of inferiority that have been made by early conditioning finds little to redeem his chronic discontent and much to aggravate it. This fact has become one of the major burdens of modern industry and a great concern to the industrial statesmen who appreciate the social menace of the discontented worker. Competition in a democratic state where classes are not so rigid and where some individuals are constantly going forward while others are falling backward to a lower economic status, necessarily tends to give more prestige to certain occupations than to others. In spite of our preachment regarding the dignity of manual labor, we have never succeeded in removing from the minds of many the stigma associated with working with one's hands. This necessarily means that the setting is present for the stimulating of the susceptible wage earner's feelings of inferiority or for magnifying those which he already possesses. Feelings of inferiority operate in industry as elsewhere to produce restlessness, antipathy, ill-temper, and an eagerness to enter conflict.

When the employee finds himself stuck with no hope of promotion to another line of work which he feels he has the skill to perform, inferiority reactions are bound to occur. Where the roadway is open for advancement in industry and achievement is immediately rewarded by new opportunities, the ambitious worker is not driven toward inferiority reactions. Mental hygiene as it functions in industry is not content to handle cases of inferiority feeling, but endeavors constantly to influence what may well be called the general atmosphere of the organization so that inferiority feeling will be largely prevented. This is one of the most important functions of mental hygiene in modern industry.

Ambition and capacity.   In industry as elsewhere there are many individuals who have ambitions far beyond the possibility of attainment.   Sometimes they struggle on through life dissatisfied because of their misinterpretation of their own gifts and their lack of understanding of the requirements that go along with the kind of work they think they would like to do.   It is important and humane that gifted people who have been temporarily stranded in an inferior position in industry should be rescued and given an opportunity to attain to that for which they are fitted.   Mental hygiene, however, finds a larger problem in dealing with those whose ambitions have outrun their capacity and who have no serious desire even to attempt to work out their daydreams.   It has been found in practice that when these individuals can obtain prestige in their present occupation or can find considerable enjoyment in the things they do outside their work, their impossible ambitions shrink and they accept without protest the work they can efficiently do.   Since the unreasonably ambitious as well as those that are gifted but locked into a minor position can cause disturbance and contribute to a general restlessness among the workers, this problem of dealing with those who misunderstand their ability is an important task of mental hygiene.

Fatigue and rest.   Some of the interests of mental hygiene in industry shade over into the field of general hygiene.   Among these is fatigue.   This is so significant to industry that it has been studied from many aspects, especially by psychology, and to-day we know a great deal in regard to the nature, the origins, and the results of fatigue.   Although we speak of unskilled labor, in our attempt to classify employees, strictly speaking there is no operation carried on in industry that does not have an element of skill in the sense that there are efficient and faulty means of carrying it on. All labor, also, includes the problem of fatigue. For purposes of analysis this problem has been catalogued by Anderson[6] as due to: (1) physical conditions of the worker, (2) the social strain, especially in home life, (3) the nature of his job and his situation while working at it, and (4) personality make-up, the product of previous experience.

Of these elements the second and fourth especially concern the mental hygienist. It must not be thought, however, that these four aspects are easily isolated in practical cases of industrial fatigue. They reënforce one another, and trouble along one line encourages difficulties with regard to the others. For example, persons fatigued because of physical disease will be excessively sensitive to social strain and will be irritated by unfavorable conditions while at work although these may be trivial in character, and at the same time such persons will reveal defects of personality that previously in a state of health were concealed.

Much attention has been given by both psychiatry and psychology to the problem of monotonous labor. No occupation is free from monotony, but there are certain kinds of labor connected with automatic machinery that we are in the habit of thinking of as especially monotonous. Monotony, however, is never merely an objective fact, because the reaction of the worker himself is the decisive element in determining the amount of monotony in any experience. There has been much experimenting with the conditions that make for monotony and these investigations have been carried on both in the laboratory and under conditions of actual work in industry. It has been found that monotony and fatigue are both complex. The question of the intelligence of the worker enters into

[6] V. V. Anderson, *Psychiatry in Industry*, p. 175.

both problems, for if the work in hand does not utilize reasonably the mind of the worker, the subsequent monotony tends to be more fatiguing. This brings out the significance of interest. Monotony is felt not because of the automatic character of the operation but because of lack of interest. Thus the entire state of the individual is involved in estimating the monotony he feels and the reaction he makes to it.

If his automatic labor permits reverie which he carries on as a pleasurable activity, his feeling toward the entire situation is colored by his reverie. Fatigue will be decreased and the monotonous occupation grow less irritating. The reasonableness of this becomes clear as soon as an analysis is made of the mental state of the worker who is beginning to feel fatigue. As he labors to keep his mind on his job he must suppress desires and thinking that are incompatible with the thing in hand. He has no difficulty in doing this when he is interested, but as soon as he feels the monotony of his task as something unpleasant, he has to fall back on effort for control. Immediately tension arises as he attempts to inhibit the thoughts that would be more agreeable. From time to time the mental processes that have more interest intrude and he is called upon to use still greater effort to direct his attention. In such a situation, it is evident that the strength of the contending intrusions, the degree of monotony felt, and the mental stability and habit practices of the individual are all concerned.

It is easy to exaggerate the fatigue that comes from monotonous labor, forgetting that there are workers who find relief in a definite routine which requires little initiative once habit has been organized. Those who interpret the psychology of industry are apt to overstress the effect of monotonous labor since they read into the experience of others what would be true if they themselves were assigned a mechanical task. Undoubtedly there are persons who are protected from stress in their employment by being permitted to follow a routine that has little variation. The discontent that such workers express is probably often due to their feeling that they are looked down upon because of the nature of their work, to the lesser wage that they receive compared with that given to those who have greater demands of adjustment put upon them, and to the difficulty that the person only adapted to routine work has in obtaining promotion. These conditions rather than rebellion against the monotony of their labor, in many instances at least, explain the workers' dissatisfaction that the critic of industry misinterprets as protest against monotony.

Fear and anger are two of the most forceful competitors that the worker who is trying to keep himself attentive to his work has to struggle against. Worry and anxiety, both members of the family of fear, are, in the experience of the mental hygienist, common causes of fatigue. It is hard to keep worry out of consciousness; security and happiness seem to be at stake and the individual has strong feelings moving him toward concentration upon the predicament which gives him fear. Since these experiences of worry may be the product of an anxiety neurosis which has possession of the entire life of the worker, mental hygiene has to treat the fatigue problem arising in the worker captured by fear in the same manner in which the psychiatrist deals with such a morbid state in individuals who are not tied up in industry. The difference is that, in the worker, worry is more likely to result in a problem of fatigue than when it occurs outside of industry.

Fatigue in industry concerns not merely the worker,

since it operates also in the conduct of executives and of those in important positions of management. The risks of fatigue and the menace of anxiety as an influence upon those in control of other men in industry have become generally understood and efforts are made to safeguard any large undertaking from the harmful results bound to come when executives show overstrain. An exception seems to be the tradition of the sea which still permits the captain, because of his responsibility for the vessel, to retain command over such a long period of time that he as a physical being necessarily suffers from body fatigue, lack of sleep, and anxiety. Out of experience the railroads, however, have learned the necessity of removing from the engine the man at the throttle before he has become overtired as a result of the length of the run. Smith points out that it is part of an executive's job to safeguard himself against excessive fatigue; that keeping fit becomes an obligation on account of the influence that any failure to do this may have upon the responsibility which has been given into his charge.[7]

Accidents. What has been said regarding fatigue is also true with regard to industrial accidents. Accidents are produced by conditions similar to those that make fatigue. The importance of accidents in industry has led to a series of investigations and it has been found that the rate of accidents reveals a sensitiveness on the part of workers to all sorts of physical and psychic conditions. Fatigue itself is one of the influential causes of accidents. Weather, time of day, the age of the worker, are also factors that are important in the understanding of industrial accidents. As one would expect, there have also been discovered by careful study great differences between individuals with reference to their risk of accidents.

[7] E. D. Smith, *Psychology for Executives,* p. 103.

Mental hygiene tries to deal with those individuals who have a high record of accidents. In some cases a study of the personality reveals the causes of the trouble, making it possible to turn the person into a safe employee. In other cases it is evident that inherent awkwardness or some other personality defect makes it unwise for the worker to continue in his employment.

Industrial accidents become a greater problem because compensation laws have been so widely adopted in this country. An important task of mental hygiene is the treatment of various types of what the management is likely to interpret as malingering. There is a disposition on the part of the employer and the executives either to think of the worker's suffering as directly due to the physical injury, or to regard his request for compensation for an accident as an attempt falsely to get aid. To the specialist, acquainted with the mechanism of the human mind, these cases of apparent deception are regarded as indirect results of injury. They may come out of the attitude of the worker toward the company, for if he feels that the accident was not his fault but the fault of the organization or if he is chronically dissatisfied with his work or has received morbid suggestions from the doctor, who in treating him has not thought of the psychic elements involved, or if the worker fears some permanent harm from the injury, he will unconsciously delay his recovery in an attempt to receive compensation that to the executive may seem unjust.

In the study of concrete accidents the mental hygienist often comes across evidences of mental disorder, and doubtless the discovery of these mental deviations before they are expressed in some accident saves the company much loss and trouble. For example, Anderson reports a case of a man arrested for stealing a drum, who was upon examination found to be a sufferer from general paresis. He had been a motorman and within a year had had five accidents, one injuring thirteen people. The value of discovering such persons before they have a chance to do great damage is obvious.

Students of psychoanalysis will recognize also the subtlety involved in the interpretation of accidents. As Freud and others expert in psychoanalysis have pointed out, many accidents might more correctly be described as unconscious volitions. In other words, they are explained by underground feelings and unadmitted motives that, under stress, issue in action. This it is that makes Freud think of certain accidents as being really attempts at suicide, the result of mechanisms that have not clearly entered conscious volition. Industrial conditions give opportunity for such experiences, and the individual suffering from fear complex or from guilt feeling may not only satisfy strong emotional impulses that lead toward self-destruction, but at the same time may have the false sense of protecting himself against the very thought of self-injury. His state of mind is so inconsistent, and so much of his emotion is kept under cover, that to any but the specialist the description of the motivation behind his act seems far fetched. It may be that these occurrences are also complicated by the fact that the worker in industry has a chance to conceal the meaning of his act and at the same time to bring security to his family that would not come were his death or injury to take place under other circumstances. Of course in mental disease the risk of self-injury is sometimes one of the major symptoms. Regarding this matter of great importance to the employee, Freud writes as follows:

It is known that in the more serious cases of psychoneuroses one sometimes finds self-mutilations as symptoms of the disease. That the psychic conflict may end in suicide can never be excluded in these cases. Thus I know from experience, which some day I shall support with convincing examples, that many apparently accidental injuries happening to such patients are really self-inflicted.[8]

Industrial poisoning and mental hygiene. Since the majority of the symptoms of industrial poisoning appear in psychological form, the contribution of mental hygiene to the problem is very definite. The psychiatrist especially contributes from his experience an important part in differential diagnosis when poisoning is suspected. Psychological evidences of the working of certain poisons are especially significant to the physician. Poison often shows itself in excessive fatigue and incapacity that causes accidents, so that in dealing with other problems the mental hygienist discovers the work of poison that would not otherwise have been noticed until its results had become more marked.

Mental disease and industry. Candidates for the various sorts of mental diseases are present in industry as everywhere else, and from time to time some individual begins to show symptoms of definite disorder. Such persons are a decided menace to their fellow workers as well as to the industry itself. Their malady may lead to accidents that will cause some catastrophe in the factory or store or it may lead to some occurrence that will damage the good will of the organization in the minds of the public. Since the first violent expression of the increasing disorder may occur within the industry, the need of early detection of mental malady becomes an important function of industrial mental hygiene.

[8] *Psychopathology of Everyday Life,* p. 198.

Limits of industrial mental hygiene. There is a disposition among some to exaggerate the benefits that business and industry can obtain from a program of mental hygiene. This same over-confidence is found in other fields where the mental hygiene program is at work. There are doubtless conditions which can never be entirely changed, which will bring us always serious problems of maladjustments in industry. No mental hygiene program can expect entirely to eliminate personality defects and the symptomatic expressions of the various sorts of mental disease. At present, however, we are not in a position to know what the limits of the mental hygiene program are, since it has not yet traveled outside the experimental stage. What has been accomplished gives us confidence that mental hygiene has for industry as for other human activities an enormous usefulness.

ILLUSTRATIVE CASE

A young Scotchman, a skilled mechanic and most industrious, living in a mill village, won rapid advancement, being appointed first overseer of a department and finally at the age of thirty-five superintendent of a small factory. As the result of consolidation he was transferred to a much larger factory in a different community. In all the positions he had held he had been a driving and exacting person, but as soon as he became superintendent these traits increased until he was a literal slave-driver. As a consequence he was both feared and hated and his labor turnover increased noticeably year by year.

His domestic life appeared to mean little to him, for although he was kind to his wife and children his only interest, aside from his ambition to save, was the mill. The only son of a widow, he had tasted during childhood the bitter fruits of poverty, and, being sensitive, had reacted strongly to his experience.

In the mill he was a constant nagger in his dealings with his men, disregarding his overseers and going directly with any complaint or threat to the worker whom he considered unsatisfactory. He realized his growing unpopularity and met it with more bullying and various sorts of restrictions. Finally, due to one of his obnoxious regulations, a strike occurred. This in time led to a reorganization of the company and his discharge. After a few futile efforts to get a position in the same industry, he bought a small farm. At once his attitude toward his family seemed to change. He became brutal to both wife and children. The latter all left home early and had as little to do with their father as possible. Once in a fit of anger the man so unmercifully whipped his horse that he was arrested and fined for cruelty to animals. About this time his wife left him and went to live with her oldest son. The husband, who never had been a successful farmer, after the departure of his wife became more careless and less prosperous. He continued a hermit-like existence for five years and then, as a result of careless exposure, died of pneumonia. After his death it was found that his property, which was larger than had been suspected at the time he left manufacturing, had been nearly all lost through carelessness and dissipation.

SUGGESTIONS FOR CLASSROOM DISCUSSION

1. What is the mental hygiene program in industry?
2. What is the function of the psychiatric social worker in industry?
3. What hampers the growth of mental hygiene in industry?
4. What are the common maladjustments in the factory? In the department store?
5. How does mental hygiene contribute to industrial peace?
6. What forms does inferiority feeling take in industry?
7. How does mental hygiene decrease industrial accidents?

SUGGESTIONS FOR WRITTEN REPORTS

1. Development of mental tests in industry.
2. The experiments of Münsterburg in vocational guidance.

3. Childhood experiences and adult choices of vocations.
4. Opportunities in industry for mental conflict.
5. Mental hygiene as a preventive of industrial fatigue.
6. Effects of the influence of monotony in industry.

SELECTED BIBLIOGRAPHY

ANDERSON, V. V. "The Problem Employee: His Study and Treatment." *Personnel Journal,* 1928, Vol. VII, pp. 203-25.
—— "A Psychiatric Guide for Employment." *Personnel Journal,* 1928, Vol. VI, pp. 417-41.
—— *Psychiatry in Industry.* New York, 1929.
BARTLETT, F. C. "Psychological Qualities in Leadership and Management." *Report of the 25th Lecture Conference for Works Directors, Managers, Foremen, and Forewomen,* Balliol College, Oxford, September, 1927, pp. 21-25.
BURTT, H. E. *Principles of Employment Psychology.* Boston, 1926.
—— "Psychology of Industrial Efficiency." New York, 1929.
BUZZARD, E. FARQUHAR. "Traumatic Neurasthenia." *Mental Hygiene,* April, 1924, pp. 425-37.
CAMPBELL, C. MACFIE. "Mental Hygiene in Industry." *Mental Hygiene,* July, 1921, pp. 468-78.
—— "Personal Factors in Relation to the Health of the Individual Worker." *Mental Hygiene,* July, 1929, Vol. XIII, pp. 483-95.
CARLTON, F. T. "Psychology and Management." *Scientific Monthly,* 1928, Vol. XXVI, pp. 350-52.
CRAIG, D. R., and CHARTERS, W. W. *Personal Leadership in Industry.* New York, 1925.
DYE, V. E., and UNGER, E. W. "A Technique for Job Analysis." *Personnel Journal,* 1928, Vol. VII, pp. 367-75.
ELKIND, HENRY B. "Industrial Psychiatry." *Mental Hygiene,* April, 1929, pp. 378-92.
FEUTINGER, JOSEPHINE. "The Mental Factor in the Economic Adjustment of 500 Disabled Ex-Service Men." *Mental Hygiene,* October, 1926, pp. 677-700.

FISHER, BOYD. "Has Mental Hygiene a Practical Use in Industry?" *Mental Hygiene*, July, 1921, pp. 479-96.

FRASER-HARRIS, D. F. "Some Psychophysiological Aspects of Industry." *Journal of State Medicine* (London), October, 1929, Vol. XXXVII, pp. 594-601.

FRYER, DOUGLAS. "Psychology and Its Vocational Application." *Mental Hygiene*, January, 1927, pp. 124-39.

GILLILAND, A. R. "The Use of Psychiatry in Industry." *Religious Education*, September, 1929, Vol. XXIV, pp. 650-51.

HERSEY, R. B. "Periodic Emotional Changes in Male Workers." *Personnel Journal*, 1929, Vol. VII, pp. 459-64.

LIPPMAN, O. "The Human Factor in Production." *Personnel Journal*, 1928, Vol. VII, pp. 87-95.

MACALPINE, JEAN DOUGLAS. "A Study of the Underwear Industry with Special Reference to Opportunities for Subnormal Girls." *Mental Hygiene*, January, 1923, pp. 70-101.

MCKAY, MURIEL. "Mental Hygiene in Industry." *Canadian Nurse*, July, 1929, 25:361-62.

MYERS, CHARLES S. *Industrial Psychology in Great Britain.* London, 1925.

PARKER, CARLETON H. "Motives in Economic Life." *Publications of the American Sociological Society*, Vol. XII, pp. 131-51.

PARTRIDGE, GEORGE E. "Psychopathic Personality and Personality Investigation." *The American Journal of Psychiatry*, May, 1929, pp. 1053-55.

PEAR, T. H. *Fitness for Work.* London, 1928.

PRATT, GEORGE K. "The Problem of the Mental Misfit in Industry." *Mental Hygiene*, July, 1922, pp. 526-38.

PRUETTE, LORINE, and FRYER, DOUGLAS. "Affective Factors in Vocational Maladjustment." *Mental Hygiene*, January, 1923, pp. 102-18.

SCOTT, AUGUSTA. "Neuropsychiatric Work in Industry." *Mental Hygiene*, July, 1923, pp. 521-37.

SMITH, ELLIOTT DUNLAP. *Psychology for Executives.* New York, 1928.

SOUTHARD, E. E. "The Modern Specialist in Unrest: a Place

for the Psychiatrist in Industry." *Mental Hygiene,* July, 1920, pp. 550-63.

TEAD, ORDWAY. *Instincts in Industry.* Boston, 1918.

TIEBOUT, HARRY M. "Psychiatric Phases in Vocational Guidance." *Mental Hygiene,* January, 1926, pp. 102-12.

VITELES, M. S. "The Clinical Approach in Vocational Guidance." *Vocational Guidance Magazine,* 1928, Vol. VII, pp. 1-9.

—— "Psychology and Psychiatry in Industry; the Point of View of a Psychologist." *Mental Hygiene,* April, 1929, pp. 361-77.

WRIGHT, WADE. "Industrial Hygiene." *Mental Hygiene,* July, 1921, pp. 497-98.

CHAPTER XI

RECREATION AND MENTAL ADJUSTMENTS

The need for recreation. In primitive society, the dividing line between work and play was much less finely drawn than in our modern civilization. Early religious rites insured a close association between the two activities. We have only to recall the ceremonial song or dance of primitive peoples to insure good hunting or to bring about a fruitful harvest in order to understand the intimate relationship between work and play in earlier stages of social evolution. Moreover, in a non-industrial economic order, all work was of a simpler nature, and while perhaps accompanied by greater physical hazard (in hunting or fighting) it did not result in mental strain and fatigue like that which follows the steady day-after-day application of the office or factory worker.

The primitive occupations of hunting, fishing and agriculture, as practiced in a non-industrial society, depended very largely upon physical strength and skill. But the factory or office worker of this modern age must make use of finer neuro-muscular coördinations and exert constant attention to his task. Again, the hunter, fisherman, or early agriculturist could be his own pacemaker; but the factory worker must keep up to the pace set for him by a machine and the office clerk must work under considerable pressure. Speed and accuracy are demanded of the laborer in modern methods of production. Prior to the industrial revolution and the introduction of machinery, even manufacturing, as done by hand, did not call for such effort with respect to sustained attention, rapidity and precision of movement. It is this aspect of the modern worker's life which separates his work so completely from any play element.

Other factors contribute to the strain of the modern worker's life. Competition is keen and he must be on the alert to guard against it. His purpose is intense and very often he falls below the standards of achievement which he has set up for himself. Work is highly specialized and varied and the opportunities for making choices are multiplied. Myerson emphasizes the rôle of "over-intense purposes, failure to realize ideals, and the difficulties of choice" in the production of mental fatigue.[1] Even the executive and the professional are open to these experiences which create mental tension.

Social conventions enforce upon the individual the necessity of suppressing many of his natural emotional reactions in the interests of courtesy and good taste. This self-control which is imposed by the demands of group adaptation is wearying and increases fatigue. With all these sources of tension, it is imperative that some means of relaxation be provided.

In order to preserve mental health, some form of recreation is vitally important. It must permit the dropping of serious purposes, forgetting of cares and worries, and relaxation of emotional inhibitions. Almost any activity which has no vitally serious purpose, which provides release from inhibitions and relief of mental tension may take on a recreational value to the individual.

Active and passive recreation. In modern civilization it would seem that we have two different kinds of recreational movements. One favors a return to outdoor

[1] A. Myerson, *Foundations of Personality*, Chap. XV. New York, 1921.

life; it fosters parks and playgrounds and summer camps for city children, and municipal tennis courts and golf links for adults. It favors every form of recreation in which the individual is an active participant. The other trend is toward recreation in which there is only a passive participation: motoring, watching competitive athletics, attending motion pictures, listening to the radio. It has been estimated that at least half the money spent on recreation by the people of the United States goes into these passive forms.[2]

Commercial interests favor the passive types of recreation and make them easily accessible to the city dweller. It is far easier to walk a few blocks to the nearest motion picture theater or sit at home and listen to the radio, than to seek farther afield for more active play. The yielding to the easily available, passive forms of recreation does not necessarily represent a real preference for these. For example, in a recent study of young working women in Cincinatti, the three most frequent recreational activities reported were reading, theater attendance, and visits to amusement parks, although athletics and dancing were given as favorite recreations. Personal preference had simply yielded to differences in opportunity for gratification.

Even when we study the play activities of children, particularly in the city, we find that passive recreation takes care of a great amount of their leisure time. Lehman and Witty, investigating the play of Kansas City school children, find that auto riding, watching athletic sports, attending movies, listening to the radio and reading vie in frequency with playing ball. Furthermore, playing ball is about the only really active kind of play reported

[2] Stuart Chase, "Play," Chap. XIV of *Whither Mankind*. New York, 1928.

for more than 25 per cent of the boys, unless we can count such things as card games, writing letters, chewing gum and whistling as in the active classification. The active list of the girls is still more reduced by their lack of interest in playing ball, being limited to writing letters, chewing gum, playing the piano or singing.[3]

The increasing prevalence of passive types of recreation gives rise to rather serious speculations. Is the progressive urbanization of the country removing the opportunity for active play for both adults and children and replacing it by recreation of a predominantly sedentary nature? And if this be true, what will be the effect upon the mental health of the people?

Recreation in rural life. In the old pioneer days, and to some extent up to the introduction of farm machinery and modern methods of agriculture, there was occasional community participation in labor, such as roof-raising or harvesting, followed by dancing and games. The rural school and church also served as recreation centers in addition to their primary purposes of education and religious worship. While church and school still serve as social centers to some extent, the older customs of community gatherings for work and play have virtually disappeared. For the most part, the adults in rural neighborhoods have turned to more sophisticated and passive recreations, resembling those of the city dweller. The farmhouse has its radio or victrola; villages boast of motion picture theaters, and many rural families have automobiles. While all of these tend to promote a passive type of enjoyment, they have been exceedingly effective in breaking down the isolation which was once a chief characteristic of country life. They have therefore most

[3] Lehman and Witty, *The Psychology of Play Activities,* Chap. V. New York, 1927.

fortunately relieved the monotony and loneliness of rural existence, with excellent benefits to mental health.

The introduction of farm machinery has had a decided effect upon the play of country children. It has released them from long hours of labor before and after the school day and has helped to do away with the practice of keeping children out of school at the planting and harvest seasons. Thus rural children have far more time for education and recreation than was formerly the case. The country child has always had plenty of space for play, and with adequate leisure is placed in a far more fortunate situation than the city child. Lehman and Witty's inventory of the play activities of country children show conspicuous differences from that of city children. There is much less dependence on sedentary recreations, such as reading and the movies, with a predominance of running and romping, throwing rocks or stones, horseback riding and playing with pet dogs, etcetera.[4] Where once we pitied the country child because of his recreational deprivations, it seems that our sympathy must now be reserved for the child in the city. Even the girls in rural communities have far more active play interests than do the city girls.

Play as a factor in personality development. If the adult needs recreational activities as a means of relaxation from the strain of modern life, the child has no less need of opportunity for play. The play life of the child contributes materially to his proper physical development and to his personality adjustments. The kind of playthings, the type of games and the character of playmates are important.

The factory produces an unending supply of mechanical toys. The only activity required of the child is winding

[4] *The Psychology of Play Activities,* Chap. VIII.

the springs that make them move. If playthings of such a nature are given to children, the incentive for constructive activities in their play is greatly reduced. For some time, however, the children's magazines have been educating parents to show more discrimination in the selection of playthings. Fortunately, the factory turns out not only mechanical toys, but also a liberal supply of carpenter's tools, and meccano and erector sets. These are a source of great satisfaction to older children and can be provided at no great expense. For the younger child, there is play equipment for the nursery or back yard which encourages climbing and other exercises that strengthen the muscles. If this equipment is too expensive for the single family purse, it is possible for families living in the same neighborhood to combine in preparing a playground where it may be shared by all the children.

Just as the wise selection of playthings may foster physical and mental health, so participation in group games aids in socialization. When a group of children engage only in aimless activities the struggle for individual supremacy may be keen, but without more or less organized team games the spirit of fair play and coöperation is unlikely to be developed. If the opportunity for group games is offered, and a child persistently refuses to join in them, preferring solitary play activities, ill health or social maladjustment is to be suspected. Such a child needs careful diagnosis and treatment of his condition, whatever it may be.

While the personality traits and behavior patterns of the child are influenced most of all by his family life, nevertheless he takes over some of these from his playmates. The most striking example of this is his response to the gang. Whatever the gang decides the individual must carry out or else risk the likelihood of ostracism.

If he does not belong to the neighborhood gang, the child's life may be made exceedingly unhappy by the hazing which he encounters from it. Thus the gang influence is a powerful factor in shaping the habits and character of the individual child. Even where there is no actual gang formation to enforce conformity to the group, the influence of playmates is still felt, although the pressure which they are able to exert is less intense.

The gang thrives in the city streets, and it is therefore the city child who is most frequently exposed to gang contacts. With the rural child there is another handicap to be considered—the lack of playmates near his own age. This is also a serious matter, for as has been said the child needs group play for his proper development. Whether in the city or the country, some way must be found of providing the child with desirable playmates if there is any possibility of doing so.

Community efforts to provide recreation. Within the community there are many provisions for public recreation and also different private enterprises which consider this one of their functions. Parks and playgrounds are provided by most cities, although there is seldom adequate preparation to serve all those who are in need of such facilities. The Y.M.C.A. and Y.W.C.A., or Y.M.H.A. and Y.W.H.A., usually furnish club activities, swimming pools, gymnasiums and other recreational opportunities for both adults and children. Many churches sponsor recreational activities for their members. The social settlement in the city and the community center in smaller towns take care of certain kinds of recreational needs.

The clubs for business men—Rotary, Kiwanis and Lions—and similar clubs for business and professional women, afford social contacts and at the same time introduce an element of recreation into their meetings through the singing and general atmosphere of jollity which accompanies their more serious business. The Rotary, Kiwanis and Lions clubs all have boys' work or child welfare programs. A part of their contribution is in the interest of recreation, and certain of the local clubs maintain camps for under-privileged children, or support other child welfare enterprises.

There are a number of national organizations for boys and girls which aim to combine recreation and character development. They are familiar to all of us, for they include such organizations as the Boy Scouts, Girl Scouts, Woodcraft League, Camp Fire Girls and Boys' Club Federation. On the recreational side, they foster such healthful activities as hiking, camping and many other outdoor sports. In the local branches, a great deal depends upon the energy and initiative of the young man or woman who is in the position of leadership, so that the value of these organizations varies from one community to another.

Commercialized recreation. Despite the efforts of public and private recreational agencies to meet community needs, the vast bulk of people depend upon commercialized amusements for the occupation of their leisure time. In the Cleveland Recreation survey, for instance, the following figures as to patronage of commercial recreation enterprises were reported:

Annual attendance at motion picture theaters about 26,000,000; at dance halls, 1,500,000; amusement parks, 1,250,000; professional baseball, 500,000; lake excursion boats, 170,000. These, of course, represent only the most popular kinds of commercial recreation. Pool parlors, bowling alleys, and other minor enterprises are omitted from the estimates.[5] In other cities, it is undoubtedly also true that motion pictures, amusement parks, dance halls and professional sports are the most heavily patronized commercial recreations.

From the viewpoint of mental adjustments, all of these offer both positive and negative values. On the negative side, there is chiefly the fact that motion pictures and professional sports offer only a passive participation on the part of the audience, while the dance halls and amusement parks may lead to informal acquaintanceships which carry opportunities for danger to young women. On the positive side, all these amusements provide relaxation of mental tension, an exciting break in the monotony of everyday life, and a temporary escape from painful realities.

Recreational value of motion pictures. Since the opening of the first motion picture theater in 1905, this has become one of the most popular forms of commercialized amusement. By 1920 it was drawing an audience of at least eleven million daily. Since it caters to so large a number of people, its advantages and disadvantages as entertainment must be briefly mentioned.

All sorts of accusations are lodged against the motion picture, but many have no foundation in fact. Superficial observers have frequently tried to saddle the movies with the causation of crime. Recently there emanated from a prominent statistical organization the statement that the movies are to be considered as the "basic cause of the crime waves of to-day." Aside from the fact that "crime wave" is a newspaper phrase, of statistical dubiety, no real evidence was advanced in proof of the above state-

[5] Figures quoted from the *Cleveland Foundation Survey*. A community Recreation Program, p. 34. Cleveland Foundation Committee, 1920.

ment. Apparently it was based on the opinion expressed by school principals of New England, 70 per cent of whom believed the motion pictures to be more influential in character formation than the home, the school or the church.

When we consider the careful studies of adult crime and juvenile delinquency which have recently been made, some of which were reported in Chapter IV, the absurdity of believing that the motion picture has more effect upon behavior than family influences is obvious. Yet there is little doubt that a large section of public opinion accepts this viewpoint. Neither directly nor indirectly is it supported by clinical studies in delinquency. Burt, in his careful investigation of juvenile delinquency in England, found only four or five cases out of two hundred in which crime seemed to be "directly inspired by the cinema." [6] Healy and Bronner, in their intensive case studies of 4,000 young offenders in Boston and Chicago, found that in only one per cent of these could movies be connected with misconduct.[7] As reported elsewhere, our experience with behavior problems in the Child Guidance Clinic would confirm these findings as to the exceedingly slight rôle played by the movies in causing delinquency.[8]

This is by far the most serious criticism leveled at the movies, just as it is the most unfounded. Criticisms of the failure of the motion picture to live up to its possibilities for artistic achievement are rather more justified, although it has in the past given examples of its capacity to contribute to the field of art. The sound-synchronized films which have recently been introduced into this branch

[6] Cyril Burt, *The Young Delinquent*, pp. 137-143. New York, 1925.
[7] Healy and Bronner, *Delinquents and Criminals: Their Making and Unmaking*, p. 281, table 57. New York, 1926.
[8] P. Blanchard, *The Child and Society*, pp. 200-203. New York, 1928.

of entertainment promise to conform more creditably to artistic standards, since the early mechanical imperfections have been corrected, than did the general run of the old silent pictures. The technicolor process is also contributing to esthetic improvement.

The chief value of the motion picture, from the recreational viewpoint, is the complete release from daily cares which it affords to the major portion of the audience. It provides a vicarious satisfaction for all sorts of desires which are denied fulfillment in actual life. The person restricted from wide travel may sit in the motion picture theater and be transported to strange lands; the universal love theme may be shared with the actors on the screen; the relief from a monotonous existence through the excitement of perilous adventures may be obtained. For the mass of people, the motion picture becomes an easily accessible means of a temporary flight from reality, a way of forgetting trouble and anxiety. And until we have a society which is more perfect than any which has thus far been evolved, the masses will continue to need such wholesome flights from reality, as an alternative to taking refuge in religious fanaticism, mob spirit, and all the more or less pathological ways of escape in which suffering humanity has sought to find some solace for its woes.

College and university athletics: College and university athletics are of two kinds: intercollegiate athletics, in which the actors are few and the spectators many, and intra-mural athletics in which nearly all the students participate. Theoretically, the college sponsors athletics in order to favor the health and socialization of the students. It is generally agreed that intra-mural sports and games advance these ends. But with intercollegiate contests, the situation is somewhat different. In particular football, which has become the great American collegiate sport, has taken on many of the aspects of professionalization and commercialization.

The stadiums where the important football games are played have been built to meet the demands of the public for a spectacle. The capacity of the University of California stadium is 90,000; the University of Michigan stadium seats 86,000, and that of Yale 80,000. Accommodations for 75,000 or more spectators are provided by the stadiums of Ohio State University, the University of Pennsylvania, and the University of Pittsburgh. Between 50,000 and 70,000 people may witness games in the Chicago, Illinois, Minnesota and Northwestern University stadiums. At all the big games, this seating capacity is strained to the limit. Hence football ranks with the world series baseball games and other professional sports in providing entertainment for tens of thousands of passive participants.

Financially, football is referred to as "a million dollar sport," both because of the money spent to maintain it and the enormous gate receipts which it brings. And indeed, it is no exaggeration to say that it has reached that figure. In 1925-26 the gate receipts from football at Yale were $244,807.40; in 1927-28, the gross receipts were $1,033,211.98 at the same university. It must be remembered, however, that football is practically the one college sport which can show any profits; from its proceeds all the other intercollegiate athletic contests must be financed, for ordinarily these are carried on at far more expense than the gate returns. Besides taking care of the whole intercollegiate athletic schedule, the funds from football contribute heavily to the building of stadiums, and, in some institutions, to the maintenance of the intra-mural sports which offer an opportunity for active participation to the student body as a whole.

One of the reasons, aside from its being a preëminent financial resource, for the marked interest in football, is its publicity value. The football victory pushes the institution into front-page prominence all over the country, while the death of a college president may be relegated to the inside pages, except in the local press. Since alumni like to see their alma mater hold a front page place, they bring pressure to bear upon the educational executives to organize and maintain a winning team. This forces the restriction of players upon the college or university team to a highly selected group of star athletes.

This state of affairs is certainly not the will of the students themselves; the tension of feeling that they must live up to the demands placed upon them robs their sport of spontaneity and pleasure. Nor is it the will of the president or faculty. Those who have carefully studied the situation agree that the prominence of football is due to the desire of the alumni for a gorgeous spectacle in which they may revel, and their demand for an achievement which will bring their college into the headlines. Since the business of education is becoming increasingly expensive, and alumni must be humored in the interests of financial endowment, their will must be obeyed.

While for the public football has distinctly a recreational value comparable to that supplied by any professional sport for its passive spectators, its usefulness in the interests of student welfare has been called into question. Since it provides opportunity for active participation to only a few picked men, it is certainly of no more than neutral significance in that respect. Many in close contact with college life are agreed that it often has an injurious effect upon the student body. They look upon the tense emotionalism which surrounds the football season as a kind of crowd hysteria, in which all sense of perspective is lost and finer values are distorted. A few colleges and universities have become so convinced of the harmful nature of football on the grand scale that they have abolished intercollegiate athletics altogether, and there seems to be a concerted movement to try to reduce it to proper proportions in institutions which still see some good in it and which depend upon its financial returns for the support of other student sports.

The public, seeing only the newspaper reports of football and other intercollegiate contests, might well believe that this represents the whole of athletics in student life. Such is not the case, however. In a recent study of twenty-three well-known institutions of higher learning, including the University of Chicago, the University of Pennsylvania, the University of Illinois, Yale, the University of Michigan, Amherst, Dartmouth and Princeton, it was estimated that from 75 to 90 per cent of the whole student body takes part in some form of intra-mural athletics. At the University of Michigan, in 1924-25, out of a total enrollment of 10,068 students 6,984 participated in intra-mural sports. Mental hygiene, concerned with the welfare of the student as an individual, would give hearty approval to the tendency to develop athletics for the many instead of for the few.

Individual differences and recreation. To be of real value, recreational activities must be suited to the physical and mental needs of the individual. Certain types of sports require physical robustness, and while improving the health of the average person would be injurious to those with physical handicaps. It is for this reason that schools and colleges and community recreation centers require a physical examination before admission to gymnasium classes or prior to athletic training.

The mental differences which help to determine recreational interests are still more varied. Esthetic pleasure and the joy of creation may be meaningful to the talented person (in the arts, music or writing), but exceedingly irksome to the unimaginative mind. To read Shakespeare or Sudermann or Aldous Huxley may be a delight for the person of keen intellect, but the tabloids and the art and sex magazines are undoubtedly more pleasant reading for the mind which has remained at the sixth grade level. The subtleties of Bernard Shaw or Eugene O'Neill appeal to one mental type, but others prefer musical comedy or vaudeville, and the masses turn principally to motion pictures. It must simply be accepted that what is recreation for one person may not be pleasurable to another.

Even in the play of children, indications of mental differences may be observed. The mentally deficient child shows little initiative or leadership, and very often displays an imperviousness to boredom which permits him to repeat the same playful acts untiringly over and over again. The normal or superior child shows a wide range of play interests and is exceedingly versatile in his play life, except when restricted by environmental deprivations, by ill health, or by some mental maladjustment. The highly gifted child, according to studies made by Lehman and Witty, and by Terman, has about the same number of play interests as the average child, but these are somewhat different in kind. The gifted child turns more to reading and to solitary interests requiring intellectual activities, while the average child depends more upon group games and motor activities to occupy his leisure time. This is a comparative statement, however, and does not mean that the average child neglects reading entirely, or that the gifted child refuses all participation in active sports and games.[9]

Not only physical and mental differences, but also age differences, must be taken into account in the individual selection of recreational activities. Below the age of ten or eleven, the child is interested in a large number of different kinds of play activities; as he grows older, the range of recreational activities diminishes. This is clearly brought out by data Lehman and Witty report in their survey of the play activities of Kansas City school children.[10] Other investigations indicate that adults tend to rely more and more upon sedentary and passive forms of recreation as they advance in age. It is probable that we have our modern life, with its urban domination, to thank, at least in part, for this increasing tendency toward the passive forms of recreation.

The modern view of recreation. The ancient civilizations, such as those of Greece and Rome, glorified play and consciously utilized it in the development of citizenship. Thereafter, during a long period of social history the attitude toward recreation was decidedly negativistic. Early Christianity condemned it, and not so very long ago, in our own country, the influence of Puritan ideals still caused it to be held in low esteem. Play was regarded with suspicion by those generations which were trained in the harsh precepts of self-denial and which regarded any indulgence in pleasure as sinful, or at best, as a waste of time.

A better understanding of the principles of physical and mental hygiene has materially altered our viewpoint. We

[9] *The Psychology of Play Activities,* Chap. IV. L. M. Terman, *Genetic Studies of Genius,* Vol. I, Chap. XIV. Stanford University Press, 1925.
[10] *The Psychology of Play Activities,* Chap. V.

know that physical energy and vitality are refreshed by active participation in games and sports, and that mental tension is relaxed by recreational pursuits even when these are passive in nature. It is as necessary for a properly balanced life to have enjoyable play outlets as to find a congenial occupation. The devotion of some leisure time to recreational pursuits is of positive value outside of the enjoyment which it affords, for it enables the individual to return reinvigorated to the more serious routine of study or work. The realization of this fact has caused society to look with approval upon play activities for the child, the adolescent and the adult—an attitude which is eminently encouraging to those who have the health of the people at heart.

ILLUSTRATIVE CASE

James was referred to a child guidance clinic because of truancy, lying and stealing. At that time, he was nine years old, and had high average intelligence. His home life was decidedly bleak, as his father belonged to a certain religious sect which had very strict rules of conduct. All pleasure activities were frowned upon, games and sports being considered a waste of time and such things as dances or the movies being held actually sinful. Strict discipline for children was believed quite proper, and for minor misdemeanors, even before he had committed any of the serious ones which caused him to be brought to clinic, James had been given corporal punishment, shut up all night in the cellar, and had his sins taken to the Lord in his father's prayers.

James was very frank in discussing his misconduct. He said that he played truant because he could go to the woods with a group of older boys who were building a cabin there. He had stolen money to go to the movies; he had purloined toys from stores because he was never given any playthings; his last and largest theft of five dollars had been invested in an express wagon which he wanted very badly. His lying about his conduct was done in order to escape the severe punishments which he knew would follow if his father discovered his misdeeds.

It would have been unwise, even if possible, to try to alter the father's personal religious convictions. His religion was the stabilizing influence in his own life. Prior to his conversion, at the age of thirty, he had been an alcoholic and a vagabond. After accepting this religious faith, at a revival, he had settled down. All that could be done was to induce him to relax his attitudes sufficiently to permit James to have some wholesome recreational outlets.

At the suggestion of the clinic, James was permitted to join some of the boys' classes at the Y.M.C.A., where he could learn swimming and other sports. The father was too poor to give him an allowance, but a way was arranged whereby the boy could earn some money, and he was allowed to use this to purchase playthings and to attend a movie occasionally. His father was induced to ameliorate his disciplinary methods.

These changes in the boy's life were sufficient to remove the need of truancy, stealing and lying. Once he was launched on a program which provided wholesome recreational activities, he was no longer forced to obtain amusement in these furtive ways. Thus recreation became of primary importance in bringing about James' adjustment to social requirements, and probably checked him in a career which if continued might have led him to become a chronic delinquent.

SUGGESTIONS FOR CLASSROOM DISCUSSION

1. How does modern civilization differ from primitive society in respect to work and play?
2. Why do we need recreation?
3. What types of recreation are most readily available in the city?
4. What effect has city life on the play of children?
5. In what way does the play life of the child in the country differ from that of the city child?

6. To what extent does athletics provide play activity for the majority of college students?

7. Why do different individuals enjoy different types of recreation?

SUGGESTIONS FOR WRITTEN REPORTS

1. Play in the Machine Age.
2. Play in Primitive Societies.
3. Play as a Socializing Agency for the Child.
4. The Motion Picture as a Form of Recreation.
5. Make a list of the forms of recreation which you like best; then make a list of those which you take part in most frequently. From the viewpoint of mental hygiene, would you wish to make any changes in your present recreational outlets?

SELECTED BIBLIOGRAPHY

APPLETON, L. E. *A Comparative Study of the Play Activities of Adult Savages and Civilized Children.* University of Chicago Press, 1910.

BLANCHARD, P. *The Child and Society,* Chaps. V and VIII. New York, 1928.

CHASE, STUART. "Play." Chapter XIV of *Whither Mankind.* New York, 1928.

CULIN, S. "Hawaiian Games." *American Anthropologist* (new series), 1899, Vol. I, pp. 201-247.

CURTIS, H. S. *The Play Movement and Its Significance,* Chaps. X and XI. New York, 1917.

EDWARDS, ARTMAN and FISHER. *Undergraduates,* Chap. IV. New York, 1928.

FRAZER, J. G. *The Golden Bough* (abridged edition), Chaps. III and LXII. New York, 1922.

GILLIN, J. L. "The Sociology of Recreation." *American Journal of Sociology,* 1914, Vol. XIX, pp. 825-834.

GROVES, E. R. *An Introduction to Sociology,* Chap. XXV. New York, 1928.

GULICK, LUTHER. *A Philosophy of Play,* Chaps. IX-XVII. New York, 1920.

KIDD, D. *Savage Childhood,* Chap. V. New York, 1906.

LEHMAN and WITTY. *The Psychology of Play Activities.* New York, 1927.

MYERSON, A. *Foundations of Personality,* Chap. XV. Boston, 1921.

PATRICK, G. T. W. *Psychology of Relaxation,* Chap. II. Boston, 1916.

SEASHORE, C. E. *Psychology in Daily Life,* Chap. I. New York, 1913.

SIES, ALICE C. *Spontaneous and Supervised Play in Childhood,* Chaps. I and II. New York, 1926.

SUMNER, W. G. *Folkways,* Chap. XVII. Boston, 1906.

THOMAS, W. I. *Source Book for Social Origins.* Part V. Boston, 1909.

THOMAS, W. I. and D. S. *The Child in America,* Chap. IV. New York, 1928.

TUNIS, J. R. "The Great God Football." *Harpers,* November, 1928, Vol. 157, pp. 742-752.

WALKER, J. R. "Sioux Games." *Journal of American Folk-Lore,* 1905, Vol. XVIII, pp. 277-290.

WEGENER, A. B. *Church and Community Recreation,* Chaps. I, III, IV and X. New York, 1924.

WOODWORTH, R. S. *Psychology,* Chap. XIX. 1929.

—— " 'Sportsmania' in the Colleges: Pro and Con." *The Literary Digest,* December 8, 1928, Vol. XCIX, pp. 48-54.

CHAPTER XII

MENTAL HYGIENE AND RELIGION

There is, and since the days of the Greek thinkers there has been, much speculation regarding the origin and the significance of religion. This is not strange since religion, whether thought of as an individual or social experience, is one of the most impressive of human interests. In importance it rivals the family, the state, and industry, and no discussion of mental hygiene would be complete if man's religious experiences were ignored. The diversity of these experiences, however, makes treatment difficult. The term religion has to be highly abstract, since it attempts to generalize the greatest differences possible in emotion, thinking, and behavior. The multitude of creeds, the striking peculiarities of beliefs, the various sorts of worship, all having appeal for certain individuals, and the great diversity in moral preachment in the different faiths and churches, reveal the complexity of the experiences that we designate religious. Fortunately, mental hygiene is not directly concerned with the origin of religion, nor is it obliged to tie itself to some particular form of religious experience and insist upon this as the norm. Avoiding any attempt to standardize religion in the effort to define the most desirable type, mental hygiene is free to recognize both the social and personal values and also the problems associated with religion as an expression of human needs.

The opportunity for speculation regarding the nature of religion and its beginning has not been neglected by those interested in psychology, and some of these theories do carry practical consequences for mental hygiene. Psychoanalysis in its literature has also given much thought to religious experience and the genius of Freud has expressed itself in interpretation of the religious motive.[1] In these various treatments of religious phenomena, the thing that most concerns the mental hygiene student is the significance of fear as an emotion in religion. If, for example, such a Freudian explanation as the following is accepted, immediately it influences the mental hygiene program:

Fear is the determining stimulus to the regressive myth-making phantasy. Of course the fear that stimulates modern religious faith is not a primitive fear of certain places or persons. It is rather a complex dread of life and its tasks as a whole. When dangers threaten mental peace or physical health, the instinct of fear counsels men to retreat from an intolerable situation. Viewed thus religion appears to be a psychical flight from a dark and threatening reality. The sensitive person who feels inwardly incapable of resisting the blows of fortune seeks escape from the real present in a religious world of phantasy or faith. Religion is indeed a safety valve for the strained mind.[2]

Religion is many-sided and perhaps since the first it has been less simple than in theory we are wont to think. Growing knowledge of the religious attitudes of savage people shows us that fear has a large place in their beliefs, but it does not follow, as many claim, that religion was in its beginnings an expression of fear. Leonard's statement seems more reasonable:

[1] See C. Moxon, "Religion in the Light of Psychoanalysis," *The Psychoanalytic Review*, January, 1921, pp. 92-98.
[2] *Ibid.*, p. 96.

There was in the beginning no conscious effort, on man's part, to develop any religion. On the contrary, his suspicions and fears, his confidence and veneration, were but the spontaneous outcome of his natural instincts—an outcome of the emotions that he could no more check than he could cease to exist or to propagate.[3]

Primitive man found his environment saturated with fear, born of his ignorance, and in his efforts to escape from the dangers that faced him on every side he was irresistibly drawn toward the supernatural, pulled both by his yearnings and his need of security. This interpretation is at least closest to the attitude that mental hygiene has to take as it deals with religious experience in the modern world.

The relation of mental hygiene and religion. There are many points of contact between mental hygiene and religion. Each deals with human nature in the effort to produce right ways of living. In the religious motives of each individual mental hygiene finds either a strong ally or a stubborn antagonist. Likewise religion furnishes a goal for human achievement and the character of this decides whether mental hygiene obtains support in the working out of its program or meets an opponent that may defeat its best endeavors. Everything depends upon the type of religious experience that has become characteristic of the individual. Although mental hygiene cannot always count upon religion as an ally, it never safely ignores the religious life of any individual, for if the religious experience furnishes no assistance in the working out of a wholesome life program, it necessarily builds up an outlook upon life that antagonizes wholesome behavior. Since religion offers such a powerful motivation, the mental hygienist usually finds it a help-mate in

[3] A. G. Leonard, *The Lower Niger and Its Tribes*, p. 88.

any effort to reconstruct character and reëducate the individual to meet with success the demands life puts upon him. On account of the variations of religious experience, which may appear in forms suggesting perversity because of the unsocial attitudes encouraged, it is not sufficient to think of religion as determining the purposes of life, and mental hygiene as developing a technique for their attainment. When the goal is in accord with mental hygiene's teaching, this desirable relationship follows. Such a situation is not always present. The emotional appeal of religion gives opportunity for a morbid slant upon life which leads to feeling and acting exactly contrary to the teachings of mental hygiene. When this is true there is a sharp clashing of emotionalism on the one side with science on the other. In cases such as these mental hygiene treats the religious influence as a major part of the problem presented by the individual's maladjustment to life.[4]

Conflict and religion. Within the domain of Christianity, especially Protestantism, religious conflict, primarily during the adolescent period, has been so common as to seem the normal experience. As mental hygiene views this, it is one aspect of the growing-up process and represents much more than may appear on the surface. In part it is a collision between earlier habits, both of thought and emotion, and new ideas. In part it is also a breaking away from parental authority and the development of personal beliefs rather than clinging to the doctrines that have been conveyed by church and home and accepted until now as a matter of course. History records

---

[4] The desirable relationship between mental hygiene and science and religion is clearly brought out by an article by Rev. P. M. Grant, "Moral and Religious Life of the Individual in the Light of the New Psychology," *Mental Hygiene*, July, 1928. For a discussion of pathological types in religion, see W. F. Swisher, *Religion and the New Psychology*, Chap. VII, "Pathological Religious Types."

a multitude of such conflicts, and until religion changes as rapidly as do the other characteristics of one generation compared with another, such occurrences are inevitable. Nor does mental hygiene think of them as necessarily harmful in their influence. Possibly a more desirable development would be so gradual as to make no sharp breaks, but aside from the erratic individuals who are unable to stand the ordeal, religious conflicts are merely the growing pains of a maturing character.

There is another sort of conflict that centers about religion, which also concerns mental hygiene. This represents the effort to attain moral security. It also is often an awakening that comes to the individual who, interpreting his past conduct as evil, develops a feeling of unworthiness. Even in such cases there is a wide variation in the motives given emphasis. In one person the feeling is that the past is something unworthy that ought to be repudiated, while another individual flees from the wrath of a righteous God, and fears eternal punishment unless he finds an opportunity to save his soul. This latter type of conflict flourished in Puritan culture and gave a morbid tinge to the entire life of the believers. Hawthorne, who was one of the first of the psychoanalysts, used his literary skill to portray religious careers so highly emotional as to reveal what to the scientist of our day would be clearly pathological. It would be, however, unfair to charge religion with responsibility for these morbid upheavals of personality and to forget that religion ofttimes should be credited not with the cause of the upheaval, but with power to bring it to a successful conclusion. The sense of guilt is too fundamental and too easily aroused to be thought of merely as the product of religious teaching artificially built into the life through morbid instruction. Mental hygiene finds guilt too common an experience to be thought of as something brought into existence by ecclesiastical effort.

Guilt and religion. The guilt feeling that mental hygiene frowns upon, because it has associated with it such morbid possibilities, appears in religion as the sense of sin which is often made the basic concept upon which the doctrine of the church is built. Thus guilt as an emotion has in religion a prominence far beyond that given in mental hygiene. The sense of sin, however, must not be thought of as something superimposed upon human nature, for, as nobody knows better than the mental hygienist, guilt reaction is a characteristic behavior of men and women under the stress of conflict.

Religion has taken over one of the most disturbing of human reactions and has made use of it as a means of influencing character and giving motive to life. In this way religion has opened up relief for those in the throes of sin and by replacing fear with assurance has reëstablished courage to face the ordeal of living. In thus ministering to those genuinely afflicted with a tremendous inner conflict, religion has run the risk, from which it has not altogether escaped, of encouraging and even artificially inducing guilt feeling. In extolling the victory of one man it has incited imitation in many others who have been led to express a guilt feeling that they otherwise might not have had. In organizing its doctrine so as to show its power to deal adequately with personal sin, it has been tempted to insist upon the experience as necessary for a normal start in the religious life.

The value of religion's service will be discounted unless it is frankly recognized that organized religion has had to deal with human nature in the mass as it concretely shows itself and that the emotional behavior of most men and women has not traveled far from childhood experience.

Mature in many respects, they make little headway in emotional growth. On the level where their emotional life is lodged, the feeling of guilt becomes for many of them, especially the most sensitive, as spontaneous as it is among children who develop conflict. In the adults, however, the feeling is largely self-made, or at least appears to come from the individual's own feeling; while in the case of children, if guilt arises, it is frequently associated with the pronouncement of blame by older persons. Thus the self-appraisal that leads to a sense of sin is a step toward maturity, because it contains an element of self-judgment. It is because of this feeling of failure that religion has a chance to give assurance and to furnish an incentive toward a better-adjusted and more social way of living. It is the bane of any doctrine that attempts to satisfy human needs that it easily becomes formalistic and mechanical and operates without regard for personal differences. When this occurs in religious experience what otherwise would be a means of relieving a sense of failure and of giving inspiration becomes instead the forcing upon the individual of a fictitious experience which is doubly morbid, being both artificial and unwholesome. When the guilt feeling arises there is need of assurance from some source outside the person. Self-forgiveness seems to be impossible. This fact lends force to the interpretation of the psychoanalyst who finds in the experience a reversal to childhood dependency. Just as the child developing a feeling of blame-worthiness seeks from the parent forgiveness and reinstatement into good graces, so the guilty sinner seeks from some outside source the security that once he had from the father or the mother. Viewed from this angle guilt is lack of self-sufficiency, the feeling of need of support. It is the reaction of the emo-

tional orphan who must escape his loneliness and helplessness and again have the sense of belonging.

This insistence upon outside security was vividly impressed upon me years ago when as a college student I
had charge of a small church in a remote country village
in Maine. Near me was a young fellow of about my own
age ill with consumption. I had seen him once and recognized as did his neighbors that it was impossible for him
to recover. He had gone out from this small community
to earn his living in New York City, and had returned to
fight the dread disease. I was visited one morning by his
sister who said that her brother was very ill and was
saying that he could not die without seeing me. At once
I went to the house, and as soon as I entered the room, in
the faintest of whispers he said, "I want to be forgiven."
"You are," I answered, and instantly he died. Desperate
as he was in the clutches of fear and remorse, he turned
to a stranger because he sought authority for an assurance
that he could not give himself.

There is a great difference between the attitude mental
hygiene takes toward the experiences that issue in guilt
and the interpretation of the churches. The latter puts
upon the individual the full responsibility and offers him
the means of release. To the theologian sin is personal.
The scientist goes behind the individual and finds a social
situation of which the individual is a product. He is a
victim of events and of tradition. Even if his guilt is
purely imaginary, his predicament is not charged to him
directly since it is the consequence of preceding influences.
To the theologian this dilutes the sense of sin by spreading
it through the community, and since sin cannot be per-
sonified, it loses its dramatic element and has less force
as a motive to reconstruct the life. The student of mental

hygiene, on the other hand, sees in the orthodox procedure a failure to get at the sources that control character, leading either to the torturing of the individual for not changing what is beyond his power, or permitting him to cover over or drive out of consciousness his fundamental difficulties in adjustment to life.

The situation is parallel to what once was true when physical diseases were thought to be the direct edict of supernatural forces attempting to bring vengeance upon men and women for going astray. Finally the microscope and the laboratory convinced most people that there were specific causes for the various infectious diseases and soon science began to conquer and to prevent because it had a clew to the source of trouble. The movement of psychological and social science is irresistibly toward finding in the social situation that determines character the causal influences that lead to the bad adjustment so frequently expressed in the feeling of guilt.

In spite of these differences of interpretation, in dealing with the concrete individual who needs incentive and confidence as certainly as he requires explanation and diagnosis, the church and mental hygiene specialists work hand in hand. As will be described later in this chapter there are experiments seeking closer coöperation of church and science in the effort to minister to the mentally and socially sick.

Mental disorder and guilt. It is not surprising that we find among those seriously afflicted with mental diseases many illustrations of extreme, morbid guilt reactions. Nearly every mental hospital has a sizeable group of persons who think they have committed the unpardonable sin. Accompanying their disorder is an irresistible impulse to account for their abject failure and hopelessness. They fall back upon the terrifying passage of Scripture which announces that there is one sin that can never be pardoned. This permits them to read back into their earlier career and find some occurrence that they can interpret as responsible for their difficulty, an evil from which they cannot escape.

It is not always true that guilt wells up in the consciousness of patients suffering from mental disorders. There are times when depression has gone so far as to drive from the person the original thought with which was tied the gloom or anxiety to which the individual became captive. In such cases, although the discomfort remains, it is given a new explanation, which conceals its relation to the guilt feeling that on account of its unpleasantness has been forced out of consciousness.

Isolation and guilt feeling. There is one aspect of the guilt experience which particularly interests the mental hygienist, and that is the social isolation felt by the sufferer. He retreats within himself not merely for self-defense, but primarily because he has a sense of shame and the belief that everyone has turned against him on account of his misdoings. In mild form the literature of Puritanism is replete with illustrations of the loneliness of tortured souls who thought themselves separated by their sins from their associates. Such reactions start them on the roadway toward mental disease, for as ties of relationship are broken morbid trends gather headway and to the inner discord must be added social separation. Membership in the group whose standards are accepted as authority proves an efficient barrier against mental disorders. Perhaps no one has described the awful sense of being forsaken on account of sin with more self-revelation than the English poet, William Cowper.

The child who thinks himself estranged on account of guilt feeling from his parents, whom he loves, is driven by overwhelming impulse to confess his fault and by obtaining forgiveness to have again complete fellowship. This experience discloses in simple form the human need of reconciliation which in the adult appears as an urge to rid himself of the sense of sin by some sort of confession. The Roman Catholic Church's provision for oral confession to the priest has a moral and therapeutic value which the Protestant churches generally lack. The psychiatrist is frequently called upon to act the rôle of priest, listening to revelations of guilt that the patient dares not share with anyone except when protected by the professional code of secrecy, and assuring the patient that the guilt need not longer be carried as a hidden burden. Protestantism needs to develop a better method of dealing with personal guilt than public confession of general sinfulness. There is a craving to particularize the guilt to get definitely rid of the burden, and this impulse at present is adequately recognized only by the Roman Catholic confession.

The revival. It is apparent that man's proneness to develop guilt feeling offers those gifted in the stirring of religious emotions a tempting opportunity. How significant this has been in the history of the United States is not yet commonly understood, since we are still too near the era of the evangelist to realize fully the important function he has had as the most powerful religious leader. Theology, by building its system upon the commonly accepted religious emotion of guilt feeling, provided for the evangelist the most favorable conditions. The evangelist was the common denominator of the American colonists, and the first influence that gave the separate provinces a semblance of unity was the sweeping over the entire territory of religious emotionalism.[5]

---

[5] James Truslow Adams, *Provincial Society*, 1690-1763, p. 286.

As we look backward upon the era of the revivalist, it is the morbidity that was brought forth by the movement that attracts our attention.

As we of a different setting react against this, we are led to discount the value of the revival as a means of bringing about more adequate adjustment for the great majority of those that came under its influence. It was a crude process of therapeutics because it used mass suggestion and played upon primitive emotions, but it did influence a multitude to face squarely the realities of their time and place, leading to a moral strengthening of character and more wholesome standards of living. Its emphasis upon the individual and its democratic trend are some of its social consequences which indirectly contributed to healthier standards of living. If it taught a harsh theology and built up fears of a wrathful God, it also furnished an antidote for the feelings it created by offering a salvation which restored the lost soul to the heavenly fellowship from which he was estranged. In the days when the revival flourished, every community had its repeaters who again and again made public confession, but who as everybody expected soon became backsliders. The notoriety that they received has tended to obscure the fact that a larger number continued their professions and made an honest effort to live up to their ideals. The monotony of life in the countryside and village encouraged the revival which afforded relief from the barren life of toil endured by many. At present the movies, the radio, and the newspapers and magazines satisfy needs that once were met by the revival with its experiences of tragedy and comedy, its emotionalism and ever-present opportunity for the spectacular. In the city the revival was an expression of that crowd psychology which now seeks different outlets. The revival has probably lost ground more because of its modern competitors, among which the movies are outstanding, than because of changes in fundamental religious attitude.

Conversion. In the evangelical churches conversion has been the means of entering the Christian life. Not long since, as in remote sections at the present time, it was seriously debated by Christian leaders whether one could be a Christian unless he had first gone through a spectacular conversion which had given him the certainty of being saved. The temptation such a doctrine provided for unstable personalities is apparent, but it is surely an exaggeration to claim, as Swisher has, that all those who were converted were sick souls, expressing the neurotic needs of a divided self.[6] Such interpretation fails to take into account the influence of social fashion. When becoming converted was the standard experience expected of all rightly developing religious people, it surely had a different significance than it does to-day when the church is primarily concerned with educating the young in such a way as to preclude the necessity of any violent upheaval such as once was the expected thing. Conversion represented escape from the feeling of guilt. It was a being born again, and literally did for many reorganize their inner life. It was a point of departure from which they dated their higher aspirations.

It was in the conviction of sin that the greater risk of morbidity was lodged, and when so much was done to stimulate introspection and repentance a way of escape had to be provided. The publicity that confession received, associated as it often was with most dramatic occurrences, made it stand out in the life of the individual as the most distinguishable of all of his experi-

[6] W. S. Swisher, *Religion and the New Psychology*, p. 147.

ences. Because of this all the moral and spiritual efforts
and aspirations were built upon it. Therefore it was not
a mere fiction, but a genuine recasting of the personality,
lifting the majority to higher levels of behavior. Even
many of those who clearly revealed neurotic tendencies
as they passed through this experience, for example John
Bunyan and George Fox, were in the end better integrated
since it lessened their inner conflict and made possible a
better adjustment to life. The large place that conversion
had in the religious program during the dominance of
evangelism created special difficulty for the conscientious,
calm-minded individuals who found it distasteful to follow the prevailing religious fashion.

It is well to remember that conversion was often closely
allied to inferiority feeling, that it offered thus one distinction to many prosaic lives. Against the gray of ordinary experience appeared this vivid and public recognition of the value of the individual to the church, the community and even to God himself. This motive was played
upon skillfully by the popular evangelist, and not without
result. For a multitude conversion in the revival became
the most vital satisfaction of the will-to-power cravings
realized during their life-time.

It is important also to notice how directly the guilt
feeling was related in the life of many to their primitive
emotions, especially those connected with sex. It was in
regard to sex that strain was felt, and the conflict was
similar to the warfare between the flesh and spirit so
forcefully depicted by St. Paul. Conversion did not always give complete victory to the higher impulses, but it
usually tipped the balance on the side of self-control, thus
leading to a more unified personality. As conversion
provided entrance into the religious life, according

to the Protestant formula faith gave the vigor that made it possible for the believer to carry on. In making so much of faith the church did not create a special ecclesiastical impulse, but took over something universal among men and women and adapted it to the special doctrines and purposes of the church. In the words of St. Paul, "Faith is assurance of things hoped for, the conviction of things not seen." In its wide meaning it is a human need, for it both establishes the security we must have and at the same time gives promise of satisfactions not yet experienced. It is found everywhere because men and women, in their various contacts with life, require the feeling of security, a foundation for hope. Thus faith becomes an antidote for fear, and is especially serviceable as a means of taking away the guilt feeling, which contains so much of morbid risk. It also gives the believer, just as in former times, the means of supporting himself in periods of trial and dismay by his reminiscence of the high moments of his life. As the Christian oscillated from feelings of depression and defeat to those of elevation and success, he could draw, through faith, upon his confidence in the Heavenly Father to tide over his periods of discouragement. This has been well expressed by Browning: [7]

> The more of doubt, the stronger faith, I say,
> If faith o'ercomes doubt. . . .
>
> .   .   .   .
>
> What matter though I doubt at every pore,
> Head-doubts, heart-doubts, doubts at my fingers' ends,
> Doubts in the trivial work of every day,
> Doubts at the very bases of my soul
> In the grand moments when she probes herself—
> If finally I have a life to show,

[7] *Browning's Complete Poetical Works,* Cambridge Edition, p. 354.

The thing I did, brought out in evidence
Against the thing done to me underground
By hell and all its brood, for aught I know?

Mental hygiene recognizes that faith works wonders not only in religious experience and in the ordinary undertakings of life, but especially in psychotherapy where expectation counts so strongly in favor of the patient. The specialist welcomes as an ally strong faith without regard to the form it takes, because he knows it will give the patient a sense of security and a hopefulness which will reënforce all the influences that are making for better mental health.

Mental hygiene also knows that the subjective basis of faith carries the danger that actual facts may be pushed aside by what is nothing less than a special sort of daydreaming. Since faith issues from wishes, it is not unlike the child's reverie. Necessarily this permits faith to take the place not only of works, but of judgment. That faith must be confined within its proper territory is felt by nearly all who make use of it as a religious motive. But there are great differences in estimating where it belongs and where it intrudes. Faith, in so far as it is related to beliefs that are born of human ignorance, or to attempts to control nature through mere wishful thinking, is constantly being replaced by the accumulation of knowledge brought by science. As soon as the means of accomplishing any definite thing are thoroughly understood through experiment and investigation, we turn to the knowledge gained, rather than to faith, as a resource in our efforts to accomplish our purposes. But mental hygiene appreciates that no life is consistently scientific and that there are voids in existing knowledge which faith alone can fill. It also values the faith that gives one's life the general temper of confidence. Thus mental hygiene dreads the faith that pushes itself where knowledge is already supreme, while at the same time welcoming the same attitude as it flavors the life of the individual with assurance and serenity.

Mental hygiene senses the loss that has come to those who have given up their faith and found no substitute, just as it realizes that there is not in the modern world anything that satisfactorily replaces the old-time conversion as a mechanism for changing life in the mass and starting it toward higher levels of living.

Prayer.   Prayer in some form always accompanies religious faith.   A thoroughgoing discussion of the significance of prayer would involve exploring the entire territory of religion, since nothing reveals the characteristics of any religious doctrine more clearly than the ideas and practices of prayer.   Fortunately in treating prayer from the mental hygiene aspects it is not necessary to deal with it so extensively.   Although the interest of mental hygiene in prayer is restricted, it is extremely practical.   Prayer in the life of the believer has a definite function, and one that influences personality to a degree that makes it, according to its character, a morbid or healthful factor in the life.   Each type of prayer, however, must be judged upon the level where it appears, and it would be contrary to the principles of mental hygiene to estimate its value to any person by measuring its distance from what the investigator might choose as the norm on what to him appears to be the highest level of religious experience. Mental hygiene is not interested in standardizing prayer, but in discovering the way it functions to hurt or to help the individual to adjust himself to the environment in which he has been placed.

The motives of prayer are many, and the theorist is

likely to choose one of these and build upon it his interpretation of the nature of prayer. Human experience,
in all times and places, reveals prayer in operation. If
these various expressions can be drawn together in one
general motive, it would be that prayer comes from human
need seeking supernatural help. Prayer casts out fear,
destroys isolation, and inspires confidence. It is born of
the desire for security and is so universally found among
men that it is not strange that it has been considered the
expression of an instinct and is even yet so regarded by
many. In our time, however, a more careful use of the
term "instinct" forbids the scientist's assuming an instinct
of prayer because supplication is so common. If there be
an instinct of self-preservation, prayer is surely related
to it, for prayer issues from a sense of dependence and a
belief that help can be had. Prayer, as it is practiced, is
not merely an expression of finite helplessness; it is also,
as it appears in the lives of men and women, an attempt
at wish-fulfillment. Thus, in the experiences of some people, it is distinctly related to the magic that flourishes in
primitive society and has never yet been absent from
any civilization.

The following prayers, taken from an African tribe,
are representative of savage experience and disclose the
various motives involved:

"Ye spirits, spirits of my departed ancestors, protect me on
my journey [or, let my hunting prosper, and so on] and guard
my children and keep them safe while I am away." [8]

"Oh! Spirit of my father: who worked iron here of yore,
Listen to me, and hear my prayer.
To-morrow I, too, will work at the iron.

[8] Melland, F. H., *In Witchbound Africa,* p. 134.

I pray thee, help me, and guide my work, that it may prosper." [9]

"Ye who lived and died here long ago: ye spirits of these streams, be propitious and let these gardens that we are about to make be productive, and bring forth abundantly in due season." [10]

"Thus, God, we are all thy people. Send us rain!" [11]

Prayer in savage society, as with us, is more than a mere belief in a supernatural power. There also has to be faith that this power is approachable. This is well brought out by the following remark of an African savage:

"We never pray to God because we do not know Him, but we pray to leaves, fetishes, and to the *dead*." [12]

We, of the modern mind, think of prayer upon a higher and a lower level. On the latter it tends to be an effort to make use of supernatural power to supplement the inability of the supplicant to deal with his circumstances. The wishes turn outward and seek assistance as a means of getting security or winning success. On the higher level prayer tends to be primarily fellowship and resignation. Here the wishes turn inward, and the individual craves a sense of contact with the unseen as a means of achieving inward peace. Whatever one's theory with reference to the reality of prayer as a means of changing outside circumstances, it is important to recognize that prayer on either the higher or the lower level may act to release unused resources in the life of the individual by giving him a sense of confidence and freeing him from

[9] Melland, F. H., *In Witchbound Africa*, p. 137.
[10] *Ibid.*, p. 138.
[11] *Ibid.*, p. 155.
[12] G. Cyril Claridge, *Wild Bush Tribes of Tropical Africa*, p. 151.

the paralysis of fear or the depression of loneliness. Worcester repeats a quotation that describes the effect of Luther's prayer when he arrived to find his co-laborer, Philipp Melanchthon, apparently dying from an illness which was in part due to the feeling of remorse.

When Luther arrived he found Melanchthon apparently dying; his eyes were sunk, his sense gone, his face fallen in and hollow, and as Luther said, *"Facies erat Hippocratica."* He knew nobody, ate and drank nothing. When Luther saw him thus disfigured, he was frightened above measure and said to his companions, "God forfend, how has the Devil defaced this Organon!" He then turned forthwith to the window and prayed fervently to God . . . Hereupon he grasped Philipp by the hand: "Be of good courage, Philipp, thou shalt not die; give no place to the spirit of sorrow, and be not thine own murderer, but trust in the Lord, who can slay and make alive again, can wound and bind up, can smite and heal again." For Luther well knew the burden of his heart and conscience . . . Then Philipp by degrees became more cheerful and let Luther order something to eat and Luther brought it himself to him, but Philipp refused it. Then Luther forced him with these threats, saying, "Hark, Philipp, thou must eat, or I excommunicate thee." With these words he was overcome so that he ate a very little and thus by degrees he gained strength again.[13]

This dymogenic power of prayer which exchanges in the believer hopelessness and guilt feeling for confidence and eagerness to demonstrate repentance is familiar to the specialist in mental therapeutics who often welcomes as an ally his patient's belief in prayer. When employed to turn one from despair to face an ordeal with assurance of final victory, prayer gathers up the resources of the life

[13] Elwood Worcester, *Religion and Medicine,* pp. 310-11.

whose unity has been broken by conflict and starts the individual toward success.[14]

The following prayer of Mohammed uses the desires of a desert people to make vivid the higher need of divine fellowship. By putting the first in contrast with the second a most impressive supplication is produced:

O Lord, grant us to love thee; grant that we may love those that love Thee; grant that we may do the deeds that win Thy love. Make the love of Thee to be dearer to us than ourselves, our families, than wealth, and even than cool water. Amen.[15]

Mysticism. Although mysticism is not necessarily confined to religious experience, it almost always takes on a religious aspect and finds in religious faith its supreme expression. Religious mysticism shows itself in various forms and offers neurotics an opportunity which they have used to the uttermost. As a consequence of the morbid outlook upon life characteristic of many mystics celebrated in history, all mysticism has come to be regarded by some writers as evidence of mental unsoundness. They have found in the mystic experience the essential meaning of religion which they have described as something similar to the neurosis. Recently Freud has announced his explanation of religion: It is a clinging to childhood desires and illusions which the weakness of the individual and his fear of life or lack of preparation to deal with it forces him to nourish since, were he to face the facts as they are, he would suffer from utter helplessness.[16] The same idea was previously expressed by Everett Dean Martin in *The Mystery of Religion*. This

[14] For the relation of magic and religion see Lévy-Bruhl, *Primitive Mentality,* Chaps. I and II.

[15] S. F. Fox, *A Chain of Prayer Across the Ages,* p. 27.

[16] Sigmund Freud, *Future of an Illusion,* p. 85.

same notion of religion as a narcotic obtained through mysticism appeared in a still earlier discussion written by one of the coöperating authors of this book, but this cannot in fairness be regarded as a just description of all mysticism.[17]

Only the extreme partisan will deny the narcotic characteristic that appears in mysticism. Even Freud himself, however, admits that this sort of religious experience is advantageous for some individuals. It may not be for them the heroic facing of life, but by making use of its protection they are better able to endure their hardships, and although their policy may not be that of the healthy minded, they are hardly to be censored for finding a refuge that protects them from inevitable disaster. If under certain circumstances even insanity has a benign influence and serves as a biological protection against unendurable suffering, mysticism of the neurotic type offers a refuge that those experienced in human need would hesitate to snatch away.

There is, however, a different interpretation of mysticism, expressed particularly by Hinckley, who compares the experience with that of the artist.[18] As she sees it, mysticism is a kind of creative mechanism which suggests a capacity of which the average human being does not dream. She rules out the psuedo-mysticism of hysterical experiences, just as she would the same sort of phenomena in the realm of art, and considers true mysticism the lifting of the individual to self-possession and a sense of unity on the highest level of his experience. From this point of view the mystic has an inner source of strength which permits him to make a final adjustment of physical

[17] See E. R. Groves: "An Unsocial Element in Religion," *The American Journal of Sociology,* Vol. XXII, pp. 657-62.

[18] B. H. Hinckley, *The Re-creating of the Individual,* pp. 340-47, and 355.

and spiritual conflicts, so that with serenity he views life without disturbing conflicts and with no temptation to accept counterfeit values. It is in limiting mysticism to retreat from reality, and in failing to appreciate the different sort of mystic experience which provides a final settlement for the conflicting impulses which harass most people throughout life, that many critics of mysticism err.

Lord Shaftesbury illustrates forcefully the mystic who is strengthened for a long ordeal and who, because of the roots from which he draws his inspiration, can continue through discouragement, loneliness and misunderstanding without ever thinking of deviating from the hard path he has chosen. His religion has been described as simple, rigid, final, and exclusive.[19] The harder his task grew, the more he fell back upon God, but this was not retreat, but merely the lifting of the conflict to a level where the final victory could not be doubted. His experience literally suggests the simile of Phillips Brooks who compared the life assured of God as having the quiet of the deep sea, however tumultuous its surface. As the Hammonds say, Lord Shaftesbury, far ahead of his period in making war against exploitation and in attempting to serve those who had no understanding of the help he brought, could not have gone on calmly without the sustaining force of religion.[20] In such experiences mental hygiene sees complete commitment to the task at hand and a final settlement of emotional conflict which releases the individual from inward tension, permitting him to put all his resources into his chosen purpose. Although recognizing that this unity comes to many through religion,

[19] J. L. and Barbara Hammond, *Lord Shaftesbury*, p. 240.
[20] *Ibid.*, p. 240.

mental hygiene does not insist that such compelling motivation can come only in this way.

Spiritual healing. The title, Medicine Man, given to men who dealt with magic and the occult among savages, testifies to the intimate relationship that once existed between what we now call religion and medicine; on a still higher level of social culture the priest functioned as healer and even early Christianity maintained an alliance between spiritual leadership and the cure of the sick. In our time, however, there has been an entire separation of church and medical science, in so far as each has followed along conventional lines. The separation has become indeed an opposition for the great majority of workers in each field. On the part of the doctors there has been resentment at any encroachment of religion in their domain, while those who have used faith for healing or have insisted upon the spiritual dominance over the material have gone to the length of insisting that those who seek the physician when ill are revealing a lack of confidence in God as Christians without faith.

Rather recently there have been clear evidences of a moving away from these two extreme positions. The physicians, partly because of the new psychology, have come to realize the significance of mental attitudes and the availability of the religious motive as a means in helping the patient to use all his capacity in the effort to achieve health. Likewise those who have maintained the supremacy of the spiritual are becoming more tolerant toward those who wish also to enlist the services of physicians in dealing with conditions of the body. One sign of the closer sympathy of medicine as science and religion as a dynamic influence over the personality has been the appointment of a joint committee on the relation of religion to health, composed of representatives of the New York Academy of Medicine and the Federated Council of Churches.

In spite of the separation there has been in the past between orthodox medical science and the orthodox church, there have been within and without the churches many different sorts of efforts to use religion as a means of cure. These have usually emphasized physical disease, although the minor mental disorders have been included. Of all the various forms that this spiritual healing has taken, that of Christian Science has been most widespread, having passed from its original birthplace in the United States to all civilized countries. This is based, as is now generally known, principally upon three ideas:

1. God is all-powerful.
2. God is good, and God is mind.
3. Since God, who is Spirit, is everything, there is no such thing as matter.

Disease, therefore, is an error—a denial of the goodness of God. The person who is ill rids himself of his wrong thinking by prayer and insistence upon the goodness of God. If unable to bring himself from his error, he seeks the practitioner, who in his presence, or if necessary at a distance, helps him to strengthen his faith and win his victory. Throughout the treatment much stress is put upon the reading of the writings of Mary Baker Eddy, the founder of the Church.

There is another following which for want of a better term may be called New Thought. This, in its present form, is an offshoot from the Transcendental movement of New England. To this has been allied a special branch of psychology which gives the doctrine a semblance of science. As a matter of fact there are so many different groups in this movement that the plural, doctrines, is more applicable than anything that suggests a common belief. Much is made of the "subconscious mind" and the establishment of harmony between the individual and the infinite spirit that includes all.

Within the orthodox church we have various efforts to bring religion into the territory of disease. The Emmanuel Movement, one of the oldest of these, will be discussed later. The Church Mystical Union, established in England and now making progress in this country, aims to encourage mystical experience, and also claims to bring health to those who are sick. The Nazarene Movement started in this country as a result of the success that appeared to follow the pastoral ministrations of the Rev. Henry D. Wilson. Although this emphasizes faith cure it does not ignore the doctor. Healing missions in various parts of the country are held from time to time to which any afflicted persons may come, where without medical diagnosis it is expected that the service, which resembles the ordinary church worship, will contribute to the winning of health. There are other special types of service that the churches have carried on in their attempts to serve the sick, but these mentioned are representative.[21] The Roman Catholic Church also has its famous shrines that have come to be known as places of healing, the best known being Lourdes in France and St. Anne de Beaupré in Canada.

Although spiritual healing concerns itself mostly with the cure of physical ailments, it has a decided significance for mental hygiene. Many of the cases are clearly the

[21] The reader is urged to read Ellis B. Parkman's "Religious Healing," *Mental Hygiene,* July, 1926, a preliminary report on a survey conducted under the auspices of a subcommittee appointed by the Committee on Public Health Relations of the New York Academy of Medicine, and also the article by Rev. Samuel McComb, "Spiritual Healing in Europe," *Mental Hygiene,* October, 1928.

removal of physical symptoms of hysteria and other mental disorders. Mental hygiene appreciates the value of religious faith as a therapeutic influence. The fact that faith brings confidence, thus utilizing the resources of the patient, and the opposite fact, that in the light of science there are decided limits as to what this faith unaided can accomplish, make the proper use of faith a problem for mental hygiene, which recognizes the force of both these facts. For example, in cases where medicine at present is helpless it is possible for suggestion to give the patient an apparent cure because it turns his attention away from his symptoms and even his pain, and permits him to concentrate upon the idea that he wishes to have true. This, however, does not mean that the malady from which he suffers has disappeared, for sooner or later he succumbs to it.

This same experience comes to those who go to the faith healer when suffering from the beginning of a disease which, rightly treated, could be finally cured. The instantaneous relief the individual often gets deceives him into thinking that he is cured. Thus valuable time is lost which often means that when the case comes back to medical science it is too late to accomplish anything. Recently in the state of Massachusetts an example of this occurred. A man arrested for practicing medicine without a license brought his patients to testify to the cures that he had accomplished. One case was particularly pathetic. The sufferer insisted that he had been cured of tuberculosis. Eventually the state obtained an X-ray of his lungs, and it was found that the disease, which, at the time of its treatment by the quack, offered a certainty of recovery, had progressed so far that medical science could offer no hope of its cure. On the other hand, one of the authors, threatened with pneumonia and making a hearty effort to coöperate with doctor and nurse as he slowly made progress with his infection, finally had to rebuke his physician for a psychology which, by emphasizing pessimism, was creating unfavorable conditions that in the case of an inexperienced and untrained patient might have lessened the chances of recovery.   There is clearly need of study of this baffling problem of the relation of subjective attitude and objective body conditions, and it is not yet wise for the scientist to dogmatize. It is evident, however, that medical science has to some extent in the past neglected a resource which makes for health and assists recovery in case of illness.   There is at present a growing opinion both among doctors and religious people that there is need of coöperation in using religious confidence and scientific technique.   But the mere desire for a better working together does not solve the problem created by spiritual healing.

Since medicine, with its scientific temper, prognosticates cautiously or even at times with fatalism, there are innumerable persons who are tempted, when science offers no hope, to seek it from those who, disregarding scientific teaching, promise cure by the use of forces claimed to be superior to those of the doctor.

Church experiments in mental hygiene.   Three different types of mental hygiene service carried on by churches have been chosen for interpretation.   The first is the Emmanuel Movement which started in the Emmanuel Episcopalian Church of Boston, under the leadership of Rev. Dr. Worcester and Rev. Dr. Samuel McComb.   Although these men were not physicians, they were students of psychology and enlisted the interest of Boston specialists, including Dr. Richard Cabot of the Harvard Medical School and Dr. Isadore Coriat of Tufts Medical School.   Dr. Worcester and Dr. McComb were eager to better the physical and mental health of people in need, and finally developed a health class to which patients were admitted after a competent examination which showed that they were not suffering from an organic disease that needed medical or surgical treatment. Morning and evening clinics were held daily and a mid-week meeting at which practical problems of mental hygiene were discussed. Of late this work has been largely confined to victims of drug and alcoholic habits.

Before the Emmanuel application of mental hygiene was publicly announced, the leading neurologists of New England were consulted to determine whether they would approve the undertaking if conducted with discretion. As a result the medical men were sympathetic from the start. The work was begun, not only with confidence that religious faith could be employed to help those suffering from functional disorders, but also in the belief that such maladies were frequently caused by character disturbances of moral origin. At one time results of this work at Emmanuel Church were checked by Dr. Cabot, who made a study of 178 cases treated. The survey showed a considerable success in treating neurasthenia, alcoholism, obsession, hysteria, drug habits, and depression so extreme as to threaten suicide.

Another interesting application of religion to mental hygiene is the work of Rev. A. T. Boisen, chaplain of the Worcester, Massachusetts, State Hospital. Mr. Boisen has given much thought to the moral problems involved in mental conflicts as they appear in the insane hospital, becoming literally a specialist in sick souls. He has also investigated the religious life of persons suffering from mental disorder. Approaching his problems from a background of psychology and sociology, in his work at Worcester he is making a unique contribution from the religious angle to the field of mental disorder. His experience has convinced him of the value of giving clinic training in the mental hospital to those entering the ministry.

A third and different experiment, that is more recent, is being carried on by Rev. Moses R. Lovell of Mount Pleasant Congregational Church, Washington, D. C. In December, 1928, Mr. Lovell opened the first life-adjustment center carried on by a church offering free counsel to those needing practical help in meeting the hard circumstances of their life. For some time Mr. Lovell had been pondering upon the problem of bringing the church more actively into the life of people in need. Coming under the inspiration of Dr. William A. White, Superintendent of Saint Elizabeth Hospital for the Insane at Washington, he finally matured the idea of offering a free clinic service, wider in scope than anything that had been sponsored by churches up to that time. To use his own words, in summarizing the purpose of his undertaking, "We wanted to add science to religion in dealing with life's problems, and we wanted to open our doors widely to all types of human problems—in fact, make this truly a life adjustment center where people might come with all kinds of problems and find relief and help."

On the opening night of the clinic Mr. Lovell had gathered a staff of volunteers, including a doctor, a psychiatrist, a social worker, a general counselor, a director of religious education, all specialists of the highest standing in their several professions. One of the authors of this book was present on the night this work was inaugurated. Thirty individuals applied for assistance. The clinic, which opened at seven, did not conclude its first session until nearly midnight.

In summarizing this work for the first year Mr. Lovell reports that 96 per cent of those asking for assistance came from the middle class, troubled with all kinds of individual and social problems with which they needed practical outside assistance. Although many of the problems considered were social, especially those relating to vocational difficulties and unemployment, suggesting the need of adding an economist to the staff for the second year of the experiment, a large portion of the cases were definitely within the field of mental hygiene. This experiment is distinctive in that it is not primarily using religious belief for mental healing, but maintaining under church auspices a distributing center for modern science, for the benefit of those who need concrete assistance in dealing with the problems that life has brought them.

The training of the minister. A great part of the moral difficulties with which the Christian church deals is the result of conditions and experiences that cannot be rightly interpreted without the background of modern science. In its effort to minister to human need the Christian church is necessarily concerned with problems of mental hygiene. For the church's best efficiency its pastors should be trained to appreciate the meaning of human maladjustment and should be familiar with the practices and principles of mental hygiene. To fulfill its mission in the modern world the church must make greater use of modern science, and to accomplish this there is need of specific training in the theological seminary, that the pastor may be equipped to deal more understandingly with difficulties of personal adjustment. Mr. Boisen suggests a clinic year in an institution where mental problems are scientifically studied. Mental hygiene taught by a competent psychiatrist has more to offer the average candidate for the ministry than Hebrew or Greek exegesis. The form of religious ministration changes with varying civilizations, and there is already evidence that in the modern world, the product of applied science, the church has a large obligation for the distribution of the principles of mental hygiene in the effort to help troubled people reconstruct their lives.

Personality the goal. It has often been observed that Jesus in his public ministry dealt mostly with individuals. Perhaps it would be more accurate to say that his attention was always fixed upon the human personality. In our thought of the doings of men and women we are constantly tempted to describe their behavior by the use of abstractions, such as sin or virtue. If, however, we come close to the everyday conduct of people, we find ourselves obliged to deal with behavior that is extremely personal and altogether concrete. And when we trace our problem to its origin, we are led into the inmost life of the person. The problem becomes one of personality.

What we find true when we diagnose others is equally characteristic of ourselves. Personality is the source of all the disturbances and inner divisions that develop as people express their desires; it is also the goal of individual achievement. Everything that happens in a human career registers in personality. Nothing can be developed from any man or woman which is not a genuine product of the peculiar personality that he has become. Until we get to the personality itself we are always dealing with the outer wrappings that cover the essential heart of the person. This fact explains the difficulty that science encounters just as soon as it attempts to understand personality. The study becomes as intricate as human character. It is as vastly complex as human decisions. It is also as discordant as are the motives that are supposed to direct human activity. Indeed the motives themselves are nothing more than the outcroppings of personality.

Although the progress of science is extremely slow in

dealing with something so fundamental as human personality, it goes forward in its effort and the information it gathers is of supreme importance to anybody who wishes either to understand himself or others. The artist can skillfully catch the expression of personality and give it permanent record. He who is gifted in literary expression can dissect expressions of personality and construct fictitious characters that give convincing form to the struggles characteristic of human life.

The scientist attempts something more difficult. It is his business to interpret the personality as a product of law made by influences that can be understood and classified. Science can never assume a task harder or more fundamental. It cannot, however, ignore the challenge of life, for man is not and never has been satisfied to know things and not himself. The science that deals with personality is merely taking over an endeavor as old as man himself, but which previously has been an undertaking vexing to man because it has brought forth little substance. Its present promise is the most hopeful event in the history of man.

To this science the church cannot be indifferent if it seriously attempts to help men and women with the equipment for service that successful ministration in the modern world demands.

ILLUSTRATIVE CASE

An attractive country girl who was a clerk in a village dry-goods store became acquainted with a young college student during his summer vacation, finally eloped with him and entered matrimony at nineteen. The marriage was disapproved by his parents, but they made the best of the unwelcome circumstances, merely urging the son to continue college. This he refused to do, but instead entered a law office and after a time was admitted to the bar. From the start he lacked ambition and found the practice of law distasteful. Eventually his wife returned to the store and somewhat later bought it from the owner who was willing to give her long time credit, as he wished to retire. She was extraordinarily efficient and rapidly paid off the debt. Meanwhile, her husband left his profession and, except for helping his wife a little with the accounts, did nothing. Their married life was unhappy. Tension came from the fact that she refused to have children and from certain habits of her husband to which the wife constantly objected. He spent much of his time hanging around the hotel, where his associates were noticeably inferior to him in opportunity, training, and economic status. This she felt to be disgraceful. At times she seriously thought of getting a divorce as she was urged to do by her relatives. After several years of unhappy domestic life she began to have headaches and other physical ills which sent her frequently to doctors. Through a friend she became interested in a religious cult. Claiming that she was cured of her physical suffering, she refused henceforth to have any confidence in medical science. Her religious faith irritated her husband and separated them more widely, but her new attitude of tolerance regarding his behavior reduced the domestic strain and made their home life more comfortable. Her engrossment in her religious belief increased until, retiring from business, she gave her entire attention to it. Her concentration is now so great that she has no other interest in life.

SUGGESTIONS FOR CLASSROOM DISCUSSION

1. Why must religion prove an ally or an opponent of mental hygiene?
2. What are the common forms of religious morbidity?
3. Did Protestantism create guilt feeling or use that already developed?
4. Why is a sense of sin less common now than during the last century?

5. Why do insane people so often believe themselves guilty of the unpardonable sin?

6. Is faith in spiritual healing increasing or decreasing?

7. What position should the Christian church take concerning faith healing?

8. Did Jesus observe the principles of mental hygiene?

SUGGESTIONS FOR WRITTEN REPORTS

1. Hawthorne as a psychoanalyst.
2. Bunyan's *Pilgrim's Progress*.
3. The guilt feeling of William Cowper.
4. Famous American revivalists interpreted from the point of view of mental hygiene.
5. Modern types of mysticism.
6. The religious faith of Lord Shaftesbury.
7. Eduard Coué and his cures.

SELECTED BIBLIOGRAPHY

BARNES, C. RANKIN. "Is There a Technique for the Care of Souls?" *Religious Education,* September, 1929, Vol. XXIV, pp. 619-23.

BLACKMAN, EARL L. "Mental Hygiene Clinic in the Church." *Religious Education,* September, 1929, Vol. XXIV, pp. 636-39.

BOISEN, ANTON T. "The Challenge to Our Seminaries," reprint from *Christian Work.*

—— "Concerning the Relationship Between Religious Experience and Mental Disorders." *Mental Hygiene,* April, 1923, pp. 307-11.

—— "Evangelism in the Light of Psychiatry." *The Journal of Religion,* January, 1927, pp. 76-80.

—— "Personality Changes and Upheavals Arising out of the Sense of Personal Failure." *American Journal of Psychiatry,* April, 1926, pp. 531-51.

—— "The Psychiatric Approach to the Study of Religion." *Religious Education,* March, 1928.

—— "The Sense of Isolation in Mental Disorders: Its Religious Significance." *The American Journal of Sociology*, January, 1928, pp. 555-67.

BOISEN, ANTON T. "The Study of Mental Disorders as a Basis for a Program of Moral and Religious Re-Education." *Religious Education*, April, 1928.

BOWMAN, KARL M. "Religious Problems in Clinical Cases." *Religious Education*, September, 1929, Vol. XXIV, pp. 631-35.

COOKE, GEORGE WILLIS. *The Social Evolution of Religion*, Chap. VIII. London, 1921.

ELLIOTT, HARRISON S. "Mental Hygiene and Religious Education." *Religious Education*, September, 1919, Vol. XXIV, pp. 616-18.

EMERY, E. VAN NORMAN. "Co-operation Between Clergyman, Psychiatrist, and Social Worker." *Religious Education*, September, 1929, Vol. XXIV, pp. 624-30.

FREUD, SIGMUND. *The Future of an Illusion*. New York, 1928.

GRANT, PRYOR McN. "The Moral and Religious Life of the Individual in the Light of the New Psychology." *Mental Hygiene*, July, 1928, pp. 451-91.

GROVES, E. R. "An Unsocial Element in Religion." *The American Journal of Sociology*, March, 1917, pp. 657-62.

GRUEHN, D. WERNER. "Feelings and Emotions in the Psychology of Religion." *Feelings and Emotions*, Chap. XXXII, The Wittenberg Symposium, pp. 372-84.

HÖFFDING, HAROLD. *The Philosophy of Religion*, Chap. III. New York, 1906.

ISAACS, SUSAN. "Privation and Guilt." *International Journal of Psycho-analysis* (London), April-July, 1929, Vol. X, pp. 335-47.

JAEGER, MARTHA H. "Mental Hygiene in the Y. W. C. A." *Religious Education*, September, 1929, Vol. XXIV, pp. 640-42.

JAENSCH, ERICK. "Psychological and Psychophysical Investigations of Types in Their Relation to the Psychology of Religion." *Feelings and Emotions*, Chap. XXXI, The Wittenberg Symposium, pp. 356-71.

KAMIAT, ARNOLD H. "A Psychology of Asceticism." *The*

Journal of Abnormal and Social Psychology, July-September, 1928, pp. 223-31.

LEONARD, ARTHUR GLYN. *The Lower Niger and Its Tribes.* London, 1906.

LEUBA, JAMES H. "A Modern Mystic." *The Journal of Abnormal Psychology,* October, 1920, pp. 209-23.

LUND, FREDERICK H. "The Psychology of Belief." *The Journal of Abnormal and Social Psychology,* April, 1925, pp. 63-81.

McCARTNEY, J. L. "The Call to Foreign Missions; Its Effect on Unstable Personalities." *Mental Hygiene,* July, 1928, pp. 521-29.

MARTIN, EVERETT DEAN. *The Mystery of Religion.* New York, 1924.

MOXON, CAVENDISH. "Mystical Ecstasy and Hysterical Dream-States." *The Journal of Abnormal Psychology,* December, 1920-March, 1921, pp. 329-34.

MYRICK, HELEN L. "Mental Hygiene as a Character Builder." *Religious Education,* September, 1929, Vol. XXIV, pp. 652-56.

PUTNAM, JAMES J. "Sketch for a Study of New England Character." *The Journal of Abnormal Psychology,* June, 1917, pp. 73-99.

SCHROEDER, THEODORE. "Guilt and Inferiority-Feeling as Creator of Religious Experience." *The Psychoanalytic Review,* January, 1929, pp. 46-54.

—— "The Psychoanalytic Approach to Religious Experience." *The Psychoanalytic Review,* October, 1929, Vol. XVI, 4, pp. 361-76.

—— "Revivals, Sex and Holy Ghost." *The Journal of Abnormal Psychology,* April-June, 1919, pp. 34-47.

SHEPHERD, W. T. "A Study of the Methods of Revivalists." *The Journal of Abnormal and Social Psychology,* June-September, 1921, pp. 136-43.

SWISHER, WALTER SAMUEL. *Religion and the New Psychology.* Boston, 1920.

WORCESTER, ELWOOD. Religion and Medicine. New York, 1908.

CHAPTER XIII

MENTAL HYGIENE ASPECTS OF LITERATURE

Literature as a flight from reality. One of the chief psychological appeals of reading is the way of escape which it offers into a fuller, richer life. As we read the novel, the short story or the drama, we frequently identify ourselves with certain of the characters. Living through them for the moment, we obtain a vicarious gratification of some of our unsatisfied desires; for the time being we share with them romance, adventure or luxury. The type of reading which we enjoy depends to some extent upon which of these satisfactions we have most missed from our own lives.

The pleasure in reading is, in this respect, closely akin to that of the daydream. In daydreams we picture the fulfillment of wishes which we have been unable to gratify in actual daily life. But with many of us, after the peak of daydreaming at adolescence is passed, this phantasy method of wish-fulfillment is for the most part abandoned. Hence we turn to fiction as a substitute.

The very beginnings of literature, in the days of the wandering minstrel and story-teller, undoubtedly filled this psychological need. In a recent article, Lorine Pruette describes how the long, winter evenings in many a feudal hall were saved from utter boredom by the story-teller's arts. The folk-tale and fairy-tale, those early forms of literature, were distinctly of the wish-fulfillment type. The poor boy proves to be a stolen princeling; the beggar maid becomes the bride of the wealthy lord; the enchanted maiden is rescued by an heroic lover; all the restrictions of space and time are set aside by the wishing ring or the magic carpet.

Thus from the times when stories were passed on from one person to another by word of mouth, or laboriously recorded in ancient script upon rolls of parchment, up to the invention of printing and the widespread distribution of books among a literate people, there has always been a type of literature which would enable one to forget the everyday world in which he was compelled to live. Thus literature has served the purpose of a safety valve by permitting temporary, and usually healthy, flights from a reality that few of us, perhaps, have the courage to face squarely all the time. By furnishing a partial anesthetic for grief and anxiety, and relieving monotonous hours, it has often had a positive value. For some few persons, to be sure, when reality becomes too continuously painful, the temptation to retreat completely into the world of books is too strong to be resisted. Thus we see certain individuals taking refuge in reading to the neglect of activities entailed by the business of living and necessary for economic and social adjustment. But rarely does indulgence in reading assume this extreme form. Ordinarily, only a temporary release is sought in literature, from which we may return refreshed to take up the burdens of daily life.

The vogue of the love story. We have only to glance at the circulation figures for magazines and books which cater primarily to interest in sex to realize how many people seek vicarious thrills in this field. A popular type of sex literature is represented by such periodicals as *Snappy Stories* and *Breezy Stories,* both selling over 125,000 copies monthly; or *True Romances* and *True Stories,* which run to 650,000 or more copies a month.

True Confessions, Modern Marriage and other periodicals of similar nature may also be quoted at figures in the hundreds of thousands.[1] In New York City alone 150,-000 copies of the magazines of this type are sold monthly, while a small Ohio town with a population of 25,000 requires 1,800 copies a month for its news-stands. It is estimated that the combined total circulation for all the sex magazines reaches 55,560,000 annually for the whole country.[2]

The wide appeal of stories of love and passion is also indicated by the sales record of such novels as *Flaming Youth,* of which 160,000 copies had been sold within a year after its first appearance. Each monthly list of the ten best sellers in fiction includes such books, more or less romantic in style, but all characterized by the theme of love, in conventional or unconventional terms. On the best seller list for one thirty day period, for example, we find *Unforbidden Fruit,* which deals with the love affairs of several college girls; *Georgie May,* the story of a prostitute who is finally glorified by a great passion, and *Wintersmoon,* a dignified romance revolving around a beautiful English country estate. *Swan Song,* a love tale which carries on the fortunes of Galsworthy's Forsyte family, maintained a place on the best sellers list for three months. *Bitter Heritage, Brook Evans,* and *The Foolish Virgin,* all dealing with love in different ways, had their thirty day vogue. And these are only a few of the many illustrations which might be given.

There are many types of readers for whom the love story has an especial appeal. The working person, particularly the working girl, turns to it greedily as a way

[1] O. G. Villard, "Sex, Art, Truth and the Magazines," *Atlantic Monthly,* March, 1926, pp. 388-398.
[2] Ernst and Seagle, *To the Pure,* p. 35. New York, 1928.

of escape from the dull routine of her own life. If its setting is one of wealth and leisure the flight from reality which it offers is most complete, and both factory hand and household servant breathlessly follow the romance of the rich society girl because in identifying themselves with her they can enjoy her silks and furs, her automobiles and her ocean trips, her orchids and her diamonds, as well as her romantic lover.

The adolescent seeks the story which treats of love and passion because of unsatisfied curiosity and the stimulation of erotic feelings which may be obtained from the reading. The boy or girl, absorbed in scenes describing physical contacts between the lovers, reacts with body sensations of pleasurable nature. Or, if the tale be one of high romance, in which the physical side of love plays an attenuated rôle, it offers a phantasy outlet for sublimations of sex impulses. In both kinds of love story, through identification with the hero or heroine, the adolescent is able to reach outside the limitations of personal inexperience and to share the feelings and emotions of maturity.

Again, the love story may intrigue those who have missed love in their own experience by affording them at least a vicarious participation in this great human adventure. And for the woman who has passed the peak of her own romance and is not quite content with the more settled status of marriage it provides a means of living over again the thrilling days of courtship.

Since it fulfills the need for escape or for excitement with so many different individuals, it is not strange that the love story, in all its forms, achieves such wide popularity.

The place of the mystery story. Stories of adventure in strange lands and mystery and detective stories meet other psychological needs of the reader. With the spread of civilization to the far corners of the earth the kind of adventure story which depended upon battles with savages and the conquest of unexplored territory for its thrills becomes more or less impossible. The mystery or detective story has taken its place as a thriller, and vies with the love story in the list of best sellers. *The Treasure House of Martin Hews* and *Behind that Curtain* both appeared on the monthly list of best sellers as computed from the actual sales of leading dealers, and this despite the fact that the former had been serialized in *Collier's* and the latter in the *Saturday Evening Post*. Other best sellers of recent months include *The Green Murder Case, The Mystery of the Blue Train, The Bishop Murder Case, The Flying Squad,* and *The Seven Dials Mystery*. If you enter any circulating library, you will find many of the shelves filled with detective stories, and these libraries take care to provide the books which people want to read in order to insure adequate rental returns. If further evidence be needed, take the magazine *True Detective Mysteries,* which has a circulation of more than 150,000.

The mystery story draws its readers from all classes, even from the professions. The university professor turns to it eagerly as a means of relaxation. A member of this group has declared that it represents, for this type of reader, an intellectual game in which the objective is that of solving the mystery before it is revealed by the author.[3] While this may be true for a limited number of readers, the mystery story has a far more universal appeal. It is adventure speeded up to a high pitch, and in this present scientific age, where ordinary life moves at a rapid rate, we must have action faster than usual if we are to find

[3] M. Nicolson, "The Professor and the Detective," *Atlantic Monthly,* April, 1929, pp. 483-493.

thrills and excitement. If we wish for proof of this statement, we need only read some of the most popular mystery stories. We shall find that these are not so frequently of the type where the detective works out a long line of inductive reasoning while he sits quietly in his office or his study, but rather those in which murder follows murder, climax piles upon climax, or horror upon horror. In many respects the successful detective story follows the formula for the old-fashioned serial thriller of the movies.

Again, the mystery story is one of the easiest to read. It makes no demands upon the mind so far as character analysis is concerned; this is all done for the reader in the mind of the detective. Thus it offers not only plenty of excitement, which most of us crave as an antidote to the monotony of life, but permits a state of intellectual relaxation at the same time.

In some mystery stories the criminal, not the detective, is the glamorous figure with whom we may take on a partial identity. Thus we escape from the inhibitions which social conformity has placed upon desires which still exist, although outlawed by the demands of group welfare. The identification with the criminal is only partial, however. Although we may obtain our thrills along with him, the part of our mental life that is dedicated to law and order concedes that he must be detected and punished at the end. Because we have ourselves been thwarted through social conformity, we feel that it is just for the delinquent hero to meet with this same experience. We can identify ourselves with him to some extent, and escape a guilty conscience for so doing, because of his certain punishment.

Thus the mystery story offers relaxation and a way of escape from reality. It provides adventure and excitement, and may offer a temporary release from our own moral inhibitions. And by doing these things it relieves the tension of mental fatigue and has a definite therapeutic value.

Literature as an interpretation of life. Along with the love story and the mystery story, the realistic novel and the psychological novel appear also among the best sellers of the day. *Bad Girl,* a study of the psychological reactions to pregnancy, held its popular place over four months. Perhaps its realism was only one of the reasons for its high circulation, since it also offered satisfaction for youthful curiosity about such matters, and had, besides, a provocative title. *All Kneeling,* the portrait of a neurotic, egocentric woman, had a place on the best sellers list for a two months' period, and so did *The Children,* an analysis of the effects of divorce upon the offspring of broken unions. For different thirty day periods, other realistic novels are listed: *The Island Within, Old Pybus, Point Counterpoint, A Dead Man Dies.*

In contrast to the romance and the mystery story, which offer excitement and escape from reality, these novels bring us into closer contact with reality. Economic problems, the social relationships of individuals, family conflicts, the development of personality and character and, more recently, psychopathology are all treated in realistic literature. The importance of books of this kind for the student of human nature has been very well summed up by Crawford: "In literature that aims to be realistically revelatory of life he [the student] finds material for study such as he can hardly obtain from any group of patients. The frankness which he seeks in vain from the person with whom he comes into personal contact, he can find in literature." [4]

[4] W. A. Crawford, "Literature and the Psychopathic," *Psychoanalytic Review,* 1923, Vol. X, pp. 440-446.

There are, to be sure, some so-called realistic novels by modern writers which depend largely upon the use of words hitherto barred from print as profane and obscene, or are merely expressions of sophistication and cynicism of a somewhat superficial nature. But there are many contemporary novels which so closely parallel actual experience that they can well be recommended to the student who would learn to understand human conduct. They are as true to the principles of psychology and psychopathology as are the case records of a clinic. And they have the advantage of being much more readily accessible to the average reader. It is our purpose to mention briefly some illustrations of this type of literature and to point out the bearing upon mental hygiene studies.

Family relationships. The psychological and social problems of the family are much in the public eye at present, and it is therefore to be expected that a large group of novelists will reflect this interest. Some of the literary studies are superficial or misleading; others are characterized by profound insight. Of this latter group we may properly mention a few examples.

Warwick Deeping has given us three books dealing with varied aspects of the reactions of members of the same family upon each other. His *Sorrel and Son* is an excellent picture of the wholesome relationship between a father and son, showing how this association may help to mold a normal personality. It also indicates how domestic discord can be so treated by the parent who remains in contact with the child that even divorce loses its power to warp that child's development.

Old Pybus, another of Deeping's novels, describes the struggle of the adolescent against unsympathetic parents, particularly emphasizing conflict between father and son.

The value of a father substitute in such situations is also clearly shown.

Deeping's third novel, *Kitty*, pictures the injurious results of a mother's possessive attitude. Here, again, the corrective influence of a different kind of love relationship is suggested. It is the conflict between the good and bad forces which attack the developing personality that makes all three of these novels especially valuable studies and particularly true to life. For most people are exposed to both kinds of influences, at one time or another, and personality is made or marred by the strongest.

In *Sons and Lovers*, D. H. Lawrence has delved far into the psychopathology of a son's dependence upon his mother. The relationship with which this book is concerned is admittedly an abnormal one, from which the son is unable to release himself for marriage or for complete fulfillment through his vocation. While this represents, as has been stated, a pathological extreme, it is one which does occur in life and therefore it contributes to our understanding of distorted human nature.

John Weaver's book, *Her Knight Comes Riding*, takes up the complementary theme of psychopathology, a daughter's attachment to her father. Here we see the father ideal interposed between a girl and her young lover, turning her from the normal attraction of youth for youth to a search for a love object in an older man.

Edith Wharton's *The Children* has already been mentioned in passing as a novel of divorce. But it is somewhat exaggerated, except as it applies to the small group of people possessed of unlimited wealth. Divorce as it exists in the comfortably well-to-do class, with its capacity for devastating effects upon child life, is nowhere better outlined than in Margaret Wilson's *The Kenworthys*. This holds good in spite of the tragic ending.

Interpretations of racial conflicts. The psychology of races has become a subject for the novelist. There are several stories which analyze the difficulties of marriage between Jew and Christian, Ludwig Lewisohn's *The Island Within* being especially worthy of note. More recent is the literary preoccupation with the psychology of the Negro. Carl Van Vechten's *Nigger Heaven* is perhaps one of the most striking efforts at interpretation, although its very authentic analysis of the Negro's feeling of inferiority resulting from the superior social position of the White race is somewhat marred by a striving for bizarre and sensational style. Of much deeper sincerity is Julia Peterkin's Pulitzer prize novel *Scarlet Sister Mary*, with its account of superstitions and inconsistencies between fanatical religious experiences and everyday decisions. *Plum Bun*, by Jessie Fauset, is a striking study of the circumstances which cause the person who has Negro blood but looks all white to "pass" for the latter. *Home to Harlem*, by Claude McKay, penetrates less deeply below the surface in its psychological interpretations, but should probably be mentioned.

The feeling of guilt. One of the deepest motives underlying many emotional conflicts is the feeling of guilt. In *Theresa*, Arthur Schnitzler shows how this feeling may haunt a woman who has once wished to be freed from an unwelcome infant. Rölvaag's *Giants in the Earth* has for its primary theme the psychology and sociology of pioneer life, but with a minor motif in the feeling of guilt which persists for one of his characters until she is driven into a psychotic state.

If we would understand how powerful the feeling of guilt has been in the history of society, we have only to read some of the novels which reproduce the time in which the church was more powerful over the life of the individual than it is to-day. *The Joyous Friar,* a biographical novel by A. J. Anderson, shows the tortured conscience which followed disobedience to religious vows in other times. Sigrid Undeset's Nobel prize trilogy, *Kristin Lavransdatter,* is a remarkable study of the guilt motive in human life.

The psychology and psychopathology of sex. It has been claimed by some writers that the literary field has been too much invaded by novelists of sex. But many of their works are so true to life and provide so much enlightenment with respect to a subject that is all too little understood by the general reader that we should not issue too hasty a judgment upon this preoccupation. Several of the books which have been mentioned under previous headings also fall into this category, particularly *Sons and Lovers, Her Knight Comes Riding, Giants in the Earth,* and *Kristin Lavransdatter.*

Knut Hamsun's *The Women at the Pump* is an analysis of some of the more subtle aspects of the psychopathology of sex. The feeling of inferiority which comes with impotency and the attempt to compensate for this is the motive of behavior pictured in this novel, but the reader will need some psychological insight in order to appreciate the pathos underlying situations which superficially may seem humorous.

The Painted Room, by Margaret Wilson, is an excellent study of the sex conflicts of an adolescent girl. The remorse and anguish that follow close upon the heels of a defiance of conventionality are faithfully detailed. A very fine bit of writing, from the viewpoint of psychopathology, is to be found in the chapters describing how fear and remorse cause the girl to imagine she is about to become the mother of an illegitimate child. The hysterical simulation of pregnancy is well known to the psychiatrist, but few novelists have touched upon it.

Homosexuality has made its appearance in modern fiction in many guises. The most realistic treatments, however, have described this trait in women rather than men. One of the first studies of homosexuality among girls was Clemence Dane's account of the boarding school crush, *A Regiment of Women*. Very recently a sixteen year old schoolgirl, Carman Barnes, contributed a novel on homosexuality in the girls' boarding school to realistic literature, under the appropriate title of *Schoolgirl*. But by far the most serious work in this field is Radclyffe Hall's *The Well of Loneliness*, which is an exceptionally fine piece of literary work and is equally exceptional as a contribution to the psychology of the homosexual.

Sex literature and censorship. Whatever else we may say about censorship, it must be admitted that it is altogether too frequently perverted from the ends of protecting immature minds to an expression of the prudery and prejudice of uninformed persons. The suppression, in some communities, of *The Well of Loneliness* is a striking example of the triumph of ignorance and misinformation over truth and sincerity. D. H. Lawrence is another writer in the field of psychopathology who has felt the heavy hand of the censor. Only in one other field is censorship so active as it is with regard to sex, and that is when the novel which exposes social injustice is under consideration. Upton Sinclair's *Oil*, as we know, was not overdrawn in its exposure of graft, yet the stern New England conscience caused its suppression in Boston for a time. The author found a nice opportunity for retaliation in his two volume novel built around the Sacco-Vanzetti case, which he appropriately named *Boston*, though in all fairness it should be stated that Mr. Sinclair is probably above such petty malice.

What happens under the present conditions of censorship is that the literature most likely to be forbidden is that which would contribute to the thoughtful reader's understanding of human behavior. If we are to have a censorship, it should be placed in other hands than those of bigotry and ignorance.

Psychology in modern drama. Like the novel, the drama also upon occasion attempts to portray human nature as it is and to show how conduct is motivated. *The Silver Cord* was essentially a study of the abnormal aspects of the mother-son relationship. *The Captive* was built around the struggle of a girl with homosexual tendencies to achieve a normal married life, but like Miss Hall's novel, which has just been mentioned, it fell under the ban of censorship, despite its honesty and scientific verity. Theodore Dreiser's *The Hand of the Potter* was concerned with another phase of the psychopathology of sex.

Young Woodley gave a delightful stage presentation of adolescent boyhood, with its daydreams and its romantic aspirations. Eugene O'Neill's genius finds dramatic expression almost entirely along psychological and sociological lines—witness *The Emperor Jones, The Hairy Ape, Dynamo,* and *Strange Interlude.* The plays that dramatize the changes in family life are many; as illustrations we may refer to such widely different problems of marriage as were presented in *Craig's Wife, These Modern Women* and *The Constant Wife.* The psychology of the Negro has also intrigued the playwright; as evidence we may cite *Porgy* and *In Abraham's Bosom.*

On the whole, the drama lends itself less readily to authentic psychological interpretation than the novel, principally because its episodes are usually restricted to a shorter period of time. The forces that shape human destiny begin to act in the early years and are continued throughout the life of the individual. Thus the novel has the advantage in that it can carry its characters through childhood and adolescence and on into the later life of the adult. Therefore we are able to see the causal sequence of events more clearly in the novel than in any other form of literature. Very rarely is there a dramatic genius—an Ibsen or a Tolstoi—which can encompass life within the literary form of the play.

Emotional expression through poetry. The great psychological appeal of poetry is its verbalization of moods and emotions. Its appeal is to the few, perhaps, but for them it is the most satisfying way of putting their feelings into words. To be sure, certain kinds of poetry, the narrative or epic, merely provide the same escape from reality into a world of romance or adventure as does the novel. But a great deal of the poetry which we read exists chiefly as an expression of fundamental emotions. Because it is the most competent form of emotional expression, it is a means of catharsis which has a decidedly therapeutic value. Especially is this true for adolescence, which is more rebellious and less resigned to the necessity of emotional suppression.

Through poetry we can put our moods into words and find the solace of self-dramatization. If we are momentarily obsessed with restlessness and the longing for far places, we may build imaginary pictures as we recall the words:

"Change was his mistress, Chance his counselor.
Love could not keep him. Duty forged no chain.
The wide seas and the mountains called to him,
And gray dawns saw his campfires in the rain."

This very phrasing of our desire helps to appease it, and we may thus find peace again and again, for there is no limit to the imagery we may associate with the words.

If we love nature and the countryside, we can express our ecstasy through poetry. If it be autumn, there are such lines as these:

"The sumach burns in the brake.
The hills are a furnace of color and mellowing light
    Where junipers flame and flake,
And the blueberry dreams like a faint blue smoke on the
    height."

Or, in spring:

"There will come soft rains and the smell of the ground,
    And swallows calling with their shimmering sound;
    And frogs in the pools singing at night,
    And wild plum-trees in tremulous white."

If we feel the insignificance of humanity in the face of nature, this mood, too, has been expressed for us:

"Not one would mind, neither bird nor tree,
    If mankind perished utterly . . .
    And Spring herself, when she woke at dawn,
    Would scarcely know that we were gone."

Where else than in poetry can we find adequate expressions of love? All the phases are there, from the young passion of

"I'll break and forge the stars anew,
    Shatter the heavens with a song;
    Immortal in my love for you,
    Because I love you very strong."

to the mature tenderness of

"How do I love thee?   Let me count the ways.
I love thee to the depth and breadth and height
My soul can reach . . .
. . . I love thee with the breath,
Smiles, tears, of all my life!—and, if God choose,
I shall but love thee better after death."

and the pain of lost love:

"My peace is hidden in his breast
Where I shall never be;
Love comes to-night to all the rest,
But not to me."

Mankind, undergoing the conflict of philosophic doubts, has been given voice:

"To spend uncounted years of pain,
Again, again, and yet again,
In working out in heart and brain
The problem of our being here;
To gather facts from far and near,
Upon the mind to hold them clear,
And, knowing more may yet appear,
Unto one's latest breath to fear,
The premature result to draw—
Is this the object, end, and law,
And purpose of our being here?"

Inspirational value of poetry.   Through poetry, we find more than the simple expression of moods.   By its aid we are able to transmute our emotions and to find new courage.   The poet takes despair and molds it into an incentive to further endeavor.   How many have gained strength from Kipling's *If?*

"If you can force your heart and nerve and sinew
To serve your turn long after they are gone,

And so hold on when there is nothing in you
  Except the will which says to you 'Hold on!' ' "

Or from the heroic invocation of *Ulysses?*

"Tho' much is taken, much abides, and tho'
We are not now that strength in which in old days
Moved earth and heaven, that which we are, we are,—
One equal temper of heroic hearts,
Made weak by time and fate, but strong in will
To strive, to seek, to find, and not to yield."

The great elegies offer consolation to those who have
lost a loved one by turning from the cry of anguish and
grief to a picture of death as a happy estate, leading us
to see that we should not wish to recall the departed.
Milton dwells on the delights of heaven:

"In the blessed kingdoms meek of joy and love.
There entertain him all the saints above
In solemn troops and sweet societies,
That sing, and singing in their glory move,
And wipe the tears forever from his eyes."

Tennyson's *In Memoriam* is filled with comforting words
for those who struggle with the problem of personal loss:

"I hold it true, whate'er befall;
  I feel it when I sorrow most;
  'Tis better to have loved and lost
Than never to have loved at all . . .

"Forgive my grief for one removed,
  Thy creature whom I found so fair.
  I trust he lives in thee, and there
I find him worthier to be loved."

Shelley idealizes death as an escape from the problems
and unhappiness of life:

"Peace, peace! he is not dead, he doth not sleep—
He hath awakened from the dream of life . . .

"He has outsoared the shadow of our night;
Envy and calumny and hate and pain,
And that unrest which men miscall delight,
Can touch him not and torture not again."

For those suffering from hopeless illness, the poets also offer sustaining words. There is Browning's *Prospice*, beginning with the inquiry, "Fear death?" and ending with the optimistic affirmation:

"For sudden the worst turns the best to the brave,
    The black minute's at end,
And the elements' rage, the fiend-voices that rave,
    Shall dwindle, shall blend,
Shall change, shall become first a peace out of pain,
    Then a light, then thy breast,
O thou soul of my soul! I shall clasp thee again,
    And with God be the rest."

And Tennyson's *Crossing the Bar*, with its peaceful rhythm:

"Sunset and evening star,
    And one clear call for me!
And may there be no moaning of the bar,
    When I put out to sea. . . .

"For tho' from out our bourne of Time and Place
    The flood may bear me far,
I hope to see my Pilot face to face
    When I have crossed the bar."

In poetry we find the intellectual and emotional blended in such a way that intellectual strivings may be warmed with the glow of feeling. The work of the scientist takes

on new beauty when it is seen through the eyes of the
poet:

> "A fire-mist and a planet,
> A crystal and a cell,
> A jelly-fish and a Saurian,
> And caves where the cave-men dwell;
> Then a sense of law and beauty
> And a face turned from the clod,—
> Some call it Evolution,
> And others call it God."

Thus, in poetry, we find all the feelings of humanity
plus an interpretation which leads us to sense new values.
The ideas and sentiments given to us in this form of
literature help us to endure pain and suffering and spur
on our flagging strength. We meet with clarification of
our personal problems. We are enabled to infuse into the
threateningly monotonous round of the world's work a
feeling-tone which provides the drive to continuous labor.
Those who are fond of poetry, and who respond to the
stimulation of its word-symbols, are provided with a way
of emotional catharsis and sublimation which bears a distinct relation to better mental adjustment.

The appeal of biography. An increasingly popular
type of literature is biography. Each year of late the
number of books published in this field has been growing
and many of them have attained a wide circulation. On
the recent lists of monthly best sellers, we find such titles
as Emil Ludwig's *Goethe, Disraeli* by André Maurois,
Ludwig's *Napoleon, The Son of Man,* by the same author,
Strachey's *Elizabeth and Essex,* Fülöp-Miller's *Rasputin,
the Holy Devil,* Beveridge's *Abraham Lincoln,* and many
others. Autobiography falls in the same class of writing
and is also represented among the best sellers. Prominent
in popularity are Lindbergh's *We,* Byrd's *Skyward,*

Roamin' in the Gloamin' (which announces itself by its name as the life of Sir Harry Lauder), and Mussolini's *Autobiography.* Surely the appeal of these books is not due to the urge for information, for many of the central figures are those whose lives are already well known to the public—Lincoln, Napoleon, Christ.

Dr. Pruette has suggested that we turn to biography because modern fiction so often leaves us with a sense of futility and because in the breakdown of orthodox faith and convictions of other generations we are left a little uncertain as to the ultimate values of life. She says, in part:

"If all other values fail there still remain the everyday facts of life upon this earth. Here are men who have struggled and died without any more answer than we have found to the questions of existence. They have known moments of success and they have met their inevitable defeats. But something has kept them going just as something keeps us going. The incurable loneliness of every thinking person is a little assuaged by coming close to the life history of another human being. He is weak, as we have been; he is strong, as we may be. There is heartening and reassurance to be found in the lives of other men; there is comfort in the very design that patterns men's lives alike."

A less worthy motive which enters into the modern interest in biography centers upon it as a kind of high-class gossip. The modern biographer is likely to show the human weaknesses of the great man or the great woman very clearly. For the individual who suffers from an inferiority complex, there is satisfaction in seeing those who occupy a higher place than himself dragged down to his level. But the real value of biography, as Dr. Pruette says, is the solace it gives the reader who is struggling with personal problems.   Particularly it is helpful in showing failures in their true proportion.   For many of the tragic and noble figures who are favorites with biographers met defeat in spite of heroic efforts.   As we see their lives, in the perspective of time, we realize that this defeat was brought about by forces of fate which no single human being could have resisted.   And it may be that we are enabled to see in our own failures this element of forces too strong for us so that we are somewhat relieved of the tendency to self-reproach.   It is desirable for us to attain something of this objective viewpoint, lest we become too discouraged to continue the struggle for adjustment.

The success story and self-help literature.   It is just because sickness and pain and failure are to a greater or lesser extent the lot of all humanity that there is such a demand for literature of what may be called the self-help or inspirational type.   In this class we have the "success" story, which permits the reader to identify himself with the humble hero who, by means of trite and platitudinous rules, has achieved material prosperity.   The inference is plain: the reader has only to follow the same easy rules and he also will achieve a home, wife, kiddies and an automobile.   This kind of story has the same appeal for the adult reader that the fairy tale holds for the child; it is distinctly of the wish-fulfillment variety.

But a major portion of the self-help books feature a kind of pseudo-psychology or have a religious tone.   Some are devoted to health problems; many pose as guides to economic success; still others strike a note of faith and optimism.   There are in this field books by sincere and thoughtful writers, well known in the professional world, who have verities to offer the seeking reader.   There are also, unfortunately, the writings of charlatans who exploit the troubles of their fellows in order to secure their own prosperity.

The vexed personality, seeking aid for its problems, turns to books in this modern age where once the wise woman, the astrologer or the fortune-teller would have been consulted. The services of astrologers, fortune-tellers and mediums are still available, but the books they have written are still more readily accessible. It is difficult to know whether to condemn their chicanery wholeheartedly, or to admit that they may have some value in easing the human spirit. On the whole, their potentiality for harm is often greater than that for good, since they offer fictitious solutions of human problems and are likely to breed beliefs which may become pathological if carried to extremes.

Much more wholesome is the optimism of such popular writers as Bruce Barton and Angelo Patri, or the everyday philosophy of Will Durant when he assures the reader that "you will never find half the thrill and joy in driving a Rolls-Royce that you will get from guiding a baby carriage down the street." [5] To accept this is to assure peace and contentment, so far as the average citizen is concerned, for the baby carriages still outnumber the Rolls-Royces considerably. But there are so many men and women who have burdens to bear and who have slight abilities for great achievement that it is to their advantage, so far as individual happiness is concerned, to become reconciled to the common lot and to convince themselves that it is the best anyone could have.

Literature in the service of mental hygiene. To sum up this diverse field, we see in literature, according to its kind, a three-fold benefit. It provides for mental relaxation through a flight from reality which is usually fairly

[5] *The Mansions of Philosophy.* New York, 1929.

healthful; it is a great outlet for emotions that are otherwise inhibited and relieves the tensions due to inhibition; it helps us to understand life and to find assistance through this interpretation in working out our own adjustments. While all of these are important, it is the type of literature which aids in the understanding of human behavior which is of especial interest to mental hygiene. In so far as reading helps us to gain insight into our own motives of conduct it advances us on the road to being able to control and modify our responses. It is when we are the slaves of impulses of obscure origin, which act almost as compulsions, that we are most likely to react to situations in ways that endanger wholesome adjustment. When we have a deeper knowledge, we are less at the mercy of hidden forces within the personality.

Moreover, with a better understanding of what we are really like and how we became so, it is easier for us to become reconciled to ourselves, to spend less time in vain longings to be other than we are, and to put more energy into making the best of our abilities in spite of our handicaps. And as we free ourselves, through new knowledge, from old emotional conflicts, we release energy and vitality for other endeavors. If reading helps us to this self-knowledge and release, it is of utmost value for mental adaptation.

Equally important is the tolerance toward our fellows which real understanding brings with it. If we have insight into the sources of their idiosyncrasies, we are less impatient with them. The person who is different from others, who is slightly abnormal in some respect, may grow more normal or may have his peculiarities accentuated, according to the attitude which we display toward him. If we treat him with disgust or blame him for unfortunate traits, we intensify his maladjustment. If we have sympathy and friendly acceptance to offer, in spite of his difficulties, we may have done more than we realize toward bettering his condition.

Nothing makes a person more unhappy than the intolerance of society toward his weaknesses. The loneliness, the self-depreciation, the despair, which are engendered in the person who sees himself shut off from companionship, cannot be overestimated. If the person thus shunned is a genius, he may find compensation in creative work and thus be able to maintain his mental balance. If he is successful, his peculiarities will eventually be pardoned or even respected as the eccentricities of a gifted mind. But for the average individual it is sheer destruction to be cut off completely from the crowd. Fortunately, most of us are sufficiently like other people to be sure of a few friends. But there is no doubt that many a mental breakdown could have been averted if the person involved could have been sure of sympathy and understanding, or even compassion and tolerance, instead of denunciation and blame, when he was forced to meet a time of crisis.

As our reading gives us more and more insight into the nature of human life, we see that normality is an ideal toward which all of us strive but which no one ever completely attains. We see, too, that abnormality differs from it in degree but not in kind. We learn that all of us have abnormalities in one direction or another; that some parts of our personalities have been warped and distorted while others have developed wholesomely. As this conception is borne in upon us, we tend to be more lenient in our judgment of others, realizing that we may require their leniency, in turn. Perhaps we may even come to feel the spirit that lies behind the words—"Judge not, that ye be not judged."

SUGGESTIONS FOR CLASSROOM DISCUSSION

1. For what types of people does the love story offer a flight from reality?
2. What is the psychological appeal of the mystery story?
3. What is the function of literature as an interpretation of life?
4. What can we gain from reading realistic literature?
5. What psychological needs does poetry fulfill?
6. What is the mental hygiene value of biography?

SUGGESTIONS FOR WRITTEN REPORTS

1. Read *A Regiment of Women,* by Clemence Dane. Write a review of the book discussing the psychological aspects.
2. Read *Sons and Lovers,* by D. H. Lawrence. Then read Dr. Kuttner's article on this book. Write a review of the novel from the viewpoint of psychopathology.
3. Read *The Kenworthys,* by Margaret Wilson. Review the book in the light of its treatment of the effect of divorce upon the child's emotional development.
4. Read *The Closed Garden,* by Julian Green. Discuss the influences which led to the mental breakdown of the girl in the story.
5. Read *Kitty,* by Warwick Deeping. Review the novel to bring out the psychology of the relationships between the mother and son, and the son and his wife.
6. Make a list of the novels you have read in the last year. Classify these according to whether they have provided relaxation and escape from reality, or whether they have been books which added to your understanding of human nature.
7. Make a list of your favorite poetic quotations. What mood does each one verbalize? What help do you get from the lines?

SELECTED BIBLIOGRAPHY

Collateral Readings

BORST, HOMER. "Parental Attitudes in the Modern Novel." *The Family,* 1929, Vol. X, pp. 113-115.

BROWN, HELEN. "A Literary Forerunner of Freud." *Psychoanalytic Review*, 1917, Vol. IV, pp. 64-69.

CALVERTON, V. F. "Revolt and Reaction in Contemporary European Literature." *Modern Quarterly*, 1928, Vol. V, pp. 31-52.

—— *Sex Expression in Literature.* New York, 1926.

COLLINS, J. *The Doctor Looks at Literature.* New York, 1923.

—— *The Doctor Looks at Love and Life.* Part II, Chap. III: "Do Characters in Fiction Behave Like Human Beings?" Garden City, 1926.

CRAWFORD, W. A. "Literature and the Psychopathic." *Psychoanalytic Review*, 1923, Vol. X, pp. 440-446.

HOUSE, S. D. "The Concept of Realization in Literature and Life." *Psychoanalytic Review*, 1926, Vol. XIII, pp. 461-469.

KEMPF, E. J. "The Psychology of 'The Yellow Jacket.' " *Psychoanalytic Review*, 1917, Vol. IV, pp. 393-423.

KUTTNER, A. B. " 'Sons and Lovers': a Freudian Appreciation." *Psychoanalytic Review*, 1916, Vol. III, pp. 295-317.

LOVETT, R. M. "Sex and the Novel." In *Sex in Civilization*, pp. 677-692. New York, 1929.

PRUETTE, LORINE. "The Family in the Modern Novel." *The Family*, 1928, Vol. IX, pp. 46-50.

RIKLIN, F. "Wish-fulfillment and Symbolism in Fairy Tales." *Psychoanalytic Review*, 1913-14, Vol. I, pp. 94-107; 203-316; 322-332; 452-459; 1915, Vol. II, pp. 102-105; 203-218; 327-340.

STRAGNELL, G. A. "A Psychopathological Study of Franz Molnar's 'Liliom.' " *Psychoanalytic Review*, 1922, Vol. IX, pp. 40-49.

TOWNSEND, A. H. "Perishing Plots." *Plain Talk*, January, 1928, pp. 71-75.

VAN DOREN, CARL. *Contemporary American Novelists.* New York, 1922.

VILLARD, O. G. "Sex, Art, Truth and the Magazines." *Atlantic Monthly*, March, 1926, pp. 385-398.

Literature Revelatory of Human Nature [6]

ADAMS, HENRY. *The Education of Henry Adams.* Boston, 1918.

AMNERS-KULLER, JO VAN. *The Rebel Generation.* New York, 1928.

ANDERSON, A. J. *The Joyous Friar.* New York, 1927.

ATHERTON, GERTRUDE. *The Jealous Gods.* New York, 1928.

BARNES, CARMAN. *Schoolgirl.* New York, 1929.

BECKETT, WALTER. *Dearest Idol.* Indianapolis, 1929.

BOJER, JOHANN. *The Great Hunger.* New York, 1919.

BOWEN, ELIZABETH. *The Hotel.* New York, 1928.

BROMFIELD, LOUIS. *A Good Woman.* New York, 1927.

—— *The Green Bay Tree.* New York, 1924.

—— *Possession.* New York, 1925.

CALVERTON, V. F. "The Undertaker." (Under the pseudonym of Mark Rodson.) *Modern Quarterly,* 1927, Vol. IV, pp. 272-280.

DAKIN, EDWIN F. *Mrs. Eddy.* New York, 1929.

DANE, CLEMENCE. *A Regiment of Women.* New York, 1917.

DEEPING, WARWICK. *Sorrel and Son.* New York, 1926.

—— *Kitty.* New York, 1927.

—— *Old Pybus.* New York, 1928.

DELL, FLOYD. *Moon-calf.* New York, 1921.

—— *The Briary-Bush.* New York, 1921.

—— *Janet March.* New York, 1927.

—— *Souvenir.* New York, 1929.

—— *Upton Sinclair;* a Study in Social Protest. New York, 1927.

DELMAR, VINA. *Bad Girl.* New York, 1928.

DREISER, THEODORE. *An American Tragedy.* New York, 1926.

[6] This list is, of course, by no means complete. No one person can keep abreast of the whole list of modern fiction, especially if working in the field of science so that the amount of time free for reading fiction is limited. However, the novels, short stories and biographies mentioned here can be recommended from personal reading. I hope that authors whose works are just as realistic, but which happen to have escaped my attention, will pardon me for omissions.

DREISER, THEODORE. *Old Rogaum and His Theresa*. In *Free* (and other stories). New York, 1918.
FAUSET, JESSIE. *Plum Bun*. New York, 1929.
FISHER, DOROTHY CANFIELD. *The Bent Twig*. New York, 1916.
—— *Her Son's Wife*. New York, 1926.
GRINSTEAD, DURWARD. *Elva*. New York, 1929.
GREEN, JULIAN. *The Closed Garden*. New York, 1928.
HALL, RADCLYFFE. *Adam's Breed*. New York, 1928.
—— *The Well of Loneliness*. New York, 1928.
—— *The Unlit Lamp*. New York, 1929.
HAMSUN, KNUT. *The Women at the Pump*. New York, 1928.
HUXLEY, ALDOUS. *Point Counterpoint*. New York, 1928.
HURST, FANNY. *Apassionata*. New York, 1925.
—— *A President Is Born*. New York, 1928.
LAGERLÖF, SELMA. *The Strömstad Journey*. In *Mårbacka*. New York, 1925.
LAWRENCE, D. H. *Sons and Lovers*. New York, 1913.
LEHMANN, ROSAMOND. *Dusty Answer*. New York, 1927.
LEWISOHN, LUDWIG. *The Island Within*. New York, 1928.
McKAY, CLAUDE. *Home to Harlem*. New York, 1928.
MARKS, PERCY. *A Dead Man Dies*. New York, 1929.
MONTGOMERY, L. M. "Lost—a Child's Laughter." *The Delineator*, June, 1926, p. 15.
PARRISH, ANNE. *All Kneeling*. New York, 1928.
PETERKIN, JULIA. *Black April*. Indianapolis, 1927.
—— *Scarlet Sister Mary*. Indianapolis, 1928.
PRUETTE, LORINE. *G. Stanley Hall: a Biography of a Mind*. New York, 1926.
ROLVAAG, O. E. *Giants in the Earth*. New York, 1927.
SCHNITZLER, ARTHUR. *Theresa*. New York, 1928.
SINCLAIR, MAY. *Mary Olivier*. New York, 1919.
—— *The Romantic*. New York, 1920.
—— *Tree of Heaven*. New York, 1918.
SINCLAIR, UPTON. *Boston*. New York, 1928.
—— *Oil*. New York, 1927.
STEELE, WILBUR DANIEL. *Meat*. New York, 1928.
—— *Taboo*. New York, 1925.
—— *The Man Who Saw Through Heaven* (and other stories). New York, 1927.

SUDERMANN, H. *The Mad Professor.* New York, 1928.
SWINNERTON, FRANK. *A Brood of Ducklings.* New York, 1928.
UNDSET, SIGRID. *Kristin Lavransdatter.* New York, 1929.
VAN VECHTEN, CARL. *Nigger Heaven.* New York, 1926.
WEAVER, JOHN V. A. *Her Knight Comes Riding.* New York, 1928.
WERFEL, FRANZ. *Class Reunion.* New York, 1929.
WEST, REBECCA. *The Judge.* New York, 1922.
WILSON, MARGARET. *The Kenworthys.* New York, 1925.
—— *The Painted Room.* New York, 1926.

CHAPTER XIV

SOCIAL WORK AND MENTAL HYGIENE

The field of social work. The term social work, in its contemporaneous usage, covers a wide field of activities. Its scope can be realized, to some extent, by glancing at a volume of the Proceedings of the National Conference of Social Work. There we find such topics as child welfare, delinquency, dependency, correctional institutions, probation, health, family relief and rehabilitation, industrial problems, housing conditions, recreation, community life, settlements, mental hygiene, social service of the church, education, immigration and Americanization. With these and with many other problems social work has points of contact.

The social worker's task, broadly interpreted, is to aid in the amelioration of failures in social adjustment and to prevent the occurrence of maladjustment. Thus we find the social worker in hospitals and clinics, in institutions for dependents and delinquents, in social settlements and recreation centers, in social service departments of the church and school, in industry, and also in a large number of agencies which devote all their efforts to social welfare. The field of social work is, indeed, as broad as it must be to meet all the problems of social maladjustment that arise in a highly complex civilization.

The beginnings of social work. It was not until the twentieth century that the term social work came into general use. Previously, people had talked in terms of poor relief, charity and philanthropy. In those days, social work was not a profession, but rather an avocation for the humanistically inclined person. In the first half of the nineteenth century, public relief for the poor was provided through the almshouses, or poorhouses, as they were more familiarly called, and private charity was dispensed through the church. About the middle of the century, relief societies were organized in the large American cities. Their aim was not merely to provide financial assistance, but also to achieve economic rehabilitation for dependent members of society. Owing to the employment of untrained personnel, however, the last purpose was rarely accomplished.

The early charity organizations depended, for the most part, upon the services of volunteer workers and upon the use of "friendly visiting." Late in the nineteenth century, when social work began to be differentiated into relief organizations, social settlements, societies for the protection of children, industrial welfare agencies and other specialized branches, the necessity for a regular personnel and for some general technique was recognized. It was at this time that the method which we know in its later development as the social case work method began to supersede friendly visiting by volunteer workers and indiscriminate alms-giving.

The social case work method is based upon the attempt to study the individual in relation to his whole social situation. It inquires into the causes of maladjustment and seeks to remedy them. In the relief organizations, for example, the case work is directed toward bringing about better social adjustment, the giving of relief being regarded merely as a temporary measure. In certain cases, to be sure, relief may be continued over a period of months or even years. The death of a wage-earning father, for instance, may mean that relief will be required in a family until some of the children grow up and are able to contribute to the family needs. But the final goal of social case work, however long delayed in its achievement, is the social adjustment of the individual or of the different members of a family, and the provision of relief is incidental to this more important purpose.

Since its tentative beginnings in the relief organizations, the case work method has been improved and refined and adapted to the needs of all types of social agencies. It is the basic method for good social work with juvenile or adult delinquents, for all kinds of efforts in behalf of child or adult welfare, and is used by every social agency which seriously expects to advance human adjustment.

The professionalization of social work. The introduction of the case work method was followed by a kind of informal apprenticeship for beginners wishing to enter the vocation of social work. At first they did not receive systematic instruction, but simply picked up what they could from contacts with more experienced workers. Later, many social agencies arranged for the training of new workers by supervising their practice, assigning reading material, and planning for conferences with the experienced workers in the field.

The conception of social work as a profession, requiring academic preparation of a highly specialized type, did not find concrete expression until the present century. The first full year's course for students was offered by the New York School of Social Work (then called the New York School of Philanthropy) in 1904. The same year a "School for Social Workers"—now the Simmons College School of Social Work—was opened in Boston. An Institute of Social Science had been organized a year earlier (1903) as part of the extension work of the University of Chicago, but soon became an independent in-

stitution.   Until 1920 it existed separately under the name
of the Chicago School of Civics and Philanthropy; then
its function was again taken over by the University of
Chicago.

The twentieth century development of academic courses
for social work continued along two lines.   Separate
schools were established in many cities, but in other
places instruction was offered by colleges and universities
in connection with the departments of sociology, the academic title of applied sociology being sometimes given to
this new subject matter.   The university courses tended
to be more theoretical and supplied less opportunity for
actual practice than the courses given by the independent
schools of social work.   The practical aspects of training
have recently received more attention from the universities, however.

With the firm establishment of social work as a profession has come a gradual raising of the entrance requirements for the various schools.   Where originally a high
school graduate, of suitable age and experience, was able
to enroll, completion of a four year college course is now
more generally demanded for entrance.   Thus the school
of social work takes its place among the other graduate
professional schools, and very frequently the completion
of a full course in one of these schools confers a master's
degree upon the graduate.

Contacts between psychiatry and social work.
When psychiatry became interested in preventive measures, and psychopathic hospitals and out-patient clinics
in psychiatry and mental hygiene were established, a new
field was opened to the social worker.   Her case work
methods were then refreshed and enriched by the new
insight into human nature which she gained from her cooperative work with the psychiatrist.   Social workers con-

cerned with the problems of dependency and delinquency and child welfare also began to realize that the psychiatrist could be of service to them, and they began to bring some of their cases to the clinics. Thus, they, too, came into contact with the psychiatric viewpoint, which they carried over and applied to other cases than just those which they had brought for psychiatric study.

The coöperative efforts of the psychiatrist and social worker were conducive to mutual learning. If the social worker increased her knowledge of human behavior by assimilating something of the psychiatric technique, no less did her case work methods present new material for the consideration of the psychiatrist. Her problems presented a challenge to the science of psychiatry; her methods opened up the whole range of social treatment as an adjunct to medical treatment. In large measure this was the stimulus which operated to enlarge the perspective of the psychiatrist, and out of the alliance between the two professions social psychiatry, with all its present day applications, came into being.

For a time there was an attempt to differentiate psychiatric social work from the general field. In 1918 the Smith College School of Social Work first offered a systematic course of instruction for the training of psychiatric social workers. The course consisted of two summer sessions spent in the classroom, with the intervening months given to practice in some form of psychiatric or mental hygiene service. The New York School of Social Work soon initiated a similar course, but with class work and practice given simultaneously.

At the Pennsylvania School of Social and Health Work, the new material contributing to further understanding of human behavior and the technique of personality adjustment was absorbed into the general curriculum. This latter plan bids fair to become the eventual program for instruction, for it is apparent that all social workers need the most complete training available since all of them must deal with problems of personality and behavior. As early as 1919, Mary Jarrett emphasized the necessity for the psychiatric viewpoint in all social case work.

"Social case work habitually relies upon psychiatry for advice concerning the care of persons with mental disorder. This advice is indispensable and very important. But perhaps even more important is the help that psychiatry can give the social worker in understanding human nature and in dealing with the many varieties of human personality that come before the social agencies. Personalities that would be considered normal frequently present many irregularities and contradictions. When we have come to understand these peculiarities as they appear in exaggerated form in psychopathic cases, we can more readily understand them in the average person. . . . Whether we are dealing with pronounced psychopathic traits, or minor peculiarities, or normal mentality, the psychiatric point of view is invaluable in social case work. By the psychiatric point of view I mean the habitual recognition of mental causes of conduct, together with some knowledge of the nature of the mental processes that may cause conduct disorder." [1]

The introduction of the psychiatric viewpoint into social work has, as one social worker recently stated, changed the emphasis in the worker's approach to her case. Once the social worker's chief thought was "What shall I do?" Now it is "Why did this happen?" This intimate search for the causes of maladjustment within

[1] Mary C. Jarrett, "The Psychiatric Thread Running Through All Social Case Work," *Proceedings of the National Conference of Social Work,* 1919, pp. 587-593.

the life history and personality of the individual who seeks aid is in harmony with the principles and technique of the best and most progressive type of modern psychiatry.[2] The changes in social work technique which have resulted from the modern interest in the causes of human behavior and social maladjustment are so significant that it seems necessary to discuss them in some detail.

Modifications of the social history. The initial step of the case work method is known as taking the social history. Although this has a formal sound, in reality it is a very friendly and informal procedure. Ordinarily, when a person has applied for help in solving his problems, he is willing to discuss his situation with the social worker rather freely. Exceptions occur to this rule, to be sure. Sometimes probation officers find a delinquent's relatives inclined to be uncommunicative because they wish to protect the person involved in the inquiry. Or an applicant for relief may at first consider that the only concern of the social agency is to furnish financial aid. Other social agencies, which are called into a situation by outsiders, as may ordinarily happen with such an organization as the Society for Protecting Children from Cruelty, for example, may meet with an initial resistance to their investigation.

Whether the social worker is received frankly from the first, or whether she has to convey the sense of her friendliness and overcome early suspicions as to her motives, at some reasonably early stage of her case work she must acquire information about the people whom she wishes to help out of trouble. To be able to establish good rapport with her clients is an essential part of her equipment for her profession.

[2] Beatrice Levey, "New Trends in Psychiatric Social Treatment in the Family Agency," *Mental Hygiene*, 1929, Vol. XIII, pp. 129-131.

There was a time when the social worker concentrated largely upon material facts. Her inquiries were directed toward discovering the amount of family income, the housing conditions, the kind of neighborhood, health status, work history, recreational activities, etc. Some workers also sought to obtain a picture of the background, particularly with respect to heredity, early school career, and other pertinent facts. If a child was the object of interest, it was considered necessary to learn something of habit training, methods of discipline, health history and present physical condition, opportunities for play, character of playmates, and school record.

With the introduction of the psychiatric point of view, there came to some extent a shift in emphasis. The factual material was still gathered, but the interrelations between personalities and the whole life experience of the individual took on more importance. The dynamic rather than the static note was struck in history taking. The social worker's philosophy, underlying this compilation of an interpretative history, has been expressed particularly clearly by Karl De Schweinitz:

"Immediate environment and recent events are not always enough to enable one to understand the man in trouble. Sometimes his difficulty lies deeper. Its solution may be determined by his early life and training. . . . A man is what he has been. He is truly a part of all that he has met and there is no better key to his present than what he has thought and experienced in the past." [3]

Thus the social history becomes an attempt to picture the influences which have been operating upon the individual from the time of his birth (or even before) up to the present. His relations to his parents, to his brothers

[3] Karl De Schweinitz, *The Art of Helping People Out of Trouble,* pp. 51 and 56. Boston, 1924.

and sisters and other relatives, his school experiences, his vocational adventures or misadventures, his contacts with playmates and comrades in work, his opportunities for recreation—all have helped to mold his personality and to determine his maladjustments. But especially have his emotional relationships to other people, and particularly to his family circle in childhood, acted upon his development. The more intimate knowledge the social worker acquires of the way in which the individual's life patterns have been shaped, the more secure is her position with reference to aiding him in making adjustments.

For example, a mother came to a social agency for assistance in keeping her family together after being deserted by her husband. On the surface this might appear to be a simple problem, in which the father's desertion is the key to the situation. But as the social worker learned about the woman's life, she found that she married because she wished to escape from a domineering mother, who allowed her very little freedom. She had married her husband when she was twenty years old, not because she loved him but because this seemed to be the only way to free herself from her mother's authority. Since her mother had never permitted her to assume any responsibility she was entirely unprepared to take over the duties of caring for a house and children. The husband protested against her inefficiency and she began to feel that she had simply changed from one tyrant to another. Dissatisfied in her expectation of what marriage would bring, she refused, after the birth of the second child, to continue marital relations with her husband. There followed a period when husband and wife spent nearly all their time in quarrels, until finally the former deserted the home. With this understanding of the woman's emotional experiences, the social worker was in a position to plan the treatment more effectively than if she had limited her inquiries to the material facts of the case.

Modifications of treatment techniques. Upon her understanding of the forces which have made the person what he is depends the social worker's ability to render effective assistance in any case. The problem then becomes a broader one than giving relief to a deserted mother, or changing a maladjusted child to a different home or school, or finding a man who is out of work a new job. These material resources are not neglected, to be sure; but along with their use goes a more subtle kind of service, that of personality adjustment. To illustrate what is meant by this statement, let us return to the case of the deserted wife described in the preceding paragraph.

In this case, the social worker did indeed arrange for financial aid, but at the same time she settled down into a long period of work with the woman to help her overcome some of the difficulties which were the inevitable residuals of her childhood experiences. The woman had learned to resent authority, but the best social work technique never depends upon this superficial method of gaining ends. The social worker appeared rather in the guise of a friend, from whom she could obtain help in coming to decisions. She encouraged the woman's efforts to work out a family budget and to plan expenditures for herself and her two children in such a way that the minimum income available from the relief fund would cover essential needs. Little by little, the woman learned to manage this income wisely and to avoid the extravagances which had been so discouraging to her husband. Under the unobtrusive guidance of the social worker, she began to see into the reasons for her failure to make a satisfactory marriage adjustment. She understood why her husband had left her and the children and lost her feeling of grievance against him.

What really happened was that the social worker, with her insight into the woman's personality difficulties, was able to provide her with an experience which she had needed but had never found in her relations with her mother or with her husband. In her life, the social worker stood for security and furnished a stronger personality upon whom she could depend while she was finding self-assurance. The absence of an authoritative tone permitted this dependency so long as the woman needed it; the encouragement in working out her problems helped her to attain confidence in herself and her ability to manage her own affairs. In other words, the social worker played the part which the mother should have assumed earlier, in order to free her daughter for an independent life.

This readjustment was not a matter of days or weeks, but of months and years. After four years of absence, the husband returned. He still loved his wife and children and had not felt comfortable about his desertion. Had his wife been the same woman that she was when he left home, he would undoubtedly have deserted her again. But because of her reëducation and the emotional maturity which she had achieved with the help of the social worker, she was able to meet him at a new level, taking her share of responsibility. Thus that particular family became a complete unit once more and made a satisfactory adaptation.

Let us consider another type of problem. This is a child of well-to-do parents, who has been provided with every material comfort, who has been placed in an excellent private school, but is exceedingly unhappy there be-

SOCIAL WORK AND MENTAL HYGIENE

cause he cannot take part successfully in the games with the other children. He has no physical handicaps and from the viewpoint of strength and agility should be able to hold his own on the playground. The social history reveals that he is an only child and that his mother is devoted to him. Before he went to school, he was with her most of the time and had very few opportunities to play with other children. His mother appears to be anxious to have him make the proper social adjustments, yet she excuses his dislike of the other children at school and permits him to be excused from the athletic sports after school and to come home to her.

But the history goes deeper than this. The mother discusses with the social worker the differences between what one finds in marriage and what one expects to find in it. She tells of her romantic attitude as a girl and how she expected the attentions of a fiancé to continue from a husband. She sighs, and comments that she had to readjust her views; that her husband became absorbed in his business and that she was very lonely until their son was born. Since then she has not missed her husband's attentions so much because she has had the boy's companionship. Her husband has not taken the interest in the boy that she has, but then he has his business.

The social history continues to paint the picture. The father manifests a genuine interest in his son when talking to the social worker. He says he has left him chiefly to his mother because she seemed to wish it so. She never said anything, but he always felt that she preferred to have the boy with her and that she was lonely and unhappy if his father took him anywhere with him. Therefore he left them pretty much together.

These relationships between the parents, and the boy's relations to them, are significant to the social worker.

She sees a meaning in them which neither parent has recognized. She understands that the mother, disappointed in her romantic daydreams, has turned to the boy and away from her husband. She realizes, too, that while the mother is anxious for her son to be like other boys and to have a good time in the games and sports at school, she also finds a good deal of satisfaction in the fact that he enjoys being with her rather than staying with the other boys.

As for the boy, he has grown dependent upon his mother and upon a feminine environment. Had he been more with the father, he might have had his interest in masculine activities more stimulated. However, he is young yet, and his development can still be influenced.

In earlier days of social work, at this point the question of what to do would probably have arisen. It might have been answered in several ways. Perhaps the social worker would have pointed out to the mother that she must insist that the boy stay after school and join in the play. Perhaps she would have advised boarding school and separated the boy from the mother. To-day the technique is somewhat different. Instead of moving into precipitate action, the social worker pauses to ask Why? Why does this mother need to have such a close relationship with her son? Why was she so disappointed in her marriage?

At the next visit, therefore, the social worker avoids making any specific suggestion such as those we have described. Instead, she leads the mother into conversation about her own childhood and her relations with her own parents. The mother confides that she was somewhat spoiled, perhaps, as she was the only girl in a family of five children and that her brothers are all older than herself. She was petted by her father and also by her brothers. With a sudden flash of insight she adds that perhaps this is why she expected so much attention from her husband.

This is the social worker's cue to help the mother to work out still further results of these early experiences. A sympathetic question or two, and the mother's viewpoint becomes still further enlightened. She exclaims that she has been turning to her son for the relationship which she has missed elsewhere. The social worker's skill is again a requisite, for at this point the mother is about to blame herself for all the boy's difficulties and to assume a burden of guilt. Casually, the social worker comments that perhaps this may have been a factor in the situation; that if so, it would only be natural under the circumstances; that most of us are motivated by residuals of childhood experiences. Then she leads the mother back to discussion of her social life with her husband.

The mother cites occasions when she has refused to go out with him because she felt that she should stay at home with her boy. Instead of criticizing her, the social worker suggests that this is no longer necessary, at her son's age, and that now her husband is in a position to have more leisure time from his business they could get about more frequently together. The mother decides that she has just gotten into the habit of refusing invitations; that she will make it a point to accept more of them from now on. But this mere verbalization of the situation is not sufficient.

Slowly, the social worker continues to build up a relationship between the parents in which the mother can find satisfaction. With the father she can discuss the situation fairly openly, since he stands in less danger of feeling himself as the guilty person. He shows his wife the interest in her that he has always felt but has not thought needed any particular expression. In order that the boy may not feel deserted, the father gives him more of his companionship. This, of course, is necessary for the boy's development. The mother, however, could not have accepted it but for her own closer companionship with the father and her lessened need of her son. Little by little, the relationships within the family are readjusted. The boy, seeing more of his father, takes on a masculine viewpoint and desires ardently to be manly. Instead of clinging to his mother he wishes to be released from her. She is able to grant this release because she finds her demands upon him are less imperative.

This is, of course, an unusually successful result of social treatment. In some cases the personality maladjustments are much more complicated and less amenable to transformation. But the skilled social worker, even though she may not be able to bring about ideal conditions, can do much to improve personality adjustments even in the more complex problems.

Relation between social history and treatment. For convenience of discussion, we have been considering social case work under the two headings of history taking and treatment techniques. In actual practice, there is no clear-cut division between the two parts. The social worker assumes a therapeutic rôle even while she is engaged in obtaining the material for the history. Matters come up which can be deftly handled, even at this early stage, so as to relieve feelings of guilt or to suggest new attitudes toward past experiences. Were these left over until the history had been completed, much time and skill would have to be expended to bring them to the fore again. Moreover, this technique would be much less natural.

Quickness of perception and interpretation is necessary for the social worker who tries to make her case work significant in this way. She cannot, of course, carry therapeutic measures too far with insufficient material, lest further information cast some doubt upon premature interpretations. But very frequently certain points appear fairly clearly in the first interviews, and there is no reason for neglecting such opportunities to initiate treatment.

The social worker's attitude. Anyone who has read the social material in a first-class case work agency or in a clinic where intensive work is done, cannot but be impressed with the intimate details of personal and family life that are confided to the social worker. The novice might wonder what particular skill the social worker possesses that permits her to receive such confidence. The explanation is exceedingly simple, yet it has deep implications.

In the first place, as we have said before, many of the people who come to the social worker have already made up their minds that they stand in need of assistance with their problems. Many of them have reached a point where they feel a pressing urge to unburden themselves to someone. Long ago, they might have turned to the family physician or the minister. Indeed, they still turn to these two professions, but increasingly the professional social worker becomes the final resource of the overburdened mind. The assurance that she will be able to understand and to lend aid is a part of the concept of her vocation.

In the majority of cases, then, the person who seeks out the social worker is ready to give confidence. How fully it is given depends upon the attitude of the individual worker. The person who seeks her out soon senses whether or not she has real understanding. The kind of understanding which the social worker must have has been clearly described by De Schweinitz:

"The person who would possess it must have a fundamental respect for other people. He must feel the unique importance of each individual who approaches him and he must have a faith in human nature that is founded, not upon a sheltered optimism, but upon a knowledge of the facts. . . . He must feel neither surprise nor horror at any revelation that may be made to him, no matter how unusual. It is not enough to remain silent and refrain from expressing these emotions. They must not even exist. He must not judge. His attitude toward the person who has revealed himself must not change from what it was before the secret was disclosed. . . . It is the capacity to hear the worst or the best in human nature and to accept it neither as worst or best, but as life, which is the supreme test of him who would become the confidant of his fellows." [4]

If the social worker's training has been sound it has developed this ability to understand human nature. It is an understanding and tolerance based not upon sentimental sympathy but upon a realization of the cause and effect relationships which determine character and conduct. This fundamental attitude toward human problems is a *sine qua non* for the successful social worker. The profession should not be attempted without it.

The social worker's personality. An understanding attitude is not the only requisite essential for the social worker. If she is to see clearly into the lives of other people she must have insight into her own reactions. Very few of us have escaped entirely from unfortunate experiences which have left scars upon our personalities; very few of us are ourselves perfectly adjusted to all sides

[4] *Op. cit.,* pp. 61 and 62.

of life. But the social worker must have achieved some satisfactory readjustment of her own life, or at least be aware of the reactions in herself which rise out of her previous experiences, if she is to be of service in helping other people to work through their problems.

If we are blinded to certain cause and effect relationships in our own life experience and unable to understand our own motives of behavior in some directions, it is almost inevitable that we shall be blind to similar relationships and to like motivations when we encounter them in others. Such mental blind spots lead us to misinterpret ourselves and other people. But those who are engaged in helping with human adjustments, whether in social work or some other profession, cannot afford to be prone to systematic errors in their interpretations.

By way of illustration, take the instance of a social worker who made excellent contacts with delinquent girls and through the relationship she was able to assume with them could exert a marked effect upon their behavior. In working with the parents, however, she was less successful. She was puzzled for some time over her inability to establish satisfactory contacts with parents until she realized, through certain occurrences, that she was herself not wholly free from rebellion against her own parents. With the gaining of this personal insight, she also understood that she had been identifying herself too completely with the girls with whom she was working. Thereafter she was able to guard against this aspect of her own adjustment problems and to enter into better rapport with the parents when she came to discuss their daughters with them.

Again, a social worker concerned with family problems found that she was unable to offer much assistance to the mothers in matters which involved the behavior of their children. This worker had taken up the profession of social service after her husband's death in order to support herself and her daughters. She was always able to see the mother's viewpoint and to sympathize with her attitudes, but not until she had taken several cases to a psychiatric clinic did she realize that it had been very difficult for her to understand the child's reactions. Her own experiences had made her too sympathetic toward other mothers.

Still another worker had been forced to struggle to emancipate herself from the solicitude of her own parents in childhood. There was left from these experiences, although she was not conscious of it, a shadowy feeling of resentment toward her parents. Possibly her choice of child welfare work was motivated in part by her knowledge of the handicaps imposed upon children by their well-meaning but mistaken elders. It was several years before she realized that her failure to produce effects in certain types of family situations was the direct result of her own tendency to identify herself with the child and to adopt a somewhat critical and censorious attitude toward parents. When she perceived that she felt a certain indignation toward parents who were overprotective with their children, she reviewed the cases in which she had failed to bring about adjustment. She found that she had consistently been expostulating with parents instead of trying to find out what had caused them to assume an overprotective attitude. In this particular type of case, she had forgotten the precept of inquiring Why? and had reverted to the procedure of giving definite instructions what to do. In other cases, where the situation did not duplicate her own experiences so closely, she had used a very different technique.

Thus the social worker finds herself concerned first of all with her own adjustment. She knows that she must face her own problems frankly, and that if she cannot solve them completely, she must at least guard against projecting them into her interpretations of other people or permitting them to color her professional relationships. In so far as she is able to achieve self-understanding and to readjust to her own experiences, she will be able to serve others without prejudices and without too much sympathy for one person or too little for another. And she will be an efficient and capable exponent of this new profession.

Personality qualifications of the social worker. As we have seen, the profession of social work requires many different qualifications. A keen intelligence capable of analyzing situations and of interpreting human relationships is only one of the requisites. A broad understanding of human nature and a tolerance which makes temptation to sit in judgment an impossibility is also of primary importance. Self-understanding and the capacity to view problems from an objective viewpoint are qualifications which we have already emphasized.

But this does not mean that the social worker must divest herself of all emotion. To enter upon the profession resolved to rely upon nothing but cool analysis and intellectualization would hardly lead to success. The social worker must have a great capacity for sympathy with human weakness and failure; she must be able to warmly identify herself with individuals in order to have that intimate understanding of their problems which will enable her to be accepted wholeheartedly.

This ability to identify herself with others at the same time that she is keenly analytical and planful is something quite different from the sentimentality which found sublimation in volunteer social work in earlier days. It is also unlike the blind identification of the social worker who projects her own difficulties of adjustment into her case work problems. It is rather more like the relationship between the psychoanalyst and his patient, where emotional transference plays such an important part. Perhaps it is a quality which can not be acquired through conscious effort, unless it is based on a deep substratum of very real sympathy with suffering humanity.

Put into words like these, it has a sentimental or mystical sound, but it is a very real and vital thing. It is the sense of this fundamental sympathy of the social worker, more than the realization of her clear-sightedness, which leads the person in trouble to give her his confidence. It creates an intimate relationship between the social worker and the person who has turned to her for aid.

Perhaps one of the rewards of social work—for its financial returns alone would not enable it to compete for personnel with many other professions—is this appealing human relationship. But the social worker must have other sources of personal satisfaction, so that she may be ready to give up this relationship when the other person no longer needs her guidance. Here, again, her position is analogous to that of the psychoanalyst, who must not, for his own personal satisfaction, prolong the transference of the patient beyond its term of therapeutic value. But if the social worker has a well-integrated personality, she need not fear to enter into a relationship which makes another person dependent upon her, for the time being, for she will be ready to release this other person for a freer and fuller life after the necessary adjustment has been brought about.

SUGGESTIONS FOR CLASSROOM DISCUSSION

1. With what problems is social work concerned?
2. Discuss the origins of social work.
3. When were the first academic courses in social work initiated?
4. What do we mean by the "psychiatric viewpoint" in social work?
5. How has the psychiatric viewpoint influenced the development of social work?
6. Why does the social worker consider the social history a necessary beginning?
7. What is the purpose of the social history?
8. What material should the social history contain in order to be useful in planning treatment?
9. How does the psychiatric viewpoint influence the technique of social treatment?
10. What must be the social worker's attitude toward human behavior?
11. Why should the social worker have self-understanding?

SUGGESTIONS FOR WRITTEN REPORTS

1. The Status of Social Work in 1900.
2. The Psychiatric Viewpoint in Social Work.
3. Treatment Techniques in Social Work.
4. The Type of Personality Required for Successful Social Work.
5. Outline of Topics to Be Covered in the Social History.

SELECTED BIBLIOGRAPHY

BASCH, GOLDIE. "Some Phases of Cooperative Case-work." *Mental Hygiene,* 1929, Vol. XIII, pp. 108-117.
CABOT, R. C. (Editor) *The Goal of Social Work.* Boston, 1927.
CLARKE, HELEN I. "Personality and the Social Worker." *Mental Hygiene,* 1929, Vol. XIII, pp. 99-107.
DEXTER, ELIZABETH. "The Social Case Worker's Attitude and Problems as They Affect Her Work." *The Family,* October, 1926, Vol. VII, pp. 177-181.

DEXTER, R. C. *Social Adjustment*, Chaps. XVII and XVIII. New York, 1927.

JARRETT, MARY C. "The Educational Value of Psychiatric Social Work." *Mental Hygiene*, 1921, Vol. V, pp. 509-518.

—— "The Psychiatric Thread Running Through All Social Case-work." *Proceedings, National Conference Social Work*, 1919, pp. 587-93.

LEE, PORTER. "A Study of Social Treatment." *The Family*, December, 1923, Vol. IV, pp. 191-198.

KELSO, ROBERT. *The Science of Public Welfare*. New York, 1928.

MARCUS, GRACE. "How Case-work Training May Be Adapted to Meet the Worker's Personal Problems." *Mental Hygiene*, 1927, Vol. XI, pp. 78-123.

—— *Some Aspects of Relief in Family Case Work*. Charity Organization Society, 1929.

—— "Social Attitudes as They Are Affected by Financial Dependency and Relief-giving." *The Family*, July, 1928, Vol. IX, pp. 135-140.

—— "The Psychiatric Point of View in Social Work." *Mental Hygiene*, 1923, Vol. VII, pp. 755-761.

QUEEN, STUART. *Social Work in the Light of History*. Parts I and II. New York, 1922.

RANNELLS, MARION. "The Psychiatric Social Worker's Technique in Meeting Resistance." *Mental Hygiene*, 1927, Vol. XI, pp. 78-123.

REYNOLDS, BERTHA. "A Quest for Treatment Processes in Social Work." *Hospital Social Service*, 1926, Vol. XIV, pp. 454-63.

TAFT, JESSIE. "The Relation of Psychiatry to Social Work." *The Family*, November, 1926, Vol. VII, pp. 199-203.

WATSON, FRANK. *The Charity Organization Movement in the United States*, Chaps. III, VI and VIII. New York, 1922.

Interviews. Studies in the Practice of Social Work, No. 1. American Association of Social Workers, 130 East 22nd Street, New York; May, 1928.

CHAPTER XV

MENTAL HYGIENE AND PUBLIC OPINION

Mental hygiene and communication. Mental hygiene issues from the feeling and thinking of the group who maintain it. Since public opinion exercises so large an influence over the average person, one who is interested in mental hygiene has to reckon with it. Public opinion is made by contact and communication. Modern man has gone so far in his improvement of means of communication that we have to recognize an artificial or induced public opinion which comes from manipulation by those who have in their power the means of communicating sentiments and ideas that they know will influence a mass of people. By reflecting common attitudes and also by magnifying and multiplying attitudes belonging to those who administer the instruments of communicating thought and feeling, public opinion becomes a means of social control that necessarily interests mental hygiene because of the forceful impression it makes upon people. It also brings out into clear light the morbid features of current civilization. From both points of view public opinion is of interest for mental hygiene.

Mental hygiene and gossip. Gossip is a perverted type of curiosity. It is encouraged by emptiness of life and by isolation. Perhaps such a description over-emphasizes the seriousness of gossip since much of it is trivial in character and expresses a mild human interest in the doings of others rather than any pernicious impulse. Gossip at its worst is both malicious and morbid. When it takes this form, gossip flows out of some kind of maladjustment, revealing the weakness of the personality that turns to it for a peculiar sort of satisfaction. This sort of gossip is apt to connect itself with feelings of inferiority, having the double purpose of hurting someone, at least in public estimation, and at the same time giving the peddler of gossip a sense of power which flatters his vanity. Where ignorance prevails it is easier to spread gossip, because wild tales are not scrutinized, especially when they have to do with people and things too remote for those who receive the stories to check up on the truthfulness of what is said. Among people who demand factual knowledge gossip is restricted and seldom appears except as it is related to the intimacies of life, that, because they are private affairs, can be made matters of hearsay.

Forms of morbid gossip. One of the expressions of gossip centers about the private life of individuals, since ordinarily the person most concerned does not know about this gossip until it has become widespread and firmly entrenched in the minds of his group. It is possible for a story to start and travel far before it is checked. No better illustration of this could be found, perhaps, than the very general belief during Theodore Roosevelt's candidacy for the Presidency, as leader of the Progressive Party, that he was a confirmed drunkard. I remember how tenaciously this was held to by a lawyer friend of mine who was noted for his judicial attitude in his legal practice. On the most flimsy hearsay evidence he was convinced, finally coming to think that some of his friends had seen Roosevelt intoxicated while on a speaking trip to their community. Fortunately for Roosevelt, it was possible at last to bring the whole matter before a legal tribunal where facts soon melted away the creation of gossip. It may be that unless this trial had occurred, Roosevelt would have gone on through history as an illustration of the weakness of chronic alcoholism.

Very recently in the mountain region of one of our southern states a young woman is reported to have killed a man who was starting stories that were bound to undermine her public reputation. Only those familiar with rural life and the intense passion that gathers about maintaining one's character can fully realize the strength of the impulses that led her to commit this murder. Among her associates unquestionably what she did will seem a proper thing. In such surroundings gossip has great effectiveness and as a result men and women are quick to react fiercely when it comes to their knowledge that they are being maliciously gossiped about.

Out of such conditions comes a morbid fear of loss of character as well as morbid impulses to hurt others through gossip. The ease with which personal reputation can be destroyed opens up a temptation for the psychopathic individual who loves cruelty and craves the opportunity to inflict upon someone the suffering from which he obtains a peculiar, abnormal satisfaction. Such experiences reveal a measure of unsoundness in the social life of the group, for otherwise this gossip would not be so generally welcomed and so rapidly carried from one person to another. Busy, happy, and intelligent people react unfavorably to the passing of scandal which the idle, isolated, and emotionally immature welcome with avidity.

The psychopathic liar. Gossip is not confined to the repeating of scandalous happenings. Occasionally we find in group life individuals who make up from their own imaginations charges that menace the reputation of others. Some of these statements reveal a mean sort of character, whose motives, although malicious, disclose moral faults rather than distinctly pathological trends. There is, however, a type of persons altogether too well known to the specialist, who by their story telling evince a basic mental unsoundness. Unfortunately it is often true that the personality defect behind it does not make this gossip less injurious, for the general public is apt to be too credulous in accepting plausible but unfounded reports. These individuals who are driven by an obsession to tell things likely to create a disturbance or awaken suspicion are roughly classified as pathological liars. The point of the term is that behind their falsehoods are impulses that come forth from a dissociated, badly adjusted personality. Even cases that seem on the surface to be merely efforts to create excitement, like the tantrums of the child, reveal deep-lying mechanisms characteristic of the neurotic individual. When the pathological liar is subjected to analysis each case has its peculiarity. The compelling motives show considerable variation.

As an example of false statements that appear primarily to be merely efforts to attract attention, we have the striking case reported by Dr. William Healy of the young girl of sixteen who even convinced experienced detectives of the truthfulness of her story that she had been a prostitute, enticed into a house of ill-fame. Her confession was given with such apparent accuracy and detail that it was accepted as fact and effort was made to discover the house where she had been introduced to vice. Finally it was found that what she said had no basis in fact whatsoever, that she had not even been away from home any night. Her story had been apparently suggested by a revivalist whom she had heard describe the life of the New York City slums. She had come from the meeting much excited and finally had told her Sunday school teacher the story of her misdoings which had been taken seriously by the pastor of the church, to whom it was soon reported, and by the police. Her family were not called in until the detectives finally became suspicious. It is evident that this experience grew out of a disordered personality, which Dr. Healy describes as showing hysterical symptoms. Unquestionably there was more in this episode than merely the desire of the child to cause excitement. The method she chose for her dramatic publicity brought out the turn her disorganized life had taken. Her subsequent career gives us more evidence of her inherent unsoundness. Two years later she charged a man with being responsible for her pregnancy, and again, a physical examination that proved she was not carrying a child disclosed that her accusation was another expression of her neurotic character.[1]

Another case brings out, perhaps even more clearly, the kind of hidden desire that often leads to pathological lying. A teacher in a western rural school was found tied in her schoolroom and told the story of an assault. She did not charge any particular person in the community with the offense, but gave a vague description of a man who had come in and attacked her after school had closed, and had tied her. The community was much excited and great sympathy was shown the girl. Persistent efforts were made to discover the criminal and eventually bloodhounds were put upon the supposed track of the offender, all to no purpose. Of course, much was made of the occurrence in the public press and soon the state superintendent of public instruction became interested. He visited the community and, being a man of experience quick to detect the characteristics of an unbalanced person, became skeptical of the story that had thus far been

[1] William Healy, *The Individual Delinquent*, pp. 746-50.

accepted without question. Beginning an investigation, it was not long before he discovered that the thing never happened and after a short cross-examination of the girl he led her to confess that she had herself done the tying and that there was no truth at all in the story that she had started. The young woman was removed from her school, but she was not taken to a specialist, so that the full meaning of her experience never came out.

The credence that false charges of rape receive, particularly when they are presented by children and in detail, open up an opportunity for pathological lying of the most serious sort. We have no way of knowing how many innocent persons suffer on account of these false accusations that originate from mental disorder of mild or serious character. Dr. Robinson and others have tried to impress the public with the seriousness of this problem of false accusation of rape, but it is hard to convince the judiciary that innocent-looking little children can make up such a detailed story, or that there could be any motive to lead them to do this. Yet there are facts in abundance to convince anyone that this is just what happens in many cases. Occasionally suicide results from these false charges. Robinson reports a case of a minister who killed himself when he was falsely accused of assaulting a girl, a charge which, soon after his death, was proven to have been untrue.[2] There is great need of ministers, doctors, and lawyers, especially, realizing how frequently the story of rape, even when rehearsed by a child, is a symptom of emotional conflict or the onset of a nervous disease, and that all charges should be investigated with the greatest care. It is a terrible fact that in many southern communities a white child with psychopathic tendencies along lines

[2] William J. Robinson, *American Sex and Marriage Problems,* p. 329.

of sex can at once bring any colored man into immediate danger of torture and unlawful death. Indeed it is fortunate, both North and South, that revengeful children do not know the horrible power they possess.

Venereal diseases. In spite of considerable change toward a more helpful attitude, the general public still treats venereal disease as a topic of gossip instead of dealing with it in an intelligent way as they would with other diseases. Even in reputable medical books appears a tendency to exaggerate the risk of venereal disease and to overstate the difficulties of cure. The moment he finds himself dealing with this particular type of disease, the writer seems to lose his former scientific attitude and to mix with his statement an emotional reaction that we have become accustomed to expect. Another illustration of the same tendency is frequently found in addresses made before students regarding the dangers of venereal infection. Some of these addresses are the products of a morbid attitude and I have known instances when this was true even of doctors, who went out of their way, in talking on sex, to bring to their young listeners morbid exaggeration which could have none but harmful effects.

The policy of the press has much to do with keeping this old problem of venereal disease, as far as the general public is concerned, within the realm of gossip. It still refuses for the most part to use specific terms when it refers to venereal disease, but instead employs some circumlocution, which, although perfectly clear to the informed, conceals the truth from the very reader who needs to have an understanding of the facts. With this leadership it is easy for a taboo to persist which costs humanity much suffering since it is difficult to make the progress that should be made against these diseases so long as there is general ignorance regarding their significance. Mental hygiene is concerned because the influence of syphilis especially is so definite in the realm of mental disorders.

Insanity. There is another social problem that to some extent is kept within the realm of gossip. Mental disease is still largely misunderstood because public opinion does not tolerate in many localities and classes the frank discussion that is necessary for an intelligent understanding of the problem. Families try to conceal mental disease when they would be quick to bring one of their physically sick members to the attention of the physician. In a small New Hampshire town, I labored with a family where the grandfather was clearly suffering from a serious type of mental disease. In that community it was such a disgrace to admit that one had a "crazy" relative that it was impossible to get treatment for the man until things had become so desperate that every member of the household was in terror of the violence the old man might do. Under the stress of fear, finally one of the family called in a physician, who immediately committed the grandfather to the hospital for the insane at Concord.

The gossip type of attitude taken by many toward mental disease in its various forms is not socially dangerous merely because it prevents the treatment of the sufferer and his removal from the ordinary environment where he is dangerous, but the fear of possible insanity on the part of those who misinterpret the meaning of mental disorder in their own family history is grievous beyond description. Men and women go on through life with a hidden terror that in many cases would be easily removed if only they would receive counsel from those fitted to enlighten them as to the meaning of their relative's insanity, which they assume makes them liable to some sort of mental disease. There is still general ignorance regarding the various types of mental disorder, and especially of the fact that an insanity requiring the segregation of the sufferer may frequently be a derivative of some physical ailment rather than evidence of neurological unsoundness.

The social burden of mental disease is so great in our times that mental hygiene is necessarily committed to a program of general education. It aims to bring mental disease into the light so that it may be dealt with rationally in the same way that infectious diseases are now attacked by sanitation and medicine. Society cannot make use of its present resources in the prevention and cure of mental diseases unless it can bring mental disorders out of hearsay and ignorance so that the problem can be dealt with rationally. Public thought, much as it has already changed, is not yet right-minded in attitude toward what it calls insanity. In this task of changing public opinion, mental hygiene faces one of its chief obstacles in the way of greater social help.

Mental hygiene and the newspaper. Nothing is more representative of American life than the newspaper. From many angles it concerns mental hygiene, chiefly, however, as a most effective way of influencing public opinion. For millions, because of the attention it receives and the interest it evokes, it has come to be a means of contact that is more influential than the face-to-face meeting which in simpler society is the primary way of conveying the ideas and feelings that build up the common mind. To a very large extent the newspaper has supplanted the friendly chat which used to be a chief recreation and the source of social suggestion. What once went from person to person is now largely distributed by the press. Even when people converse, a good part of their talk is likely to be about current events as reported in the news of the day.

Mental hygiene finds the newspaper both an ally and an enemy. In its columns of news, its editorials, and its advertising appear suggestions good and bad, some leading to more normal social experience, while others create morbid suggestions. Not only is it difficult to generalize, since papers differ so widely in their policy, but it is also next to impossible to dogmatize, since what the paper accomplishes is largely determined by the personality that comes to the reading. There are many sorts of papers; there are even more types of readers. The news story that is mildly interesting to one person, repellent or even disgusting to another, is to a third a stimulant to morbid thoughts or anti-social activities. It is not difficult for the press to cater to the same impulses as those that are favorable to gossip, and from day to day there appears in print material that ranges from curiosity about unfamiliar things and people to clearly morbid interests. The paper never has space for more than a portion of the great quantity of material that comes to it, and the selection it makes is determined by what are thought to be the interests of its readers.

Since the papers do not all cater to the same type of reader their news material varies according to their policy, but anyone who will read representative papers of the same date from all parts of the country, carrying on the first page some crime or murder-trial story, will find that the difference is largely that of treatment. With the exception of the *Christian Science Monitor*, which maintains a very different policy from the others, the crime or trial featured on the front page will be treated in such a way as to make it possible on the basis of sensationalism to group the papers in various classes. In one of these groups will be found papers that exploit to the limit every sensational feature related to the news reported.   There will even be suggestions of morbidity that would not appear if imagination did not color the actual event.

It is this element of morbid suggestion that mental hygiene condemns.   It, for example, has no quarrel with the papers for reporting the crime of the day.   It is the manner in which this is done to which mental hygiene objects. If the newspapers sought merely to list the number and kinds of crimes day by day, as now they record fires, it would give a more accurate crime picture than it does to-day, but this would not be news.   It is in the process of turning the event into news that the opportunity for morbid suggestion presents itself.   In estimating this quality, it must be remembered that it varies from reader to reader—in one case exciting horror, in another a well-nigh irresistible craving to imitate what is portrayed in so suggestive a manner, while the average reader may have only a passing interest in the story reported.

In the recent Hall-Mills and Gray-Snyder trials it would seem as if the American newspapers had carried sensationalism to its utmost limit.   Nothing more impressively shows the attitude of the press than:

. . . at the Hall-Mills trial 50 reporters from metropolitan newspapers and press associations were present at the Grand Jury proceedings; 200 came for the trial itself; one newspaper in New York [the *News*] had 16 correspondents on the scene; another [the *Mirror*] had 13; 50 photographers were on duty at all hours; until the closing days of the trial 10 were stationed in the court room. . . . At the Gray-Snyder trial . . . four rows of ten tables with 3 seats to the table were installed for the reporters; one hundred and twenty correspondents filled them; papers in Buffalo, Pittsburgh, Birmingham, Syracuse, Louisville, Cincinnati, Chicago, and Atlanta sent special cor-

respondents to supplement the press association stories. . . .
The *New York Times* carried 30,000 words of testimony on
two successive mornings.[3]

This represents the high water mark in the American
newspapers' exploitation of a murder trial, but relatively
it probably has less social meaning than the reporting of
the trial of Henry Ward Beecher for adultery, which is
said to have gotten more newspaper space than any other
private event during the nineteenth century.[4]   Some of
the New York papers issued special supplements giving
the testimony verbatim and in full.   The metropolitan
press, a business highly organized and sharply competitive, as a matter of course prepares elaborately to report
whatever it knows to be of general interest.   The scale of
its reporting has changed in accord with the size of its
business just as the sales organization of the department
store is no longer that of the one-time, general-merchan-
dise retail store.

It is of course impossible to trace causally the results
of newspaper suggestion so as to measure accurately its
morbid influence.   If, however, from day to day, the
paper featured on its front page all sorts of horrifying
tales regarding physical disease, unquestionably we would
soon have countless numbers of persons suffering from
imaginary ailments, the victims of morbid fear.   In somewhat the same way, the featuring of the morbid aspects
of crime is having a definite effect in the thinking and
feeling of people that lies behind the notorious record of
this country in regard to homicide.   Unquestionably by its
publicity the newspaper helps to apprehend the criminal,

[3] Charles Merz, "Bigger and Better Murders," *Harper's*, August,
1927, pp. 340-41.
[4] "Scarlet Journalism," *Scribner's Magazine*, November, 1928, p.
565.

but through its publicity it also stimulates the cravings of the potentially morbid.

Shall we censor newspapers?   The stock answer that the press makes to the criticism of its sensationalism is that it gives the people what they want.   The same answer can be made by the bootlegger and the peddler of narcotic drugs.   In both cases a part of the public is given what it wants.   Nevertheless, there can be no discounting the fact that a newspaper's circulation increases when it is reporting in full a sensational trial, or when there is widespread interest in some gruesome murder.   If the subscribers protested by showing an unwillingness to buy the paper, or if advertisers withdrew their patronage, newspaper publishers would be quick to respond to a demand for a cleaner press.

Since the reading public, judged by the circulation of the paper, tends to encourage rather than frown upon sensationalism, there comes from some quarters a demand for legal censorship.   There is certainly need of strengthening through statutory law or court decisions the private rights of the person who wishes to protect himself from unsought publicity.   In their hunger for sensational features some papers expect their reporters to go to any lengths, and not only are private rights violated, but even ordinary decency.   In practice at present the libel law is seldom of value to anyone who does not have great wealth by means of which to defend his rights, and even the state which promises the accused criminal a fair trial finds it next to impossible to guard the legal machinery from the influence of the sensational press.   Although there is need of strengthening the law against libel and making it workable for the poor man as well as the rich, it is doubtful whether more could be done to curb the sensationalism of the press by any form of legislation.

It were better frankly to admit that the newspapers we have are on the whole reflecting the life of the people, and that unless the majority of people can be lifted above the moron level of emotionalism, we must learn to endure what we have. A hampered press, such as is found to-day in Russia or Italy, is for our country sure to prove a greater menace than any degree of morbidness on the part of the press.

It is of course true that the public opinion that tolerates modern sensationalism is itself, to a large degree, a product of the newspaper, but if any substantial progress is to be made toward greater wholesomeness it must grow out of opposition by the readers to what is spread before them. There is no reason to suppose that in time sensationalism will not bring its own reaction; indeed there is evidence that this is already to some extent happening.

It is well also for some people to remind themselves of the history of the press. Daniel Defoe, whom some regard as the great grandfather of the English newspaper, did not hesitate to be sensational, nor was he ignorant of the news value of the criminal. We certainly have made some progress away from the hangman's holiday, which in the eighteenth century in both America and England brought together immense crowds to witness a public execution. Indirect contact through the press is preferable to the experiences of the eye witness. The morbidity of the past, to be sure, does not defend that of the present, but it does reveal that the newspaper is catering to interests that have been exploited in the past. Anyone who will make an unbiased study of the American newspaper during the last seventy-five years will be convinced that there has been a general improvement that can be traced along most lines, and that there is nothing to justify the idea that the newspaper will not free itself from its morbid sensationalism as rapidly as the buying public will permit.

There are, of course, differences of opinion regarding the trends of the modern press, and with no definite standard for comparison of past and present, and extreme variability in the material even of a single issue of a large newspaper this disagreement in interpretation is inevitable.[5] The newspaper may be roughly divided into four parts, editorial, advertising, features, and news. Any attempt to classify the modern press must consider each.

If we distinguish three stages in the development of the press, at first the publishing of news, then the interpretation of news, and to-day the business enterprise of selling advertising space,[6] the editorial, appearing in the second period, flourished during the nineteenth century when personal journalism prevailed. Defoe is given credit for the emergence of the editorial when he put into *Mist's Journal* his "Letter Introductory." From 1830 to 1890 when personal journalism reached its highest development with the editorship of such men as Bennett, Dana, Garrison, Bowles, Greeley, the editorial also achieved its greatest influence. The present-day editorial has fallen from its high estate as a social influence but it also has lost its rancor, bitterness, and inflammatory appeal, characteristics which Charles Dickens called "transatlantic blackguardism which is so intense that I seriously believe words cannot describe it." It was gossip that unjustly charged the assassination of President McKinley upon the editorials of the *New York American,* but it is clear that in recent years the editorial has moved toward a milder, more tolerant and less violent type of writing

[5] See Oswald Garrison Villard, *Some Newspapers and Newspaper Men,* and R. A. Scott-James, *The Influence of the Press.*
[6] Lucy Maynard Salmon, *The Newspaper and the Historian,* p. 249.

than was characteristic even at so late a period as that of the Spanish-American war.

With regard to advertising there is no basis for difference of opinion. Even the reader of newspapers who vividly remembers the advertisements of reputable papers of two decades past notices the improvement. For example, an advertisement that ran for months on the first page of the most widely circulated paper in the largest city of an eastern state would not now be tolerated in any part of the paper even for a day. If it were published the paper would be debarred from the mails. It is interesting to contrast with their former indifference the care of most newspapers to-day in their acceptance of "Personal" advertising. A few hours spent in reading papers of twenty and thirty years ago in any large city library is most convincing. When the *New York Herald* and Bennett, its owner, for personal revenge, were indicted, convicted, and fined twenty-five thousand dollars because of the obscenities that had gotten by the vigilance of the proof readers into "personals," his paper was not the only one guilty of advertising prostitution. Of special encouragement to mental hygiene has been the change of policy in most reputable newspapers regarding patent medicine advertisements. This type of advertising, once so common, is now rare and its passing has eliminated much morbid suggestion. Instead of the patent medicine testimonial that flourished in the advertising columns of yesterday's paper, to-day's newspaper carries in its feature stories much sensible and constructive advice based on the practices and teaching of medical science.

Although all newspapers do not have the high standard set by the *New York Times* for its advertising, it is significant that one of the most prominent papers in the United States should publish the following statement:

. . . The high character of advertising is, of course, of more importance to the *Times* than the increased volume. Whenever there is reason to suspect that a firm may be undesirable, or that statements in the advertising are extravagant or misleading, an investigation is made. If the firm is one of questionable character, no advertising is accepted; if the statements made are extravagant or ambiguous, the text is censored before acceptance.

The *Times* furthermore makes a standing offer to pay a reward of $100 to anyone causing the arrest and conviction of a person or firm obtaining money under false pretenses through fradulent advertising published in its columns.

THE "NEW YORK TIMES" ADVERTISING INDEX EXPURGATORIUS

1. Fradulent or doubtful advertisements.
2. Offers of something of value for nothing; advertisements that make false, unwarranted or exaggerated claims.
3. Advertisements that are ambiguous in wording and which may mislead.
4. Attacks of a personal character; advertisements that make uncalled-for reflections on competitors or competitive goods.
5. Advertisements holding out prospect of large guaranteed dividends or excessive profits.
6. Bucket shops and offerings of undesirable financial firms.
7. Advertisements that are indecent, vulgar, suggestive, repulsive or offensive, either in theme or treatment.
8. Matrimonial offers; fortune telling; massage, unless licensed and license number is given.
9. Objectionable medical advertising and offers of free medical treatment; advertising that makes remedial, relief or curative claims, either directly or by inference, not justified by the facts or common experience.
10. Advertising of products containing habit-forming or dangerous drugs.

11. Help Wanted advertisements which request money for samples or articles.
12. Any other advertising that may cause money loss to the reader or injury in health or morals, or loss of confidence in reputable advertising and honorable business, or which is regarded by the *Times* as Unworthy.[7]

Its special features are in their present form a new and important part of the newspaper. They are good, bad, and indifferent. The authors of *Middletown* give testimony to the great influence of Dorothy Dix's column on marriage problems, and without question this influence was socially helpful. In contrast the colored "funnies" are often silly and sometimes harmful in their influence upon children. Even the worst of these have less practical suggestion than one would suppose, while the strength of their popular appeal is great. Some years ago the *Boston Herald* eliminated the Sunday comic supplement, doubtless an abomination to most newspaper men, but immediate and continued decrease in circulation forced the paper to put back the colored funnies. Many believe that this comic material is decidedly inferior to the Yellow Kid featured some twenty years ago by the *New York World*. On the other hand, is not the humor of the Metropolitan Movies, now running daily in this paper, greatly superior to that of its earlier creation? The popular feature material discussing problems of child care and personality, although of differing value, indicates the more constructive influence of newspaper writing and provides an opportunity of the largest promise for mental hygiene.

It is with reference to its news that the newspaper is most criticized. We are concerned with this indictment only as it applies to characteristics of significance to

[7] *New York Times,* July 7, 1929.

mental hygiene. The tabloid is the worst offender, but its sensationalism is largely different from that of the standard newspaper only in its form. It caters to the low-brow and at its worst is an advance over the face-to-face gossip that it replaces. The large and increasing circulation of the tabloids forces attention upon the backwater of our progressive civilization and challenges education. Depressing as it is to realize the popularity of scandals, divorces, murders, and crime as items of news among the clientele of the tabloids, it is important to recognize that the readers are advanced beyond the gossip of personal, primary contact and that even a low use of the printed page is for mental hygiene better than no use at all. Moreover, the sophisticated reader of the standard press is almost sure to exaggerate the practical effects of tabloid suggestion.

Newspapers in their sensationalism come nearest to the character of gossip. Viewed as a special type of gossip-appeal the sensational story is but a modern form of a very ancient human interest. Sensationalism changes in its outward expression but inwardly it keeps its original substance. It is doubtful, even if modern conditions of city life made it possible, that any influential paper could spring such sensationalism as did the *New York Herald*, when, as one of the first papers of America, it caused a veritable panic in New York City by its report that the wild animals in Central Park Zoo had broken loose. Thousands kept within doors, assuming that the Mayor's proclamation asking them to do so was genuine. Not until the next morning did the fear pass and for a fortnight the excitement persisted.[8]

In any attempt to judge the sensationalism of American newspapers it must be recognized that there has been an

[8] Don C. Seitz, *The James Gordon Bennetts*, pp. 304-39.

increase in readers, in leisure, and also in monotony as a conscious experience.[9] The sensational newspaper merely commercializes an opportunity presented by contemporary civilization and by so doing brings into the open a flaw which challenges mental hygiene. We cannot expect much better papers until we have better people. Unfortunately it is equally true that it will be difficult to get the latter unless the former lifts its standards.

Frequently the unwholesome suggestions imbedded in a newspaper to-day are incidental and unpremeditated, discoverable by the psychiatric expert rather than by the journalist. For that reason the newspaper that handles sensational material with the sincere purpose of reporting news as free as can be from morbid suggestion needs the assistance of someone trained to sensitiveness in noticing morbid suggestion. There is a place for the psychiatrist on the staff of the metropolitan newspaper. One comes across dangerous suggestions even in reputable newspapers that sincerely try to protect themselves from sensationalism. Not long ago a story was skillfully told by a journalist who either had a firm grasp of psychology or an unconscious twist that made it easy for him to bring out the horror of the murder of a child, who had been tempted into a basement where she was murdered by a feeble-minded boy of imbecile grade. While the child was dying—not unconscious—she was placed in a meal bag and carried on a sled to a neighboring river into which her body was dumped. The writer described the conversation between the boy and an adult who was curious when he saw the wiggling within the bag when the boy passed him on the street. The description was vivid but for a certain type of reader had distinct suggestive qualities which unquestionably would lead to desires to repeat

[9] E. R. Groves, *Rural Mind and Social Welfare*, pp. 60-65.

the crime.   In the hurry of going to press the editor who passed upon this material failed to notice the seriousness of its morbid suggestion.   A psychiatrist would have sensed the danger of the story at once and merely by a different treatment the facts would have been printed without an appeal for the perverted reader.

Newspapers and crime.   Although of interest to mental hygiene, the question, how much the news stories of crime and criminals encourage anti-social conduct, is a problem in itself.   Authorities, as one would expect, differ in their estimation of the harm done by the press.   Lombroso accused the newspaper of inciting criminals to emulation and imitation.[10]   Ferri believes that the effect of newspaper publicity is exaggerated, that it only stimulates those predisposed to crime who sooner or later would fall through temptation since they would be incited from some source.[11]   Healy, who from his practical experience speaks with special force, tells us that contrary to his own belief he has found little evidence of the influence of the press in causing crime.[12]   In not one case did he find that the reading of newspapers appeared directly responsible for the crime.   Nor does he think that his results are contradicted by anything that any other author has been able to demonstrate.   All students of the problem agree that the greatest risk of the newspaper crime story comes from its effect upon the morbid and the abnormally suggestible individuals.   The imitation that Jack the Ripper received in various parts of the world shows that the details of crimes unusually brutal, as they are reported in the press, act upon potential offenders as stimuli.   Vanity also causes crime, and when

[10] Cesari Lombroso, *Crime, Its Causes and Remedies,* p. 55.
[11] Enrico Ferri, *Criminal Sociology,* p. 277.
[12] William Healy, *The Individual Delinquent,* p. 302.

the press makes a hero of the criminal especially in writing up executions it leads some to seek notoriety through a perverted ambition. The newspaper in its descriptions of crimes suggests methods to those already committed to crime. The mental hygienist is, however, most impressed by the suggestions that come from the suicide story and from the newspaper's encouragement of mob violence. The effect of the first is seen when the method of the suicide is repeated by someone of morbid predisposition who clearly reveals by the means he uses or what he writes as his message to the world that he has become a victim to the stimulation of the press report.

We have also occasionally in cases of lynching direct evidence of newspaper suggestion. The Dayton, Ohio, and the Frank lynching [13] are characteristic examples. On the other hand, the attitude of the *Greensboro News,* the *Raleigh Observer,* and other newspapers of North Carolina is in part the explanation of the freedom of that state from lynchings in recent years. If the papers everywhere were to take a hostile attitude toward all lynchings this form of barbarism would soon come to an end.

The Hickman case, as the *Brooklyn Eagle* stated, gave the American press an unusual chance to serve its readers and to advance the cause of mental hygiene. The one thing needed was a frank publicity that would make clear the menace children face from persons of psychopathic dispositions who have developed unnatural habits. By leading parents to realize how many psychopathic persons there are who are potential child-killers and how inadequately prepared the courts and police are for the discovery of such types among the offenders who early get

[13] Robert D. Highfill, "The Effects of News of Crime and Scandal upon Public Opinion," *Journal of Criminal Law and Criminology,* May, 1926, pp. 86-87.

in trouble with the law, the newspapers could have strengthened the hands of those who are trying to make our legal system a real defense against the most horrible of crimes. Strange it is that the appeal of the *Eagle* met with practically no response.[14] The size of the menace was brought out by the *Eagle's* printing a list of recent offenses against children committed by men in New York City. The catalog was made from the police and court records. The inadequacy of present legal machinery appeared in the fact that without any psychiatric examination many of these men were on parole. Surely the explanation of the unwillingness of the press to follow the *Eagle's* lead was not lack of understanding but reluctance to invade territory under taboo. Where are the walls of prejudice so weak as at the point where parental impulses hold sway? Yet the press retreated from the challenge, although many of them did not hesitate to rehearse to the full the morbid story that could not be printed without enticing some readers to act out their pathological cravings. It was a lost opportunity but one most unfortunately that will be likely to come again to test the social courage of the American newspaper. In time some publisher will realize that parents, like mental hygienists, are more interested in preventing mutilation and death of children than in catching and punishing those guilty of such crimes.

Child delinquency and publicity. Whatever may be the policy of a newspaper regarding adult criminals, there is no excuse for publishing the names of children guilty of mild offenses. Of what advantage is it to save children from a criminal record through the juvenile court when their delinquency is reported in the public press with the name and street and possibly a vivid and exaggerated ac-

[14] "Scarlet Journalism," *Scribner's Magazine*, November, 1928, p. 567.

count of their misdoings? Experience has demonstrated that there is nothing more injurious to character than for a child to get the reputation that creates in those about him suspicion and hostility. The journalism that will destroy the future of the child for the sake of a story shows itself soulless and a public menace. In the city there are innumerable ways that the child may become a law breaker through thoughtlessness and even ignorance. His offense, even though it invokes the heavy hand of the law, does not justify publication. To hold the child up for ridicule is to hurt him just as much as to brand him a criminal. Disregard of the rights of children doubtless is responsible for starting many of them on a criminal career. There should be no ambiguity of newspaper ethics in regard to the obligations of the press to protect from publicity children, who, although naughty and mischievous, are too young to be serious criminals.

We have one careful investigation which makes clear how unjustly the newspaper may injure the reputations of children and youth. The Chicago newspapers carried headlines and news stories of the capture of a notorious and dangerous "moron-gang" on the South Side. Pictures of several boys and their addresses were given. Nils Anderson traced the unhappy results that followed this publicity both for the boys and their families. Investigation disclosed that the boys were not morons, were not members of a gang and had done no crime.[15]

The movies. As a means of communicating feeling and thought to influence public opinion, the movies rival the newspapers and possibly have already become more powerful. It is easy to criticize the movies, particularly if one looks upon them as an art and recreation which

[15] *The Child, The Clinic, and the Court,* "Trial by Newspapers," by Nils Anderson, pp. 108-19.

keeps to low levels in spite of extraordinary opportunity. Mental hygiene is concerned with the movies, however, only as they contribute morbid or wholesome suggestion to those who patronize them. There can be no just appraisal of the influence of the movies from the mental hygiene point of view unless one senses the monotony of experience to which they bring relief, the vicarious association they provide which brings new understanding of life to the poor and isolated. They offer relaxation from the hardships of life and through reverie give those who crave romance the satisfaction which in some form their condition of life makes indispensable. As Dr. Blanchard has said,[16] the mental hygienist is not so fearful of sex appeal in the movies as of suggestion related to fear and anger. So far as sex is concerned it is likely that the movies sublimate even more than they stimulate sex passion. In the case of children especially it is fear in the movies that is most likely to be damaging. For example, in a small Canadian village some years ago, a motion picture was shown to an audience of which three-fourths were children. The play presented was worked out with unusual faithfulness to scientific realism. At one point a little child, soon to be rescued of course, was kidnaped by a man who was bent upon doing her physical harm. At the moment when she was caught by this man from whom she tried to run away she fainted, and the picture proceeded to give her dreams. She was caught in the midst of a meadow of daisies and in her dream saw all about her daisies taking the form of the ugly man of passion who was about to catch her. Thousands of the ugly faces and outstretched hands rose wherever her eye fell. It was a terrifying portrayal, most decidedly harmful for some of the children who witnessed it.

[16] Phyllis Blanchard, *Child and Society*, p. 196.

So much has been said about the problems of sex in the movies that the really serious morbidity has been neglected. Here, as in the newspaper, it is not the thing that happens, but the method by which it is presented that is most likely to make the experience dangerous. The difficulty cannot be escaped by merely preventing children from attending the movies at times when especially dangerous plays are presented. This, although desirable, does not solve the problem since in an audience of adults there will be found a sprinkling of the emotionally immature and the mentally unsound who frequently run as much risk from any sort of fear suggestion as do children, even in some cases much more than would be true in the case of normal children. In the handling of this problem there is need, as in the case of the newspaper, of psychiatric censorship. It is not until one has become familiar with the consequences of morbid suggestion that he is in a position to detect the material that brings risk to those especially susceptible to morbid influence. Of course it is humanly impossible to eliminate morbid suggestion entirely, since so much depends upon the subjective character that abstracts evil from the experience, but the movies can be made more wholesome than they are.

The moving picture is primarily, and rightly, a means of recreation. To attempt to make it chiefly a form of instruction would decrease its appeal and make it in the end of less social value. An inexpensive, wholesome entertainment is its proper function but this need not mean an entire disregard of its teaching value. We already have experiments that prove the educational possibilities of the movies. These are of interest to mental hygiene for they open an opportunity to present the science of human adjustment in a form that will reach people who might never read books or articles on the subject or listen to lectures. During the World War the movies were made use of and their effectiveness proven both for educational and propaganda purposes. Occasionally a skilled artist demonstrates that entertainment and instruction can be successfully presented together, but such a happy unity is too much to expect of most writers. It is reasonable to suppose that pictures frankly educational in form and substance will be more common in the future and that mental hygiene will be given its share in the opportunity that this type of teaching provides.

The radio. Thus far the radio has not created any serious problem as a means of morbid suggestion. Much is broadcast that is worthless or at least crude, but there is seldom anything that can be objected to because of its morbid appeal. On the other hand, the radio has not been used thus far as much as it might be in distributing the principles of mental hygiene. It has not, however, been entirely neglected, for the psychologist, the child specialist, and the family counselor have been given opportunity to send into individual homes information of great value in meeting the concrete difficulties of adjustment.

In order to do justice to the social value of the movies and the radio as means of relieving isolation there is need of adding to the primary and secondary contacts defined by the sociologist a third term, tertiary contact, to represent the mechanical method of providing a reflected contact. The movies furnish through the eye, and the radio through the ear, and soon each will commonly provide for both eye and ear the contact of the spectator and the listener who is given in most vivid form an association which is independent of spatial relationships. For those in isolated places, and especially for the shut-in individual, the movie and the radio provide the supreme antidote for separation from intimate contact with their fellows.   In a recent study, Dr. L. M. Brooks has gathered most interesting data illustrating the value of the radio to lighthouse and lifesaving families who are necessarily for a part of the year denied normal associations.   Both the movie and the radio are too recent inventions for us to realize to the full their enormous social significance in providing this new type of contact.   For example in the winter of 1930 the explorers in the Antarctic region were in daily communication with the United States and Europe by means of the radio.   Although physically isolated they were in constant psychic contact.   So far as isolation is a mental hygiene problem, the invention of the movie and the radio are doing much toward its elimination.

The radical and the conservative.   Using conventional public opinion as a standard, we describe an attack upon it as radicalism and its defense as conservatism.   On account of the changing questions that arise, most of us are sometimes on the one side and sometimes on the other, but since the individual tends to be consistently in favor of or opposed to the prevailing social standards we distinguish the radical from the conservative.   Mental hygiene has presented with such forcefulness the mechanisms that lead to radical attitudes that the social rebel is rather generally understood.   In so far as his attack upon society issues from his emotional life, he is merely transferring to an outer environment the problems that he cannot cope with as he meets them within himself.   This emotionalism must be sharply distinguished from the rational breaking from current thought or feeling, such as is characterized by Darwin when he brought out his first book on evolution or by Charles Eliot when he broke from educational tradition in his early days of administration at Harvard. The emotional radical prefers the contest, even if he fails to gain what he struggles for, to the getting of success without trouble; in other words, it is the contest itself he craves. No sharper contrast could be drawn between the rational reformer who quietly works for results and the rebel-minded agitator who craves violence than the leadership of Francis Place and Feargus O'Connor at the time that England was struggling for parliamentary reform.

The radical has come to be well understood, but there is not such common knowledge of the pathology behind the ultra-conservative. The stand-patter who grows violent the moment any suggestion of change is made has his inner conflict from which comes forth the attitude that he takes. He also is covering up personal defect and emotional conflict by transferring the contest to his environment and allying himself with the prevailing social situation. Even the responsibility of a high judicial position does not take away a chronic disposition to maintain always what is and to show hostility to any proposed departure. Such individuals sometimes come to feel that any suggestion of innovation is a personal attack upon them, they are so committed to prevailing conditions.

Freedom of speech. This topic brings to the surface the emotions of both the radical and the conservative. The radical claims freedom of speech as a human right, although often what he really desires is freedom to make a disturbance. What he says frequently stirs up trouble not because of its meaning, but because it is presented in such a manner as to bring both friends and enemies immediately to a boiling point. The conservative, on the other side, fears public discussion, as if the opinions he holds are too sacred to be brought under discussion. When the conservative through the power he commands blocks the radical, sympathy is created and the significance ofttimes of what the radical would say is greatly exaggerated. Freedom of discussion is not only politically the safest policy, but it is usually the shrewdest also. Nothing weakens the radical program more than to treat it like any other project put forth for public approval. The unadjusted personality prefers to such a freedom of calm discussion an opportunity to discharge his animosity and his prejudices in some sort of riotous outbreak. In like manner the pathological conservative has no satisfaction in winning his case in open and fair discussion, since he cannot be satisfied unless the element of command enters and his opponent is crushed.

The collision between an individual radical and some ultra-conservative, powerful because of his official or social position, is one of the common tragedies of history. The latter, as proxy of the sentiment of the majority, is free to do his will. Deep-seated fear and prejudice appear in consciousness as the guardian's loyalty to the common good. He crushes his opponent, observing, of course, in modern times, the technicalities of the legal or social code. Then the feeling of the mass of people passes as the fog of passion lifts. Pity replaces cruelty; suspicion gives way to sympathy. The conservative wins the battle, but the radical gets the victory. Henceforth history has in its keeping another monument to a martyr, a reformer, or an idealist. The conservative, who was by his emotions betrayed into advancing the cause of his opponent, lives in history merely as the persecutor of the man who through unjust suffering achieved fame. Public opinion looking backward on the incident registers fear of power as once it was captive to fear of change, and what otherwise would have been a trivial clashing of opinions and emotions is perpetuated as another example of personal tyranny.

Mob spirit. When public opinion turns to an emotional frenzy in which those of calm judgment are pushed aside and the group comes under the spell of the violent-minded and irresponsible, mob spirit results. Only in such emotional debauchery do the morbid possibilities of group behavior come to the surface. This can hardly be called an exhibition of public opinion, because, devoid of rational elements, it is primarily emotional intoxication. Nevertheless it controls conduct and sets up a standard of behavior in a way that is similar to the influence of public opinion. In the mob the mental hygienist plumbs to the depths the cruel emotions that accompany morbid impulses. Not until civilization is temporarily thrown aside can we discover the frailty of that social soundness that mental hygiene seeks to encourage. The mental hygienist is also eager to know how the members of the mob feel the morning after the lynching or the burning at the stake. For the answer to this question is as significant as the study of the brutality that took place while frenzy ran its course.

Program. Mental hygiene finds in the current public opinion a challenge to its activities. Ignorance, prejudice, psychopathic outbursts, and mob spirit are products not only of social maladjustment, but of personal conflict and psychopathic trends. The problems presented are not superficial, easily remedied by some Utopian scheme. Mental hygiene does not underestimate the difficulties it faces, nor does it promise to rid human nature of all conflicts. It undertakes to distribute the recent findings of the sciences dealing with human behavior in the belief that proper education through the home, the school, and other social institutions will partially lift the burden that human nature now has to carry because of its superstitions, ignorance, immature emotional character, and its unwillingness to use the facts at its command.

ILLUSTRATIVE CASE

The atrocious murder in Los Angeles of twelve year old Marian Parker by Edward Hickman was exploited in much detail by the American press. The effect of this publicity was easily seen in several imitations of the Hickman murder. In Tennessee a youth attempted to kidnap a school girl in the same manner as did Hickman, but failed because the teacher called the police. On March 21, 1928, the United Press dispatch relates another attempt which was clearly stimulated by the newspaper account of the Hickman murder. In one instance the suggestion that issued from the newspaper rehearsal of the Hickman murder led directly to the murder of a five year old girl in Michigan. The connection between the two murders is clearly revealed by some of the questions and replies in the confession of Hotelling who admitted the crime: [17]

Q. "Did you read about the crime in Los Angeles?"

A. "Yes, sir. I thought it was terrible. I could not sleep that night. It had been on my mind and I could not get rid of it. I think about it—think about it and think about it."

Q. "About the little child in California?"

A. "Yes . . ."

Q. "What do you think is the cause of that?"

A. "I think that reading about the crime in California is to blame."

Q. "Do you think that crime had any bearing on your committing this crime?"

A. "I do; it preyed on my mind and I could not get it off my mind."

SUGGESTIONS FOR CLASSROOM DISCUSSION

1. What social conditions encourage gossip?

2. Why does the taboo regarding the facts of venereal disease persist?

[17] Joseph L. Holmes, "Crime and the Press," *Journal of Criminal Law and Criminology*, Vol. XX, August, 1929, p. 250.

3. What would be the dangers of newspaper censorship?

4. Do you believe, from the mental hygiene point of view, that the American press is improving or not?

5. How can newspapers decrease crime?

6. What are the chief mental hygiene risks of children who attend the movies?

7. What effect has freedom of speech upon the growth of radicalism?

SUGGESTIONS FOR WRITTEN REPORTS

1. Dr. Healy's studies of the pathological liar.

2. The history of social attitudes regarding insanity.

3. The development of the sensational newspaper in America.

4. Defoe and sensational journalism.

5. An analysis of the news material of one issue of some newspaper.

6. Education in mental hygiene and the use of the radio.

SELECTED BIBLIOGRAPHY

BENT, SILAS. "Scarlet Journalism." *Scribner's*, November, 1928, Vol. LXXXIV, pp. 563-69.

BERNAYS, EDWARD L. "Manipulating Public Opinion: The Why and the How." *American Journal of Sociology*, May, 1928, pp. 958-71.

BLANCHARD, PHYLLIS. *The Child and Society*, Chap. VIII. New York, 1928.

BOLLMAN, GLADYS and HENRY. *Motion Pictures for Community Needs*. New York, 1922.

CRAWFORD, NELSON ANTRIM. "Mental Health and the Newspaper." *Mental Hygiene*, April, 1922, pp. 300-305.

FENTON, FRANCES. "The Influence of Newspaper Presentations upon the Growth of Crime and Other Anti-Social Activity." *The American Journal of Sociology*, January, 1911, Vol. XVI, pp. 538-64.

HIGHFILL, R. D. "The Effects of News of Crime and Scandal upon Public Opinion." *Journal of Criminal Law and Criminology*, May, 1926, pp. 40-103.

HOLMES, J. L. "Crime and the Press." *Journal of Criminal*

Law and Criminology, 1929, Vol. XX, pp. 6-59, and 246-93.

HOLT, H. *Commercialism in Journalism.* Berkeley, 1909.

LEE, J. M. *The History of American Journalism.* Boston, 1923.

LIPPMANN, W. *Public Opinion.* New York, 1927.

—— *The Phantom Public.* New York, 1927.

LLOYD, ALFRED H. "Newspaper Conscience—A Study in Half-Truths." *American Journal of Sociology*, September, 1921, pp. 197-210.

MOORE, HENRY T. "Innate Factors in Radicalism and Conservatism." *The Journal of Abnormal and Social Psychology*, October, 1925, pp. 234-44.

MÜNSTERBERG, HUGO. *The Photoplay, A Psychological Study.* New York, 1916.

A NEWSPAPERMAN. "Sell the Papers." *Harper's*, June, 1925.

OBERHOLTZER, E. P. *The Morals of the Movie.* Philadelphia, 1922.

O'BRIEN, F. M. *The Story of the SUN.* New York, 1918.

PARK, ROBERT E. "The Yellow Press." *Sociology and Social Research*, September-October, 1927, pp. 3-11.

RAMSAYE, TERRY. *A Million and One Nights.* New York, 1926.

RICHARDSON, ANNA S. "Better Films, Better Children." *Woman's Home Companion*, September, 1926.

ROOT, W. T. "The Psychology of Radicalism." *The Journal of Abnormal Psychology and Social Psychology*, January-March, 1925, pp. 341-56.

SCHROEDER, THEODORE. "Conservatisms, Liberalisms, and Radicalisms." *The Psychoanalytic Review.* October, 1920, pp. 376-84.

SEITZ, D. C. *Joseph Pulitzer: His Life and Letters.* Garden City, 1927.

SINCLAIR, UPTON. *The Brass Check.* Pasadena, 1919.

STEPHENS, LINCOLN. "How I Made a Crime Wave." *The Bookman*, December, 1928, Vol. LXVIII, pp. 416-19.

STONE, M. E. *Fifty Years a Journalist.* Garden City, 1921.

STRONG, E. K. "Control of Propaganda as a Psychological Problem." *Scientific Monthly*, March, 1922.

SUTHERLAND, E. H. "Public Opinion as a Cause of Crime."

Journal of Applied Sociology, September-October, 1924, pp. 51-56.

TAIT, WILLIAM D. "The Menace of the Reformer—a Psychological Study." *The Journal of Abnormal and Social Psychology*, January-March, 1927, pp. 343-53.

—— "Psychology of Leadership and Democracy." *The Journal of Abnormal and Social Psychology*, April-June, 1927, pp. 27-32.

VAUGHT, ELSIE. "The Release and Heightening of Individual Reactions in Crowds." *The Journal of Abnormal and Social Psychology*, January-March, 1928, pp. 404-405.

CHAPTER XVI

THE LARGER ASPECTS OF MENTAL HYGIENE

The beginnings of mental hygiene. Mental hygiene has its narrower and its wider aspects. Its values are also both immediate and remote. In its beginning it was an effort to give the insane more humane and helpful treatment. Appearing as it did at a time when medical science had begun to realize the importance and possibilities of a preventive program, it soon outran its curative projects and boldly entered the larger field which medicine was cautiously exploring. Its development was so recent that in spite of its early interest in those already insane it had no entrenched and long-continued policy to which its new preventive program had to be adjusted. Free to follow the new lead given by the more progressive medical men, there was nothing to hinder mental hygiene from attempting an educational campaign to eliminate as much as possible of the suffering due to mental disease.

Its forward going was not, however, to be over so smooth a pathway as its freedom from tradition promised. It dealt with a problem less clearly understood than most difficulties that harass the social good. The science which represented its business capital was more meager than was needed for the sizable undertaking mental hygiene assumed. Prejudice built upon traditional attitudes and the superstitions that always firmly establish themselves where science is backward soon made it clear that mental hygiene must, in spite of its untrammeled origin, push itself through the obstacles that usually hamper progress.

Science had very recently, thanks to some epoch-making discoveries in bacteriology, started upon a conquest of physical disease which demolished all previous ideas and practices regarding body ills and made the preventive in medicine inevitable. There were not, however, with the exception of paresis, any corresponding discoveries in the field of mental disease upon which to build a preventive program. Instead of new facts clearly proven by laboratory experiment there were hypotheses which men of experience with various types of mental disease were advancing. Indications of some key discoveries that would, like what Pasteur brought forth from the wine vat, bring certainty of knowledge as to the origin of mental disease had appeared from time to time but these hopes already had proven false.

There was no lack of interest. Indeed mental hygiene was soon to find that the province into which it had entered was civilization's latest gold-mine district, where claims were being staked out by faddists, exploiters, dogmatists, mystics, as well as various types of psychologists, psychoanalysts, and others concerned with the ways of the mind. No department of life could be indifferent to the teaching of mental hygiene for it was applicable to every human value. The new movement could not assume the task of preventing mental disease without stirring up a critical attitude in those sympathetically minded, as well as suspicions in those who feared its influence.

Immediate use of resources. It was evident that the insight that would end the prevailing uncertainties regarding the causes of mental disease could come only by pushing forward vigorously the mental hygiene movement. Science, like the military strategist, brings its forces to the point where its powers are challenged. It was folly to await new conquests in the field before capturing public attention. Nor was the science destitute of information of value. It was good judgment to use to the fullest measure what was already known that would help build up healthier mental life, with the expectation that, through an effective publicity, experience would be made to yield new facts of practical application.

Area of mental hygiene. Mental disorder in all its forms has an appeal which both fascinates and terrorizes the untrained. In the emotional responses it evokes it links to the magic era of savage culture, and the modern reacts, when his impulses are driven by superstition, in ways similar to those of the preliterate. Mental disease, therefore, has one salient feature; it demands attention and forbids indifferent response. Its spectacular character offered an unusual opening for those who were determined that a beginning should be made in the use of science to lessen the burden of mental disorder, which in all its various ramifications, if not in its numerical quantity, was becoming increasingly irksome among the major ills of social life.

Whatever the future may reveal regarding mental disease, it will reënforce rather than destroy the prevailing opinion that the serious breakdown is a final issue of what has had a devious and lengthy preparation during which preventive effort has neglected its favorable opportunity. Thus, without any ambitious intention, mental hygiene has been forced into the position of dealing with the conditions and circumstances of everyday life as they increase or decrease liability to mental disaster. Mental hygiene has found it necessary, even in making a start in its prevention of mental disease, to enter the whole area of present-day living and recognize that nothing that influences people is so foreign to its interests as to be excluded from its program.   This it is that makes mental hygiene, through its wider application, as significant and far-reaching as any idea, movement, or use of science that modern life thus far has brought forth.   Mental hygiene, as soon appeared, was destined to be not a specialty confined within the province of mental disorder, but a life attitude with a fund of useful information to make it practicable.   If, however, this material be compared, for example, with that which is available for the use of the chemist, it is apparent that mental hygiene uncovers the great scientific lag of our time.   Such a situation would be discouraging were it not that the effort to deal scientifically with the problems of human maladjustment is so recent.   The most important thing, a beginning, has at last occurred.   We are leaving methods that are century old in the endeavor to use with success in human relationships the scientific procedure that has already unmistakably justified itself in dealing with material things.   That mental hygiene, by advocating a new and better way of dealing with human problems, is breaking from the past more significantly than chemistry separated itself from alchemy is perhaps something that only the future can bring out with the clearness it deserves.

The social promise of mental hygiene.   The kinds of problems that concentrate within the territory of mental hygiene are as various as human interests.   From every quarter demands are put forth with the expectation that if mental hygiene can deal with difficulties of social adjustment more wisely than those methods that have become traditional, it is in a position to give special help.   Mental hygiene has also appeared at a time when human nature is particularly restless and self-conscious and eager, if possible, to find a better way of dealing with common problems of personality and social contact. The time is not only one when there is great need of the help of science, but also a period when there is such frank and unbiased scrutiny of human failure that enthusiasm becomes difficult for the experienced, and skepticism, even cynicism, is widespread.

Mental hygiene is not the first serious attempt to create more favorable conditions for men and women and happier and healthier adjustments to life. Indeed, it is unique because of the new way it attacks age-long problems, not on account of the purpose it has, which is merely a different way of seeking a much-desired but illusive goal.

The record of past social crusading is rather a dismal one. It would be unfair to say that nothing has been accomplished, but it is true that the expectations of the enthusiastic advocate and brave worker were not justified when time at last balanced the gains and losses. In the eighteenth century, for example, the better thought of the period was bent upon finding a more equitable means of dealing with political questions, and for a time the hopes of men surged about representative government. With France and the United States leading the way, a forward step was taken, but one which, although it brought its advantages, by no means accomplished all that those who forced it forward expected. Another goal was reached only after long and bitter fighting, but when it was achieved and freedom of religious worship and freedom of discussion were at length attained, experience soon proved that, however desirable freedom of conscience and freedom of the press were, they were a long way from solving the deeper problems expressed in social and personal discontent. Of late, especially in the United States, the great investment of human hope has been in education. Much it has accomplished, as even its most severe critics will admit, but that its results thus far show an inherent lack most of its strongest supporters must confess.

More leisure also has seemed indispensable to the greater happiness of people. Without it higher standards have appeared impossible, since the entire time of most persons had to be spent in the daily round necessary for physical existence. As the long day declined and leisure came to be widely distributed, it seemed to many that at last the final social need was attained. For example, when the working men's reading clubs were in vogue in the early period of the nineteenth century and serious study was pursued by those who had most meager opportunity for reading, Maurice, Kingsley, Barnett, Huxley, John Ruskin, and others who contributed of their genius, were encouraged to believe that once the unprivileged masses had reasonable leisure, culture would rush forward, freed at last from the ignorance and prejudices that were forced upon men because of their limited time for self-improvement. The momentum of the movement, however, passed, even though leisure rapidly increased. Again, it was thought by some that the neighborly attitude that gave birth to the social settlement pointed the way to a successful functioning of society, but the facts have proven that this noble expression of idealism has a lesser rôle of usefulness. In addition to these movements that for a time raised the hopes of men and women who sought happier adjustment, there were fads and -isms of every conceivable sort. Many, like the Brook Farm experiment, the Oneida Community, and the New Harmony settlement, have been saved from oblivion only by the record that history perpetuates. Surely there is impressive evidence that man has not been well satisfied with himself and has eagerly sought various ways of escape from a situation that he has realized was not for his good.

Into this province of lost hope, mental hygiene has entered as a new social promise. It is not strange that some at once ask, Has it more substance than the others that have won the temporary allegiance of men? The strength of the prevailing confidence in mental hygiene, the great claims that are made for it, the quantity of expectations, do not secure against disappointment. It is nothing new in human history to expect much of an original movement that excites general interest. The final question, which of course time alone can answer, is, What can mental hygiene accomplish? We cannot invade the future so as to anticipate the testing that mental hygiene must go through to demonstrate that it is different from the many lost causes of the past. It is, however, possible to point out in it a new element that thus far has had no important part in any scheme that has been advanced as the solution of social maladjustment. If mental hygiene contains something new, untried in the past with any seriousness, then its fruits may be more abundant and valuable than the results that have come from preceding social programs.

Science and superior adjustment. As has been repeatedly suggested in former pages in this book, mental hygiene has an original element that thus far has been untried in the efforts that have been made to deal with social maladjustment. Mental hygiene pins its faith upon science. There can be no discounting the fact that when man turned away from magic and superstition and scrutinized his experiences, within the realm he is wont to call material, using experiments to test his thought, his accomplishments went forward with leaps and bounds. Science became such a superior method of dealing with his physical needs that there has not been any temptation to go back to the earlier methods. Science in the literal sense does not perform miracles, and there are some problems such as cancer that still challenge its power. But once scientific thinking showed itself a better way of dealing with material life, the record of its progress in one short century has made all the millions of years preceding appear empty. True it is that man merely changed his tools, but the new instruments were so much more effective that the world of things has literally been remade and the end is not yet. If science can be made to yield so much in dealing with infectious diseases, in multiplying crops, in transmitting thoughts to the uttermost parts of the earth more rapidly than human speech, in enabling man to rival the birds, no longer kept on the earth's crust in his going to and fro, what may it not do if applied to man's inner needs as it has been to those that are external? In its attempt to use science as a superior means of social adjustment, mental hygiene shows its distinctive contribution. Such an application of science for man's advantage was inevitable, even though it represented a method that antagonized all former ways of dealing with social situations and demanded a reconstruction of every institution that man has organized for his greater satisfaction. It was bound to come. The intimations of its approach were many, but no easier entrance could have been found than the attempt to popularize science as a means of preventing the most dreaded and extreme of all social maladjustments, insanity.

It is well for us to face the fact that an attempt to use science in dealing with personality difficulties is something quite different from the application of science to agriculture or to manufacturing. In one case man is doing something to things, in the other he is working upon himself. He cannot treat himself in the spirit of science, unless he is willing to give up attitudes and assumptions that insist that he is outside the realm where science works. He found it difficult to permit science freedom in dealing with his body, and even yet there is considerable reluctance to think of his flesh and bones as composing something similar to other physical organisms. Yet his success in utilizing the physical resources of his body has come from just such an attitude as this which at first was considered sacrilegious. Can he take the next step and conceive himself as the product of causation in much the same way as his body is understood by the anatomist and the physiologist?

If he makes this step he at least undergoes a stupendous change which may reveal that at last man has found a proper basis for social achievement. From this challenge science cannot retreat. Has it or can it obtain anything of value that will help man to construct his inner life with greater satisfaction and more success? Nor can man run away from his testing. He has been too long acquainted with the advantages of science in other fields easily to ignore, because of ancient prejudices, the new opening into which he is invited to enter. Why should he not apply science to himself? Why should he not regard his personal failures and the difficulties of his comrades as evidences of the need of greater understanding and better use of such clews as science has been able thus far to gather in its investigation of human behavior? It is certain that he cannot merely add psychological facts to the information that he considers useful and then proceed as if no tremendous thing had happened. If he begins to use science at all in the attempt to handle personality difficulties, he will grow more and more dependent upon it. Judging from the history of science in other spheres, it will, as it is put to use, increase and become more and more serviceable. Nor can the scientific interest be narrowed. It will appear in every quarter where human conduct is found.

Mental hygiene and other sciences. Perhaps the reader will at this point inject the protest that mental hygiene is infringing upon other sciences. Has not psychology been working for a long time with problems arising from man's mental experience? Has not sociology a long record of concern with man's social difficulties? Did it not forcefully spring forth in the writings of Comte as the indispensable discipline that would make a scientific society possible? The point is that mental hygiene is a determined effort not only to apply information that psychology has gathered regarding the mental life, and sociology, concerning man's group experiences, but every other insight that comes from any department of science. Moreover, this application is the central motive of mental hygiene, while neither psychology nor sociology has shown much disposition, until of late in the case of the first, to grapple closely with concrete problems of human adjustment. It has been possible not only to pass in and out of courses in psychology and sociology without learning anything that could be directly applied to personal problems, it has even been possible to instruct in such courses without a semblance of interest in persons or the faintest notion of applying science to life.

Either psychology or sociology could early have taken over the task that mental hygiene has assumed, but neither did. It was psychiatry, seriously wrestling with the distressing maladies that came out of human maladjustment or showed themselves in extreme abnormal behavior, that went to work to build up a preventive program to conserve mental health. Historically, the movement began as a consequence of the personal experiences of a layman who, through his own suffering, learned the need of better ways of dealing with the insane.

Mental hygiene if it prospers must be not only an application of science, but cosmopolitan in its ability to include from every quarter whatever is usable in advancing social and mental health. For the sake of investigation the various sciences that deal with man split his experiences and concentrate upon definite aspects. Whatever comes from such study that has value for application needs to be gathered as in a clearing house and reorganized, that the problems of man may not be dealt with partially. Personality as it operates is not broken in parts nor does it act according to the artificial separation that investigating science must make in order to isolate its studies. In so far as mental hygiene is a distinct science, it is the science of applying information of value in improving human adjustment. Thus it is like the science of agronomy. As the latter adapts chemistry, bacteriology, and climatology, so the former draws from psychology, sociology, and psychiatry, and any other source that has contributions to offer.

What are the resources of science? Immediately the question arises, Have the contributing sciences the information that is needed to make possible a usable mental hygiene? It is folly to exaggerate what we now have in the effort to advance the claims of mental hygiene. Psychology, sociology, and psychiatry are comparatively young sciences, undertaking investigations extremely difficult and complicated, and within the realm where human prejudices have been most stubborn. No good can come from exaggerating what these sciences thus far have accumulated that can be directly applied to human needs. It is, however, just as unreasonable to deny that much has been accomplished in the last decade in the humanistic sciences. Amid the confusion of different schools of thought, misunderstanding due to difficulties of expression and definition, and the emphasis that comes from concentrating upon one special feature of human experience, it is easy to be misled into thinking that the sciences that deal directly with men are too Babel-like to have anything worth while to guide man in his personal behavior. Somewhat the same situation would be felt by the average layman, if he could more thoroughly enter into the controversies of the material sciences as they operate upon the frontier of their knowledge. The physical sciences are, however, so definite in the applications familiar to the layman that he does not appreciate the vast amount of speculation and differences of opinion that accompany the ever-increasing progress of the sciences that deal with matter. In psychology and sociology, the lesser quantity of application and the more aggressive conflicts of opinions, due to the fact that the sciences are less mature and face necessarily a wider frontier, leads to a discounting of their practical findings. As this material is unified by the practical viewpoint of mental hygiene, it makes an appeal which is not felt as it appears in the mass of speculation that is associated with psychology and sociology.

However, the average person cannot be charged with indifference to either psychology or sociology, for, as the booksellers will testify, there has been since the days of William James and Lester Ward a persistent and intelligent interest in both psychology and sociology, and the output of both popular and technical literature which laymen have attempted to follow has been perhaps second to that in no other branch of science. The layman has been puzzled as to what to take out of this mass of ideas which bears the stamp of psychology and sociology, and frequently even more as to how to apply that which he has come to believe important. Mental hygiene has been forced from the start to attempt interpretation of what it has thought important and to popularize this material. It, therefore, has had to offer what the inquiring mind has sought. Distribution has been its function, and the prevailing interest attests its success.

Present trends in mental hygiene. The present emphasis in mental hygiene has been influenced by the recent developments of psychiatry and psychoanalysis. It moves along two directions, the stressing of the early life of the child as the conditioning period of the adult personality, and of the emotions as the least-disciplined and most determining aspect of the mental life. So far as the first emphasis is concerned there is plenty of evidence to justify the attention that is being given to the early life of the child. There is not, however, as the result of experimental knowledge, a clear-cut causal relationship between early life and later mental malady. On account of the complexity of life it is impossible to trace the influence of early happenings upon later character with the definiteness with which the anatomist can detect in the adult bone the consequences of the child's breaking his arm. It is from the study of individual cases that the specialist has become so convinced that the career of the young child registers itself significantly in the life of the later period. From such investigations confidence has developed that good adjustment in the early years means the best possible preparation for the adult period.

Mental hygiene is also in accord with the best thought of psychology and psychiatry in its emphasis on the emotional life. This does not mean, however, that there is general agreement as to the nature of the emotions, for no part of psychological science is more full of controversy than that which treats the emotions. How great these differences are strikingly appears in the printed report of the Wittenberg symposium on feelings and emotions, to which thirty-four psychologists contributed. Their different interpretations of human emotions show us how baffling the subject is, but also how important it is universally considered. Mental hygiene recognizes that, although there is much yet to be known about this element in human behavior which science only of late has begun to study seriously, there is abundant proof that the emotions are the most compelling of personal experiences. The happenings in childhood that appear later to have been most decisive in influencing character issue from the emotional experiences. Therefore, mental hygiene must stress the emotional responses of the formative years.

Mental hygiene and physical health. Science has to limit its undertakings, otherwise the various tasks that it assumes in its investigations would be too complex to handle. In dealing with man, however, it is important to keep ever in mind that the arbitrary divisions fade away when human problems are dealt with in the concrete. The basic influence of the body upon what we call mental experience has been so forcefully demonstrated in countless cases that it has become a familiar fact accepted by all who subscribe to the teachings of modern science. It is just as true that what we call mental experience brings forth results in the body. Medical science in its effort to master physical disease has necessarily kept itself within the province of the body. On account of this concentration, mental hygiene comes to medicine with an important suggestion. Since the individual who is sick evidences his trouble in both the physical and mental spheres, as we are wont to define them, any efforts to assist nature in his recovery cannot afford to forget the mental aspects of the problem.

The practicing physician is an artist as well as a scientist, who finds as he enters the bedroom of a sick patient that he has left behind him some of the exactness of his laboratory. His treatment of the sick person is an art because the physician has to adapt his methods to the peculiarities of the individual with whom he deals. His training and his major interest tempt him to consider this adaptation merely from the body viewpoint, but his neglect of the mental aspects of his problem may antagonize the skill he uses in his choice of drug, diet, or whatever the situation calls for. Unquestionably, as leaders in medical science are more and more realizing, the mental hygiene point of view has special significance for the physician, whose reluctance in the past to give serious heed to the psychic aspects of medicine, including what are often called the sociological factors, has given the charlatan and the pseudo-scientist an opportunity to exploit therapeutic resources that rightly belong to medicine. The importance of this neglected element appears, for example, in the statement of Dr. George Draper at the Colloquium on Personality Investigation, held under the auspices of the American Psychiatric Association, in which he illustrates his attempts to emphasize personality trends as an aid in physical diagnosis by referring to the prevalence of gastric ulcers among taxi-drivers.[1] The rôle of the physician himself is intricate, and even if he chooses he cannot be merely a dispenser of drugs. His

[1] *American Journal of Psychiatry,* May, 1929, p. 1132.

influence as a personality assists or obstructs the service
he attempts to render.[2]

Mental hygiene and crime.   As mental hygiene extends its principles it will be found that at no point do
they clash with current practices more than in the field
of crime.   Legal theory rests upon the doctrine that the
individual, free to choose between right and wrong conduct, willfully chooses, when he commits crime, what he
knows to be wrong.   This interpretation of human nature,
especially when in the grip of passion, runs counter to
all the teachings of psychology and psychiatry and therefore antagonizes the principles of mental hygiene.   Not
only is the legal theory the foundation of an elaborate
machinery that has been created to deal with the criminal,
it is also as firmly anchored in tradition as any idea that
has become a part of the substance of public opinion.
Under such circumstances, it is not surprising that crime
is the most baffling of all our social problems and possibly
the one that society handles with the least success.

The incompatibility between tradition and science is
uncompromising.   Fortunately we are not, as a people,
rigid in our consistency and little by little changes are
taking place that show the erosion of the traditional principles behind our legal system.   Naturally changes have
most occurred in the procedure of the court that deals
with children.   With the spread of modern philanthropy
it became apparent that to treat the child accused or
guilty of crime as the adult offender was commonly dealt
with was most contrary to normal humane impulses, and
socially ineffectual.   Unfortunately, however, for the legal
theory this departure brought into relief the false premises

[2] See the suggestive article by William A. White, "The Dynamics
of the Relation of Physician and Patient," *Mental Hygiene,* January,
1926.

of conventional practices in the treatment of adult crime and the uncompromising difference between what science teaches and the law assumes, for the deliberating, self-determining criminal that the legal theory of responsibility postulates is not the sort of creature psychology finds. In the entire province of present day behavior, there is no place where traditional practices must more radically change to conform with science than in those that have gathered about our criminal courts, jails, and prisons. The history of the juvenile court has demonstrated also that merely changing the procedure will not give society the full benefit of modern science. A scientific personnel is also required if a better way of dealing with anti-social conduct is to bear fruit.

No well-balanced person expects or desires the rapid changes necessary to bring court procedure, legal theory, and the custody of the criminal into full accord with scientific teaching. Society cannot switch itself from track to track with such rapidity. What must take place is a gradual adaptation as the teachings of science become more generally known, more clearly proven through experience, and more a part of the substance of our everyday thinking and living. In bringing this about, mental hygiene has much to contribute.

Mental hygiene and war. The protest against war is by no means recent, but it carries with it now a new feature. Undesirable as conflict between man and man has seemed to the most sensitive people of the recent past, there has been little to encourage those who wanted to see it replaced by something more in accord with modern sentiment. Science, by increasing the penalties of war, has made clearer and clearer its irrationality, and the fruitlessness of military success under modern conditions of life. The opposition to war still remains, however, primarily emotional and untrustworthy. Under stress of circumstances the horror of war can easily be turned to a passion for war, which pushes aside the statesmen who desire to prevent its coming. On the other hand, as the past abundantly demonstrates, those in high places if they so choose can bring about a situation that hurls people, however they may personally shrink from the ordeal, into war. We have science to aid us in the conduct of war, but there has been little attention given by science to the causes of war, for the purpose of making it unnecessary. The social group, even when a victim to the passions of war, is merely a gathering of persons whose emotions are individual, spreading through contagion from one to another. As mental hygiene forges ahead and makes entrance into every problem of social and personal maladjustment, it will surely bring forward the significance of the maladjustment which we call war. As Professor James years ago made so forceful in his essay on "The Moral Equivalent of War," it is folly to pin our faith in the elimination of conflicts between nations on any sort of negative policy. If there is anything certain about war, it is that in the past it has had an extraordinary appeal to the great mass of people concerned, when the conditions have been ripe for its coming. When this urge to war is understood and sublimation provided, civilization should be secured against what is now its greatest menace.

In its effort to apply to human needs the usable information that assists men in their social adjustments, mental hygiene is strengthening the attitude which more than any other will protect future peoples against war. The scientific attack upon war, motivated entirely by the desire to understand it, is well illustrated by Dr. William A. White's *Thoughts of a Psychiatrist on the War and After*. Until the mechanisms that impelled to war are better understood, in our efforts to secure peace we are searching for the light but still in the dark, for we cannot abolish that which we do not clearly apprehend. Physical science has already made war a world menace; the mental sciences may prove that, although it is a human folly, it will tempt man until it loses its emotional appeal through being fully understood.

Mental hygiene and philanthropy. The history of human philanthropy is both inspiring and depressing. It represents a noble endeavor, but one unfortunately that has often brought greater credit to man's heart than to his head. It is a record of high expectations and miserable failures. The philanthropist, without question, has often done greater injury to the social good than if he had preserved indifference to the suffering about him. The trouble has been that many times relief has been offered with little knowledge of the effect of this upon the personality of the recipient. Even now it is seldom that any philanthropic organization announces that it has accomplished its mission and therefore comes to an end. Although a philanthropy is usually organized to put an end to human misery along some particular line, its problem persists with such vigor that the charitable organization becomes indispensable. Progress has been made, however, in understanding where the difficulty lies, and it more and more appears that, although relief of suffering may be brought about, its elimination is impossible unless assistance is given which changes personal behavior. Indeed there is risk always that in relieving the sufferer, a stimulus may be set loose that will encourage growth of the burden that society has assumed. As is proving true in delinquency, better understanding of conditions that lead to the necessity of philanthropy shows the need of constructive education or reëducation of personality.

Thus the problems that enlist sympathy and lead to organized philanthropy are clearly linked with mental hygiene.

Society as it deals with chronic poverty is even yet too much like the sick patient who spends all he has from time to time to relieve his suffering and therefore cannot afford to take the treatments necessary to get well. The quantity of thought, energy, and money spent in philanthropic relief is appalling and its curative results disheartening. Sympathy, as it appeared with the evolution of society, lessened individual suffering, and organization, as it appeared in recent times, made relief practices more efficient, but only prevention built upon a program of science can accomplish much in the elimination of the problems that will punish a backward society.

Mental hygiene and eugenics. About the beginning of the nineteenth century when interest in the improvement of the human product by eugenic methods developed attention was directed especially to the problem of feeblemindedness. It was felt that the need of decreasing the offspring of degenerate family strains was both the most pressing and immediately promising of the various elements of the eugenic program. This attitude was strengthened by the fact that at first those near to the problem of feeble-mindedness were dealing mostly with institutional cases and because of this were led to exaggerate the significance of inheritance. In the first effort to enlist the sympathy of the public in practical efforts to decrease the size of the feeble-mindedness problem, under the leadership of Walter Fernald and Henry Goddard in this country, stress was put upon the possibilities of segregating the higher aments, who, having the power of reproduction, were able to transmit vicious strains of heredity. Continued study of the feeble-minded, especially those outside of institutions, led to an accumulation of facts that showed that the most exacting program of segregation, even if tolerated by public opinion, could not by itself eliminate the feeble-minded. With greater insight the number of those deficient in mental capacity would seem to be much larger than was at first supposed, and, clearly, legislation leading to the segregation of the higher types of feeble-minded, often biologically the most dangerous, could not be expected unless there was a complete reversal in the attitude of the public regarding the rights of marriage and parenthood.

In recent years science has gained a more accurate knowledge of human heredity and has come to realize that the problem of feeble-mindedness is more complex than was at first supposed. There has been considerable change in the attitude of both the scientist and the layman in regard to sterilization. The legal right of the state to sterilize the individual whose offspring are likely to be feeble-minded has been upheld by the highest court. There also has been a growing conviction that sterilization is more humane, as well as less expensive than segregation. Thus far California has had recourse to sterilization more than any other state or any country. Fortunately the experience of California is being carefully studied,[3] with the result that the attention of eugenists everywhere is attracted to this modern effort to protect the population from offspring that must be expected to become in some form or other a mental hygiene burden.

Mental hygiene and morals. There is no part of social experience where science at present has less direct influence than in morals. This fact is apt to mislead us into supposing that morals are forever to be independent

[3] See studies of Paul Popenoe.

of the findings of science. On the contrary, even our present situation in the field of morality discloses more influence from science than at first appears. So far, science affects morals indirectly. Through discovery and invention our ways of living and finally our ideas are changed. This leads to new adaptations of moral principles and from this point of view no influence is operating upon morality more effectively than science. There is no reason to suppose that science will always be restricted to this indirect way. Society conserves its values and protects itself as it enters the future by the moral standards it establishes. In none of its activities has error more serious consequence than when moral teaching runs contrary to the welfare of the individual and the group. The supreme importance of morality has made people more dependent upon tradition in this particular experience than in any other. Tradition cannot uncover its own mistakes. It is only as we look backward into earlier civilization and the life of preliterate people that we detect the danger of allowing past experience to sway moral judgment.

In the end morals, like every other human effort to establish the good life, must be tested by its accomplishment and no satisfactory appraisal can ever be made of human behavior except by the methods and with the temper of science. It would seem, therefore, as man matures and becomes more conscious of the need of safeguarding morality, his most precious asset of social control, that science will increasingly be called upon to pass judgment upon the value of contemporary moral standards and also, if possible, to change the future so that moral progress may be more rapid and more free from the set-backs that come when the better impulses are led astray through lack of knowledge.

At the present time science is contributing most to morality by the influence it has on the training of the child. In actual practice it is impossible to attempt to establish good habits and fortunate attitudes toward life and at the same time ignore the beginnings of practical morality. Moral growth is largely achieved in the early childhood, and it is significant that just now there is no place where science is doing so much to modify conduct as in this period. As adults deal more consciously with problems of child behavior, they will find themselves depending more and more upon mental hygiene to interpret moral obligations in terms of good adjustment.

It is supposed by some that a morality built upon science will be less exacting than the traditional code, even to the extreme of license. There is, however, reason to expect the exact opposite as morality is increasingly influenced by the factual knowledge of the scientist. The way that science has undermined the long-accepted idea of a double standard of sex morality is a good illustration of this. The greater promiscuity of men and the acceptance of prostitution were based upon three ideas that science has shattered. First, that the prostitute protects the family. Investigation has proven that she is one of the most dangerous enemies of family happiness. She provides the worst possible introduction to physical sex experience and thus encourages sex misinterpretation on the part of men and finally incompatibility in the marriage relationship. She also is mostly responsible for the persistence of venereal disease which is a deadly menace to the family. Second, that women find chastity easy and men find it difficult. This proves, when subjected to scientific study, merely rationalization without a shred of biological substance. Third, that prostitution protects the virtue of women. Science refuses to accept either the implication or the fact. The implication is that it is morally justifiable to allow the exploitation of the weaker group of women for the happiness of the rest. This attitude, to one who recognizes the social penalty that falls upon the prostitute, is monstrous. The fact assumed also proves false. The prostitute by establishing an easy code of sex conduct leads individuals, especially when the opportunities of commercial prostitution have been exhausted, to seek in perversions, and even through violence, satisfactions that because of their morbid and anti-social character are, of all things, most dangerous to the safety of women.

The rural setting. Country life in its normal activities provides conditions for personality growth that are more favorable than those encountered by the majority of urban children. The meaning of this, however, can be easily exaggerated, leading to the idea that there is little need of the science of behavior in country places. Like most advances in the organization of science, mental hygiene has functioned more in the cities than in the rural environment. The movement is so vital that country people cannot be permitted to lag behind in this effort to apply principles that conserve human character. The strategic points of attack for mental hygiene directed toward social welfare are at present the ministry and the medical profession. The theological seminary and the medical school from which ministers and doctors go to the country are places where even a meager instruction in the principles of mental hygiene will yield abundantly. Mental hygiene and its allied sciences as they advocate progressive legislation will find stubborn resistance coming from rural sections unless greater effort is made to familiarize country people with the teachings of science as they have to do with problems of personality.

The implications of mental hygiene. Mental hygiene is the application of science in an effort to help men, women, and children make sane adjustments. It recognizes the biological meaning of adaptation to environment and endeavors to enlist man's most precise intellectual instrument, science, in furthering his ability to adjust to the variegated life of the modern world. It frankly seeks personal and social happiness in the belief that this normally follows wholesome adjustment. It is concerned with the processes society uses, both by accident and by deliberation, in the making of personalities, and believes that where social disturbances arise, revealing maladjustment, the difficulty harks back to the ways by which the character trends were formed, except when the troubles are clearly due to heredity or to some catastrophe, such as an earthquake, for which society is in no way responsible. Clearly recognizing human limitations and the tragedies inherent in the finite, mental hygiene is optimistic in believing that through science, applied practically to problems of human adjustment, a larger degree of personal and social happiness is bound to come. What other method of dealing with individual or social problems has equal promise? Science insists that we seek facts whether we like them or not, and that through scrutiny we learn to handle them more and more effectively. It keeps us close to our problems and conscious of the only means we have for their solution. Thus in the end mental hygiene may exercise its greatest influence by making society conscious of the processes by which civilization is built, and by insisting that the flaws which appear in social life bring out earlier failure in the building process. Science has its inning and mental hygiene is called to the bat to show what it can do. It faces a supreme testing of the scientific procedure which along so many lines has already demonstrated its extraordinary power. The present movement may be disappointing and may in time even appear to have been premature. Final failure is, however, impossible unless nature's conditions are so adverse to man that no amount of thought and care and experimental knowledge will aid him in accomplishing that in which he is most interested, the achievement of happiness both for himself and his fellows.

SUGGESTIONS FOR CLASSROOM DISCUSSION

1. Why have the social sciences developed more slowly than the physical sciences?
2. What social conditions now favor the development of mental hygiene?
3. How does mental hygiene differ from tradition?
4. Why is mental hygiene superior to tradition?
5. Is war the result of human impulses?
6. What are the special mental hygiene problems of country people?
7. Can morality be made scientific?

SUGGESTIONS FOR WRITTEN REPORTS

1. Recent developments in psychology of value to mental hygiene.
2. The psychiatric contribution to mental hygiene.
3. The constitution clinic conducted by Dr. Draper at the Presbyterian Hospital, New York City.
4. The legal theory of criminal responsibility.
5. The psychiatric clinic and the courts.
6. The psychology of war.

SELECTED BIBLIOGRAPHY

BARNES, HARRY ELMER. "The Social Basis of Mental Health." *The Survey,* January 15, 1928, pp. 490-91.
BEALE, JOSEPH H. *A Selection of Cases and Other Authorities upon Criminal Law,* Chap. V, Sec. I. Cambridge, 1915.

BEERS, CLIFFORD W. *A Mind that Found Itself.* New York, 1923.

BIANCHI, L. *Foundations of Mental Health.* New York, 1930.

BURR, CHARLES W. "Crime from a Psychiatrist's Point of View." *Journal of Criminal Law and Criminology*, February, 1926, pp. 519-36.

BUZZARD, E. FARQUHAR. "Some Aspects of Mental Hygiene." *Mental Hygiene*, July, 1922, pp. 449-62.

CAMPBELL, C. MACFIE. "Crime and Punishment: From the Point of View of the Psycho-Pathologist." *Journal of Criminal Law and Criminology*, August, 1928, pp. 244-51.

CANADIAN NATIONAL COMMITTEE FOR MENTAL HYGIENE. "Mental Maladjustment Responsible for Enormous Human and Economic Loss." *Bulletin*, May-July, 1929, Vol. IV, pp. 1, 6.

CARROLL, ROBERT S. *The Mastery of Nervousness.* New York, 1917.

COOK, WILLIAM G. H. *Insanity and Mental Deficiency in Relation to Legal Responsibility.* London, 1921.

DAVIE, MAURICE R. (Editor). *Social Aspects of Mental Hygiene.* New Haven, 1925.

DAVIES, STANLEY P. "Mental Hygiene and Social Progress." *Mental Hygiene*, April, 1929, pp. 225-49.

DOE, JUDGE CHARLES. *State vs. Pike, 49 N. H. 399.*

EAST, W. NORWOOD. *An Introduction to Forensic Psychiatry in the Criminal Courts*, Chap. III. New York, 1927.

ELWOOD, E. S. "The Place of Psychiatry in the Medical School Curriculum." *American Journal of Psychiatry*, April, 1925, pp. 767-74.

EMERSON, CHARLES P. "Mental Hygiene: Wise and Unwise Investments." *Mental Hygiene*, July, 1926, pp. 749-63.

EMERSON, HAVEN. "The Place of Mental Hygiene in the Public Health Movement." *Mental Hygiene*, April, 1922, pp. 225-33.

GLUECK, SHELDON. "Psychiatric Examination of Persons Accused of Crime." *Mental Hygiene*, April, 1927, pp. 287-305.

—— *Mental Disorder and the Criminal Law.* Boston, 1925.

GLUECK, SHELDON. "Psychiatry and the Criminal Law." *Mental Hygiene*, July, 1928, pp. 569-95.

—— "A Tentative Program of Coöperation Between Psychiatrists and Lawyers." *Mental Hygiene*, October, 1925, pp. 686-98.

HART, BERNARD. *Psychology of Insanity*. New York, 1912.

HAYNES, F. E. "The Individual Delinquent." *Journal of Criminal Law and Criminology*, May, 1927, pp. 65-74.

HEALY, WILLIAM. *The Individual Delinquent*. Boston, 1915.

—— "The Mental Factors in Crime." *Mental Hygiene*, October, 1928, pp. 761-67.

—— "The Newer Psychiatry." *American Journal of Psychiatry*, January, 1926, pp. 391-402.

JOHNSON, LOREN B. T. "The Psychiatrist Looks at Medicine." *The Psychoanalytic Review*, July, 1928, pp. 247-60.

KARPMAN, BEN. "Impulsive Neuroses and Crime: A Critical Review." *Journal of Criminal Law and Criminology*, February, 1929, pp. 275-91.

KASANIN, J. "Mental Hygiene in a Social Agency." *Survey*, 1929, Vol. LXI, pp. 666-69.

LARSON, J. A., and WALKER, A. "Paranoia and Paranoid Personalities: A Practical Police Problem." *Journal of Criminal Law and Criminology*, November, 1923, pp. 350-75.

LOWREY, LAWSON G. "Some Trends in the Development of Relationships Between Psychiatry and General Social Case-Work." *Mental Hygiene*, April, 1926, pp. 277-84.

LYDAY, JUNE T. "The Place of the Mobile Clinic in a Rural Community." *Mental Hygiene*, January, 1928, pp. 77-89.

McCORD, C. P. "Social Psychiatry—Its Significance as a Specialty." *American Journal of Psychiatry*, October, 1925, pp. 233-40.

MARCUS, GRACE. "The Psychiatric Point of View in Social Work." *Mental Hygiene*, October, 1923, pp. 755-61.

MARTIN, WALTER B. "The Development of Psychoses in Prison." *Journal of Criminal Law and Criminology*, November, 1927, pp. 404-15.

MAY, JAMES V. *Mental Diseases: A Public Health Problem*. Boston, 1922.

MAY, JOHN WILDER. *The Law of Crimes*, pp. 40-57. Boston, 1905.

MEAGHER, JOHN F. W. "Crime and Insanity: a Discussion of Some Modern Radical Theories." *Journal of Criminal Law and Criminology*, November, 1925, pp. 360-87.

—— "Crime and Insanity: The Legal as Opposed to the Medical View, and the Most Commonly Asserted Pleas." *Journal of Criminal Law and Criminology*, May, 1923, pp. 46-61.

MITCHELL, T. W. *The Psychology of Medicine*, Chap. IX. New York, 1922.

MYERSON, ABRAHAM. *The Foundations of Personality*. Boston, 1921.

MYRICK, HELEN L. "Psychiatric Social Work, Its Nurture and Nature." *Mental Hygiene*, July, 1929, Vol. XIII, pp. 505-13.

OLSON, ELMA. "Psychiatric Social Work in the Field of Education." *Mental Hygiene*, April, 1929, pp. 263-70.

OVERHOLSER, WINFRED. "Psychiatry and the Courts in Massachusetts." *Journal of Criminal Law and Criminology*, May, 1928, pp. 75-83.

—— "Psychiatry and the Treatment of Offenders." *Mental Hygiene*, April, 1927, pp. 306-23.

PARTRIDGE, GEORGE E. "Psychopathic Personality and Personality Investigation." *American Journal of Psychiatry*, May, 1929, Vol. VIII, pp. 1053-55.

RAVEN, ALICE. "A Contribution Towards a Psychological Conception of Insanity and Its Relation to Crime." *The Sociological Review*, October, 1928, pp. 274-92.

—— "Murder and Suicide as Marks of an Abnormal Mind." *The Sociological Review*, October, 1929, Vol. XXI, pp. 315-33.

SANDS, IRVING J., and BLANCHARD, PHYLLIS. *Abnormal Behavior*. New York, 1923.

SCHROEDER, M. G. "Mental and Emotional Factors in Illness." *Medical Woman's Journal*, June, 1928, Vol. XXXV, pp. 160-64.

SHEPHARD, HAROLD. "The Psychopathic Laboratory." *Journal of Criminal Law and Criminology*, February, 1927, pp. 479-93.

STRECKER, EDWARD A. "Mental Hygiene and the Practice of Medicine." *Mental Hygiene,* April, 1929, pp. 243-60.

SWIFT, E. M., and BOYD, C. S. "The Pullman Porter Looks at Life." *The Psychoanalytic Review,* October, 1928, pp. 393-416.

TANSLEY, ARTHUR G. *The New Psychology and Its Relation to Life.* New York, 1920.

TROTTER, WILLIAM. *Instincts of the Herd in Peace and War.* New York, 1926.

TRUITT, RALPH P. "Community Aspects of Child Guidance." *Mental Hygiene,* April, 1926, pp. 294-99.

WELLS, FREDERIC L. *Mental Adjustments.* New York, 1917.

—— "Psychology in Medicine." *Mental Hygiene,* October, 1922, pp. 700, 707.

WHITE, A. MORESBY. "Legal Insanity in Criminal Cases: Past, Present, and Future." *Journal of Criminal Law and Criminology,* August, 1927, pp. 165-74.

WHITE, WILLIAM A. *Insanity and the Criminal Law.* New York, 1923.

—— *Thoughts of a Psychiatrist on the War and After.* New York, 1919.

WILLIAMS, FRANKWOOD E. "Community Responsibility in Mental Hygiene." *Mental Hygiene,* July, 1923, pp. 496-508.

—— "Psychiatry and Its Relation to the Teaching of Medicine." *Mental Hygiene,* April, 1928, pp. 331-42.

INDEX

ture of, 28; and nursery school, 198; organizations, 6, 7; and philanthropy, 448; preparation for life, 219; principles of prevention, 27; program of, 228; psychology and psychiatry, 29; and religion, 308; and science, 436; science and superior adjustment, 436; in schools, 184; social promise of, 433; and temper in industry, 270; trends in, 442; use of, 431; values of, 430

Mental Hygiene Surveys, 13

Mental Pathology and therapeutics, 20

Mental processes, study of, 24

Mental strain, and modern civilization, 34; and illness, 50

Meyer, Adolph, 10; emphasis on living patient, 42

Morals and mental hygiene, 450

Morgan, J. J. B., 48

Motivation, pleasure, 99

Myerson, Abraham, 237, 287

Mysticism, 326

National Committee of Mental Hygiene, 3; clinics, 8; division on community clinics, 10; financial resources of, 8; publications of, 5, 14

National Mental Hygiene organizations in Bulgaria, Germany, Hungary, Italy, New Zealand, Spain, Switzerland, 6; in formation in Australia, Czecho-Slovakia, Denmark, Greece, Holland, India, Norway, Russia, Sweden, 7

Nervous system, diseases of, 24

Neurosyphilis, 24

New York, Hospital for Insane, 20; Pathological Institute, 23; School of Social Work, 374

Newspapers, censorship, 407; and crime, 415; mental hygiene of, 403; and psychiatrist, 414

Nursery school, needs of, 200; purpose of, 198; studies, 198

Nutrition classes, 196

Occupation, choice of, 261

Paranoid conditions, 36; personality traits in, 44

Paresis, general, 35, 38; behavior in, 62

Parents, ambitions of, 133; and child, 111; and college, 204; education for, 7; fixation, 167; hygiene for, 126; problems of, 95; reaction to child, 176; scientific interest in, 96, 97; and the visiting teacher, 201

Parent-Teacher associations, 201; work of, 202

Parole system, 89

Pathological Institute of New York, 23

Patri, Angelo, 364

Pennsylvania, Frankford Hospital of, 21; School of Social and Health Work, 376

Personality, in adolescence, 148; abnormal, 42, 43; defects in, 159; development of, 290; physical disease and, 50; and failure, 203; formation, 45; genetic conception of, 45; literature on, 54; maladjustments, 210; in marriage, 161; psychoneurotic, 44; and religion, 337; of school teacher, 187; shut-in type of, 45; and success, 202; studies in mental disorders, 41; traits in paranoid conditions, 44

Philadelphia children, behavior symptoms, 211; personality maladjustment of, 210; physical condition of, 209; social condition of, 210

Pinel, Philippe, 19

Play, and personality development, 290

Poetry, emotional expression in, 356; inspirational value of, 358

Pratt, George K., 237

Pre-school child, study of, 26

Probation officers, training of, 89

Pruette, Lorine, 268

Psychiatry, and the legal profession, 85; in mental hygiene, 11; early texts on, 30; modern texts on, 31; in war, 40

Psychiatric, clinics, 8; examinations, 89; for school children, 7; Institute, 23; tests in army, 41